Once upon a time...............

Therapeutic Stories
That Teach & Heal

by Nancy Davis, Ph.D.

Illustrated by Valerie Solarz

Stories also by:
Karen Custer, L.C.S.W.
Marcella Marcey, Ph.D.

Published by: Nancy Davis, Ph.D.
5321 Palmetto Point Drive
Palmetto, FL 34221
703 472-3886
nancydavisphd@yahoo.com

Copyright: 1996

Printed in the U.S.A. by
InfinitPrint Solutions, Inc.
www.InfinitPrint.com

This book is dedicated to:

Karen Custer, L.C.S.W., my mentor. Karen used images to open my potential and gave me ideas for stories that blossomed into a book. Karen is a brilliant and creative woman who has helped many people live life in a healthier way.

Ken Lanning, M.S., a Supervisory Special Agent of the FBI, assigned to the Behavioral Science Unit of the FBI Academy at Quantico, Virginia. Ken is easily the world's leading authority on child abuse and pedaphiles. Ken may have no idea that he was instrumental in redirecting my life to working with abused children and other victims. Ken has helped thousands of children and adolescents by training law enforcement officers in identifying and prosecuting child molesters and training professionals who treat victims of child abuse.

All of the victims of trauma that in some way, have become a part of my life. You have helped me to learn and grow and have given me the will to discover new ways to heal exposure to trauma through your strength and your incredible will to survive and to heal.

ACKNOWLEDGMENTS

Many friends and business associates have helped me successfully complete this book:

My husband of thirty years, Joe, who spent many hours editing this book and preparing it for the publisher. Joe is my childhood sweetheart, my friend, my strength and the most intelligent man I have ever met. Joe and my children have always believed in me, allowed me the freedom to write this book and given me the love I needed to balance the trauma that I experience through my job.

My office manager and friend, Pat Galloway, who has typed, organized and assisted in editing this book. She has also listened and cried with me about the trauma experienced by many of the victims. Pat has believed in my ability to finish this book and I couldn't have done it without her.

Kathy Saville, a friend and associate, who typed, organized and edited many of the stories, She also put up with my disorganization and my promises for years that I would put the new stories she worked on into another book. Kathy also inadvertently provided me with a sense of the power of images. When I create an image for a patient, Kathy often types them for a future book. Liking one of them, she began listening to it as she exercised on her treadmill. Kathy tells me the tape relaxed her so completely that she fell off the treadmill.

Valerie Solarz, the artist who created the delightful pictures. She has consistently improved with each picture and delights children and adults alike with her interpretation of the stories through her drawings. To retain her services, contact Valerie at (410) 757-8330.

Marcella Marcey, Ph.D. is the author of several of the therapeutic stories and co-author of the article on Post Traumatic Stress Disorder. She has been a good friend and business associate for many years. Marci is one of the few people in my life who, while encouraging me, never told me that anything I wanted to do was impossible.

Karen Custer, L.C.S.W., a brilliant and creative therapist who wrote one of the stories in this book, provided the roots for many others, and helped me to learn the skills that allowed me to write these stories. This book is dedicated to Karen.

Karolyn Holdren and Maryanne Blackford, my sisters, who helped to edit the stories and constantly asked, "Haven't you finished that book yet?"

Julie Dolenga, who helped to edit the punctuation and grammar of some of the stories.

All the professionals who have written me, called or in some way let me know of someone these stories helped. You are the reason that this second book was created. It is important to find something positive when treating trauma and abuse to balance the pain, and I appreciate your calls and letters.

INTRODUCTION

I have learned much since <u>Therapeutic Stories to Heal Abused Children</u> was published in 1988 and revised in 1990. Understanding Post Traumatic Stress Disorder (PTSD) has allowed me to meaningfully link the symptoms of abused children, rape victims, battered women and victims of violence. As individuals who had experienced a wide range of traumas described how they were functioning, it became clear that, although their traumas were significantly different, their symptoms were remarkably similar.

An article on PTSD, co-authored by Dr. Marcey and myself, is included at the beginning of the first chapter of this book. This article not only identifies the symptoms, but also contains quotes from victims. This allows the reader to share in our new understanding of PTSD, and use this knowledge to heal victims experiencing a variety of traumas.

In my experience, victims of child abuse, rape and battering have been more difficult to treat than the individuals exposed to other types of traumas. Therapists must therefore be creative and open to new techniques to treat victims in these areas.

Dr. van der Kolk, the director of the Trauma Center at Harvard University, and his associates (1995) used brain imaging to study volunteers having flashbacks. They discovered that during a flashback, the right side of the brain, where images, vision and emotions are located, was extremely active. In contrast, the left side of the brain, where speech and logic reside, was completely shut down, particularly the portion which allows the victim to talk about his/her experiences. This research helps explain why therapeutic stories and other techniques which are aimed at right brain functioning are effective in treating victims. Metaphor and symbols are the language of the right brain, and they form the core of therapeutic stories (Mills & Crowley, 1986; Rosen, 1982). In my experience, other techniques which also create conditions for quick healing are: Eyemovement Desensitization and Reprogramming (EMDR)(Shapiro, 1995); audio tapes; visual imagery and hypnosis (Erickson, Rossi & Rossi, 1976).

The knowledge I have gained through working with victims is interwoven throughout this book, particularly in the introduction to each story. In reading and using these stories, you may find that some part of you is healed and that your unconscious learns how to create stories of your own.

Therapeutic stories can be used in a classroom setting; individual, group or family therapy; in individual testing with a resistive child or adolescent; in preparing a child witness to testify, or by parents, guardians and other caregivers.

Do not interpret the stories when they are told; it diminishes their power. As mentioned previously, therapeutic stories are designed, through metaphor and symbols, to speak to the right brain. Often, when the left or logical brain becomes involved (as when the story is interpreted), resistance to change may set in, and become another roadblock to healing. An explanation of the theory and construction of therapeutic stories is available in <u>Therapeutic Stories to Heal Abused Children</u> by this author.

If your role is to take care of others, you must learn to take care of yourself or you may find that you are in a chronic state of stress or burnout similar to PTSD. Symptoms of this type will impair the ability to function in your job and your personal life and become roadblocks to the learning and healing that you want to accomplish. It is, therefore, important that you learn ways to clear out the pain and tragedy that you take in from others. Use these stories, EMDR, and other right brain techniques on yourself. I created visual imagery tapes for my own use; "Letting Go" and "The Waterfall" enable me to clear the pockets of darkness I take in as I treat a large number of traumatized individuals. I have made these tapes available for other professionals, as they have been so effective in helping me. They can be purchased through my office.

As you read and use the stories in <u>Therapeutic Stories that Teach and Heal</u>, let the message be clear . . . although trauma is an inevitable part of life, there are ways to heal and find something positive in enduring even the most difficult trauma.

The author gives permission to therapists and counselors to make copies of individual stories for clients and patients in order to help with their treatment or counseling; this book is, however, copyrighted and permission is not granted to reproduce the book or individual stories, except as previously stated.

Nancy Davis, Ph.D.
Oxon Hill, Maryland
1996

Table of Contents

CHAPTER ONE

Stories that Empower and Treat the Symptoms of Trauma and Post Traumatic Stress Disorder

These stories were created specifically to deal with the symptoms of PTSD (Creamer, 1993; DSM IV, 1995; Ellen and Van-Kammen, 1990; Everly, 1994; Foa et. al., 1995; McFarlane, 1993; Rosen and Fields, 1988; Sample, et. al., 1993; Schreiber and Galai-Gat, 1993; Vargas and Davidson, 1993) outlined in the article at the beginning of this chapter. Many of these stories are, of course, applicable to the trauma caused by child abuse. In this chapter, the stories use metaphors of hurricanes, tornados, lightening, vandals, etc. to symbolize trauma. Listeners will personalize the metaphors; these stories, therefore, are appropriate for symptoms caused by a wide variety of traumas.

POST TRAUMATIC STRESS DISORDER

Nancy Davis, Ph.D.
Marcella Marcey, Ph.D.

Post Traumatic Stress Disorder (PTSD) is a common reaction when a person has been exposed to a traumatic event in which "the person experienced, witnessed, or was confronted with an event or events that involved actual or threatened death or serious injury, or a threat to the physical integrity of self or others". The response to this traumatic event "involved intense fear, helplessness or horror" (DSM IV, 1994). Symptoms may also be triggered by the sudden and/or violent death of a loved one. Long term exposure to trauma generally causes more severe symptoms than a one-time event. Symptoms resulting from trauma may change in intensity from day to day. A diagnosis of PTSD requires that symptoms continue more than thirty days. If these symptoms last less than 30 days, this is considered an Acute Stress Reaction. Reactions to trauma may be delayed, beginning days or months after the trauma. PTSD can even occur years after an event, if the traumatic event or some emotionally powerful aspect of the trauma has been "forgotten" and then is suddenly recalled.

PTSD is the result of exposure to extreme trauma and appears to be caused by the inability of the brain to process a traumatic experience. Exposure to trauma may cause changes in a variety of hormones. These hormones, in turn, appear to cause change in the functioning of the brain, particularly in the hippocampus and noradrenaline system. Electrical firing between cells in some parts of the brain, can increase significantly. Research now supports that PTSD, and the resulting symptoms, are the result of changes in the way the brain can change after exposure to trauma. PTSD is the result of the brain becoming neurologically sensitized causing it to over-react to small stimulation (like a car alarm that goes off when someone walks close to the car, but doesn't touch it). Fortunately, many individuals recover on their own from traumatic stress. Those who need assistance can benefit significantly from the newer techniques which often eliminate the symptoms of PTSD in a short period of time.

Having experienced other significant traumas, even in early childhood, may increase the symptoms of PTSD. Having a loved one die suddenly and/or violently and witnessing violence in the past can influence the severity of symptoms from a recent trauma. However, exposure to lesser traumas can immunize a person to stress, decreasing a stress reaction to a more serious trauma later in life. Some of this immunizing effect appears to be due to the development of problem solving and coping skills. There is also theory that some immunization may be due to brain changes from prior trauma that allows stress to be handled differently on a neurochemical level.

The symptoms related to PTSD fall into three categories:

Intrusive
Arousal
Avoidance

Intrusive Symptoms

1) Flashbacks or intrusive memories: This involves re-experiencing the traumatic event in such a way that it feels as though the event were happening again. The traumatic event may be re-experienced through intrusive memories of the event, images, thoughts, body sensations, feelings, or perceptions. It is as though the traumatic event is "stuck" in the present memory because the mind is unable to process the thoughts, feelings, and sensations that surround the trauma and move them into past memory. Events that were not directly experienced, but vividly imagined, such as a loved one dying in pain and alone can be experienced over and over in the same way. Dr. van der Kolk (1995), director of the Trauma Center at Harvard Medical School, used brain scans to understand the functioning of the brain during flashbacks. He indicated that the right side of the brain, particularly those involved with vision and terror, were overstimulated. The left side or language areas of the brain completely shut down, particularly the area which translates experiences into speech.

Flashbacks are often stimulated by **anchors** or **triggers.** These are reminders of the trauma and can be activated through any sense, (i.e., smell, sight, hearing, or touch) or by a thought or feeling. The re-experiencing of the feelings associated with the traumatic event is often excruciating. Because of this, reminders of the trauma are often avoided, especially talking about the event. Therapy is rarely sought because "talking about" the trauma reactivates flashbacks. Depending upon where the trauma occurred and what is associated with it, the world can become a mind field of things that can cause overwhelming emotions. With children, flashbacks are often recognized when the child re-enacts the trauma in play. Flashbacks or intrusive re-experiencing of the trauma <u>must be present</u> for PTSD to be diagnosed.

- *"I felt like I was thinking about it every minute of every day."**

---

* *Quotes from persons who have experienced PTSD.*

- *"I see the gun pointed at me and my stomach is tight, my head pounds, my whole body feels weak and the fear is so intense, I sweat and shake."*

- *"The seizures she had. I try to wipe out the noises, but I can't."*

- *"I won't drive by the hospital. I see him there. Once I couldn't breath, I felt that something was going in my throat just like that tube they put in him. I always leave 10 minutes early so I can go all the way around and not see that building."*

- *"If I have too much time on my hands, I start remembering, like it's happening again."*

- *"It's like I get the feeling that I did then. Pictures come in my mind. It feels like it happened this morning."*

- *"I had a flashback today. I couldn't think. It's like I was there. You know he never took a bath or brushed his teeth. I've been smelling that smell all day, and I had forgotten about it. I can't believe it."*

- *"I try not to think about it, but I can't. It never leaves my thoughts."*

- *"I think about it every day, 10 times a day. I used to think about it a 1000 times a day."*

- *"They opened the casket for me. He was burned all over. I still smell that smell every time I think of that."*

- *"If I go downstairs and open up the room where it happened, it's like I'm there. It's that sound, it's that smell, it's that darkness".*

- *"When I get in situations where a car gets too close, I feel like my head is going to blow off or my kids head is exploding. I never saw the girl whose head was cut off, but I imagined what she looked like and I can see it happening to me."*

- *"When I saw that train on the news last night....it was on fire... people were screaming because they couldn't get out, It took me to a memory where I could see that guy throwing the fire bomb. I saw a man burn alive. He was screaming and throwing up. It was 30 years ago, and it seems like it just happened."*

- *"I got home from the morgue that morning and I couldn't sleep. I turned on the TV and she was being put into a body bag. Her hair was out. A garbage bag. I thought I heard the* zip. *Why would they show that? I see that over and over, a 100 times a day. And at the trial, the drunk who killed her, one girl said that he spit on her while she was lying on the pavement. I know she was dead, but what is he? I think of killing him. It comes into my mind over and over, when I pick up a knife or anything. I see him spitting on her and I see his smile at the trial when he got one month. Nothing really. And he smiled at me. Killing him or anyone, that's not me. I feel I'm going crazy sometimes. I'm here, but most of me is there."*

2: Night Terrors are dreams which occur in a different stage of sleep than normal dreams. They seem to be flashbacks occurring during sleep, as the mind attempts to process the traumatic experience. Often the dreamer wakes up in fear, but can't remember the content of the dream.

- *"He's shooting me and I'm trying to get away, but I can't move. I wake up with sweat all over my body."*

- *"I wake up crying, like I'm drowning. I know I'm still asleep, but I have to wake up but it's so hard."*

- *"I wake up and I'm scared, but I never remember what I'm dreaming about. I'm getting up at least two times a week and throwing up."*

- *"My husband wakes me up about twice a month. I'm dreaming he has bombs on his stomach and I'm trying desperately to knock them off before they explode."*

- *"When he's having these night terrors, his body becomes so stiff. He's so strong. You can't do anything with him. It's like he's awake but not awake." (young child)*

Arousal Symptoms

Exposure to a traumatic event(s) causes the body to release stress hormones. The brain reacts to these stress hormones in many ways, often significantly increasing the speed of electrical firing between cells in certain areas (Everly, 1995). These changes typically cause the following symptoms:

1) Tension, Anxiety, Irritability, Hyperactivity: These symptoms involve feeling jumpy, on edge, shaky. Little things become very upsetting. The response to small irritations may be screaming or tears. Emotions move from being absent to being intense almost instantly, without going through any stages of escalation. For example, stages of anger may be described as irritation, annoyance, being really angry, and finally, being enraged. In PTSD, emotions often skip the middle stages, moving from irritated to enraged in an moment. Sudden and intense feelings of sadness, depression, jealousy, and other strong emotions are experienced and expressed. Children may seem okay one minute and be sobbing hysterically the next.

- *"I had to stop work. I had a desk job. I loved it but I couldn't sit still. Still can't. That would be OK if I was doing something, but I just move."*

- *"I have to stay in agitation to keep from getting angry."*

- *"I came out of the courtroom and saw all the reminders of the bombing and I started to cry. It was embarrassing."*

- *"I over-react. Like not feeling calm-like. Things are bothering me. I feel like that all the time."*

2) Interruption of Sleep Cycle: This may involve either difficulty falling asleep or waking after short periods of sleep with an inability to return to sleep. If interruption of the sleep cycle results in chronic sleep loss, other symptoms related to sleep deprivation occur.

- *"It feels like something is on my mind, but I can't figure it out and it won't go away. It keeps me awake."*

- *"The police came and knocked on the door at 2 AM. I never sleep past 2 anymore. Sometimes I wake up thinking I heard the knock again."*

- *"I have to read or watch TV to fall asleep. I have to fill my mind with something or I'll never fall asleep. I wake up four, sometimes more, a night. Now it seems normal."*

- *"That's why I have trouble falling asleep, 'cause everything goes to my head."*

- *"I can't sleep all night if I have to talk about the rape to the prosecutor or my therapist. I wake up again and again all night."*

- *"I go to bed at 8:30. I stare at the clock. It's usually 11:00 at least before I fall asleep. Then I get up to go to the bathroom and I can't go back to sleep. I feel like something is bothering me or irritating me."*

3) Nightmares are usually related to the event, either directly or symbolically. When the trauma is a crime, often the dream centers on lack of safety, i.e., the criminal harming or killing the dreamer and/or his family. These dreams often begin by mirroring the traumatic event and become more symbolic over time.

- *"I dream of him all the time, but he's alive. He's a child, a baby, crying. I'm trying to get to him. I have to feed him or he'll die, but I can't get to him. I look.. He's there and then he's gone, but he's a child. Then I wake up and realize he's dead and he died alone and I will never change that. Which is the nightmare? When I'm asleep and frantic or when I'm awake and there is nothing I can do?"*

- *"I keep dreaming that I'm being buried alive; when I wake up, I'm so upset I don't sleep the rest of the night."*

- *"I dream that my father is coming to kill me. He's hunting me down and when he finds me, I wake up. I dream that over and over again. I can't sleep because I don't want to dream."*

- *"If he gets scared at night, he's not comfortable until he's in our bed, stuck to us like glue. I used to be a teacher but the stress of staying up with him when he can't sleep or has those night terrors; I had to quit my job."*

4) Hypervigilance, easily startled: Feeling constantly on guard against attack, often to the point of paranoia. Body may seem braced. Nerves are on edge. Small sounds, movement, or shadows may cause intense response of fear or flight. The feeling that attack or traumatization is going to recur is often present. An innocent bystander may seem to be attacking or dangerous.

- *"I saw the gas meter man and I thought it was someone trying to get in the house. I got my gun and barricaded the door. I positioned myself at the side of the window. When I realized who it was I felt stupid."*

- *"Every sound made me nervous. The house seemed alive at night, creaking. I thought I'm in charge, I have to calm down. I would check the locks over and over."*

- *"If I'm walking someplace, I'm constantly looking behind me. I stop like I'm paranoid and let them pass. If the leaves shuffle, I jump."*

- *"Like when I'm looking at T.V. I try to concentrate, but all of a sudden I look around to see if my blinds are closed. I try to keep them closed all the time."*

- *"If he hears a noise outside, he comes running. Jumps. Says "What's that?" He's hard to calm down. If he's in the car and he gets scared, he has to touch me or hold onto something." (young child)*

5) Fear and Loss of the sense of safety: PTSD takes a person back to the level of feeling unsafe. Other things don't matter. Perceptions of the world often change. If the traumatic event(s) occurred in the home or areas traditionally felt to be secure, the loss of a feeling of safety may be more intense. The perception of the world may become distorted. Phobias or intense fear may develop, especially about being traumatized again or reminded of the trauma. Elaborate techniques to avoid reminders of the trauma may develop. Children may wet or soil their pants because of the intensity of their fear or flashbacks.

- *"I see the way these guys look and they remind me of him and I freeze up."*

- *"Those guys were never caught and I never saw their faces. I could be standing beside one in the store and not even know it. I think about it. It will come into my mind and my heart will start beating so fast. I want to run. One time I had to leave a store. Just put everything down. God, it was hard to drive home. Come to think of it I've never gone there again."*

- *"At first I just wanted to stay away from stuff that upset me but then a friend said 'you know you never leave the house anymore.' Well, I was angry, but then I tried to leave and I thought I was going to die, like a heart attack. I fell down and my neighbors called an ambulance and they took me to the hospital. I just wanted to be home, where I never had something like that happen."*

- *"It took away some kind of innocence. I feel I'm not safe anymore."*

- *" Every time I go home I search the house. I search every closet, look under every bed. We have a dog that makes the kids feel safe, but nothing makes me feel safe. I always feel like someone is going to come in again."*

- *"I used to take things for granted. Now I know that I could die or be injured any time. Sometimes I try to be careful and sometimes I just stop caring altogether since I can't do anything about it. And my daughter. I'm terrible to her. I'm so scared for her all the time. I'd do anything to protect her."*

- *"He's potty trained except when in a new environment. All of a sudden, it's like everything let's loose."* (young child)

6) **Aggression/Rage:** Intense feelings of rage and thoughts about punishing or killing the attacker or abuser. The degree and the intensity of the rage experienced may be terrifying because it is unlike any emotions previously experienced. This aggression may be misdirected toward friends, family members or work associates.

- *"I curse a lot. People really get to me."*

- *"At first I was angry 80% of the time.. Furious at everyone and everything. So mad I couldn't talk to people. They would avoid me, I know, and that made me mad. I was mad when they were around and I was mad with they weren't. I was crazy, never knew what would set me off next."*

- *"At work, everybody says I've changed. I look more angry. It doesn't feel good when people say they want back the old me."*

- *"I got in a fight with a defense attorney. We were screaming at each other. I used to be so calm and let everything roll off my back. The judge wrote a letter to my supervisor."*

- *"He has temper tantrums where he falls out uncontrollably. Screams. It takes 45 minutes to calm him down. Will hurt himself or hit me. He banged his head, chipped a tooth. He wrings his hands. He's impossible to stop."* (young child)

7) **Problems in Concentrating, Reading, Writing, Speaking, Short Attention Span:** Inability to think things through because the mind and thoughts are so speeded up that thoughts are fragmented. Reading and writing may be a problem because of the inability to concentrate. Problems in listening are common because the mind keeps drifting off to other places or re-living the traumatic event. These symptoms cause missed appointments, forgetting important events. In children, these symptoms of PTSD may be misdiagnosed as Hyperactivity or an Attention Deficit Disorder.

- *"It really affected my work. I would start to tell a story and after I said the first sentence, I would forget what I was going to say. It happened all the time. I got afraid to talk to anyone."*

- *"Like if I'm reading something. Like I'm trying to pay attention to it, but I can't. Like my eyes are on it, but my mind's not."*

- *"I stopped teaching police schools. I stopped teaching Sunday school. I couldn't remember what I was going to say from one minute to the next. I just stopped doing anything which would let people know I couldn't remember."*

- *"My dad will start talking to me....I'm hearing him, but it's like an echo. My mind's thinking a million other things."*

- *"When I'm giving my lecture, I focus on one particular part of the slide and my mind goes blank. I have to cover it up and continue to talk."*

- *"I'm listening, but it's not registering."*

- *"I don't even know how I drove up here today. My mind escapes me. I'll be talking to someone and I hear their voice, but I'm not listening."*

- *"When I'm supposed to do something in class, I can't do it. I can't focus on it. I read it over and over again and it won't stick in my head."*

- *"It's like my eyes are looking at the page, but my mind's not."*

- *"I used to read all the time. Now I read the first sentence and I think of something else. I feel like my mind is racing."*

8) Sense of Being Stuck; Problems in Making Decisions: The inability to make even small decisions is often present. Inability to initiate common activities. Inconsistency in problem solving is part of this symptom, as well as constant shifting from one point of view to another.

- *"I can do the things I use to do, but I can't do new things. A friend of mine asked me if I wanted to go shopping. She was pushing me to get new things. I couldn't make any decisions. How do you explain that you can't decide things. I need to go back to work, but my job requires me to make decisions. I can't decide what to do."*

- *"It's like running on a treadmill and grasping for something to latch on to to gain control, but I can't grasp anything and I can't get control. I feel like a gerbil running round and round on an exercise wheel....running as fast as I can but getting no where."*

- *"I look for excuses so I won't have to do my reports. I go to lunch; I talk on the phone. I keep putting them off and I'm not getting anything done. I'm not paying my bills either."*

11

- *"I used to be a neat and organized person. You could come in my house at any time and it would be so clean you could have a party. Now all my summer clothes are in a pile in the corner of my bedroom. I want to clean it up, but I just can't get started."*

- *"When I tell him to get a book, he goes in to get one. You go in there and every book is on the floor. He can't decide which book to get. He does the same thing with his toy box."* (young child)

Avoidance Symptoms:

Because the flashbacks and the feelings and thoughts associated with the trauma are terrifying, painful, and disabling, efforts to avoid any thoughts, feelings, conversations, people or places that trigger reminders of the trauma are common. Numbing of responsiveness is an additional factor. Numbing and avoidance are part of the phases seen in PTSD. These cycles move from intrusive symptoms to numbing and back again. Individuals in the numbing stage of PTSD are often mistakenly thought by professionals or their friends and co-workers to be okay. Avoidance and numbing by the following means is common:

1) Inability to recall parts or all of the traumatic event: Because the traumatic event is not being processed, and the reactions to any reminder of the trauma are intense, some aspect of the traumatic event may be difficult or impossible to remember. Facts related to the event may become unclear. (This is not a conscious process). Although forgetting provides some measure of relief from flashbacks, the loss of memory may also be upsetting, especially if testimony about the event must be given. It appears that in this way, childhood trauma that is intense and/or long term, may be forgotten.

- *"I don't think I felt anything at the funeral. I don't really remember anything from when I left the house to go to the hospital until about three weeks later. They tell me I made all the arrangements and I was at the funeral and I didn't cry at all, but I have no memory."*

- *"It's like I can remember pieces of it, but it just won't come....I can't remember."*

2) Numbing and Diminished Interest in Significant Activities: This is generally a "shutting down", suggestive of depression. "Don't feel, don't think, don't see, don't hear." This symptom is commonly seen in children who have been through long term or intense trauma resulting in undiagnosed PTSD. If this type of "shutting down" extends into months and years, the child's developmental growth is affected and the child may be mis-identified as retarded. Numbing and withdrawal from life is also a characteristic of battered woman syndrome.

12

- *"I want to do things, but I can't get to it. I want to do it, but I just don't try."*

- *"I feel like this. On Thursdays, people are planning what they're doing for the weekend...like skating. They say, 'do you want to go?' I say I have something planned, but I don't. I really want to go, but I don't go."*

- *"I've let my husband's business go to hell in a hand basket. I've stopped cooking. I used to come home every day and cook, clean and wash clothes. Now I just sit. My kids and husband just have to take care of themselves."*

- *"I feel shut-down. I don't have anything to say. I can't join in conversations. I'm very uncomfortable."*

3) Dulled or blunted sense of feelings: Through "numbing" a sense that nothing is real may evolve. Feeling "not human" or "in another dimension" while going about daily routines is often related. When asked to relate details of the trauma, an individual may relate the experience as though it was watched in a movie. Emotions may become so numb they are not experienced. <u>When in this state, others may believe that the trauma is being handled well by the person because there is no reaction to details of the trauma.</u> Children in this state often draw pictures without details, such as outlines of people without faces.

- *"It's like I want to get excited, but I just don't get excited."*

- *"Everyone kept saying, 'you're doing so well, you're a rock', stuff like that. I read the grief books and I didn't have any of those feelings. I just did and did. There was so much to do. Then, I was alone for a week. No one home. I began to feel like all the skin had been peeled off me, like every movement, every breath was intensely painful. I thought I was sick, but the doctor said I was just feeling the grief. I don't see how you can feel nothing for two years and in one week just fall apart."*

4) Problems with Relationships or Attachment: (The belief that everyone is an enemy may be present.) Pulling away from social situations and the common activities of everyday life is common, as is isolation from friends and relatives. There is often a loss of love or feeling for loved ones. Laughter disappears, as does a sense of humor. Withdrawal sometimes is an outgrowth of shame resulting from believing that others think that the victim is to blame for the trauma. Feelings of love may become so numb that they seem to have disappeared. Victims may use work as a way to isolate and avoid.

13

- "I didn't tell you this. I stopped eating. I stopped drinking. I stopped talking to my familiy family and friends. I thought I could handle it alone, but what happened just kept going over and over in my head."

- "Sometimes I'm talking and they're listening, but it seems like I'm just having a conversation with myself or sometimes they're just not there and I'm talking to myself."

- "Like last year when the teacher came to test him. He shut down and they just couldn't test him. They would ask him questions and he would just repeat it 'cause he didn't want to be bothered." (young child)

- "I thought everyone in the office was against me, talking about me, trying to get me fired or put on disability retirement."

- "I couldn't talk to people. I felt that I was in a different reality. In my world terrible things could happen, it was always cold, there was no future. People would say 'you have to put this behind you'. I knew they thought I was doing something wrong or that I was weak, but I began to feel that they weren't human at all, just noises. Sometimes I felt like laughing at them, but mostly I felt terrible."

- "I don't want to talk to friends; I don't want to talk to anyone."

5) Lack of Sexual Interest: Because feelings are "shut down", sexual feelings may disappear and inability to function is common. In some individuals sexual interest increases as a way to stay connected when human interaction is avoided in other areas.

- "I really don't want to hug him, but I do 'cause he wants me to."

- "I still have a boyfriend, but I just don't let him come round that much."

6) Absence of Fantasy/No Sense of Future: Because PTSD causes thoughts to be stuck in an endless loop focusing on the present, the result is a lack of fantasizing about doing things in the future, making lists of what must be accomplished or daydreaming about being successful. An inability to think about the future may involve an inability to consider consequences of present behavior. The lack of feeling safe also can result in being pessimistic about having a rich rewarding life or a normal life-span. Many adults with this symptom report that they no longer pay their bills on time or clean their house because this requires a future orientation.

14

- *"The future----why bother? Nothing was really as important as being a mother. No other accomplishment matters."*

- *"They asked what do you want to do when you graduate. I never think about it. I feel like I don't have a future."*

- *"Sometimes I think I'm going to be dead by 14. When I was 12, I never thought I'd reach 13. When I was 11, I never thought I'd reach 12."*

Other related problems can also accompany PTSD:

1) Territorial Issues: The belief that others are trying to get what is yours and intense feelings of possessiveness may occur. This suspicion may extend to fellow employees, bosses or family members. In traumatized children, this symptom may be expressed by fighting or aggression. Children often fight among themselves over getting their fair share. Stealing may be a way of symbolically claiming what is theirs.

- *"My brother came to visit me. I didn't want him there. I watched him all the time and I wouldn't tell him anything. He kept asking questions."*

- *"You were right about being territorial. Someone put their coffee cup on my desk and I went nuts. My partner wanted to put some of his papers in my filing cabinet and that really upset me. He's my best friend but I was upset about sharing my space."*

- *"He gets real selfish. He won't let anyone near his toys. He doesn't want me kissing my husband or other kids." (young child)*

2) Poor Boundaries: This symptom may include saying or doing things that break rules, are outrageous, or show poor judgement. Children often regress to younger behavior, and seem out of control.

- *"He gets in everything. We had a visitor at out house and he came in the kitchen carrying a tampon he has found in her purse asking, "What's this grandma?"*

3) Guilt/Shame: Feeling responsible for the trauma or believing that behavior during the trauma was 'wrong' can cause intense feelings of shame or guilt. These feelings may result from the intensity of the rage and the desire to kill during or following a traumatic event which involves an attacker. The guilt and shame may lead to intense feelings of self-hate. If the traumatic event involved a near-death experience, the shame may be more intense if religious beliefs conflict with the feelings, thoughts, and behavior that occurred during the event. Guilt can be triggered by the action or lack of action that one took in the traumatic situation and/or by one's reactions afterwards. These feelings may also arise over reactions of fear such as wetting or soiling pants, freezing, poor accuracy of a police officer in returning shots during a gun battle or responses that seem childlike. Guilt may arise from the belief, in retrospect, that the trauma is punishment by God for failing to be a good or perfect person. The guilt and shame are experienced after self statements that begin with, "If only I had....If only I hadn't...I should have...This is my fault." This guilt may be about normal things that, in hindsight, seem wrong. It may be brought on by thinking about the things that had to be done to survive in the traumatic situation.. Guilt is often an attempt to say "I really did have control."

- *"I believe that it could have been prevented. If I have not let her go out that night. I gave her the car keys. If I had said 'no', she'd be alive today."*

- *"I just ran. I didn't think of anything but getting out. I should have made sure everyone else was okay."*

- *"I should have known he would hurt my sister. If I hadn't gone off to college maybe I could have stopped him. Maybe he would have left her alone."*

Information in this article came from DSM IV, numerous research articles, and workshops in the bibliography (particularly those of Dr. George Everly and Dr. van der Kolk) and from personal experience of the authors in dealing with the people they have treated.

The Path in the Woods

Problem(s) Addressed:

The intrusive and arousal stages of Post Traumatic Stress Disorder, including circular thinking, flashbacks, thinking that seems to be racing and problems concentrating (Ellen, et. al., 1990; Epstein, 1993; Everly, 1993; McFall; et. al., 1989).

Appropriate for:

Adolescents and adults who have been traumatized.

Message:

The symptoms of PTSD can be eliminated and you will discover how to heal yourself

Symbols and Metaphors:

Running: the increase in brain activity and electrical firing between brain cells caused by PTSD.

Lightning: a sudden trauma

Burns: symptoms caused by exposure to trauma

Disconnected from logic: the understanding that flashbacks occur in the right side of the brain or symbolic side of the brain; this side is not logical

Berries: techniques that heal the symptoms of PTSD

Elements of the Story Which Can be Changed:

Change of sex of main character; any symptoms unique to the listener.

Note:

This story was created from the description of symptoms given by a law enforcement officer who had been in acute PTSD. He described the experience as follows: "I never told you this but I stopped drinking, I stopped eating, I stopped talking to anyone. I thought I could handle it myself, but my thinking just went round and round."

18

The Path in the Woods

Once upon a time a man sat on the steps of his porch. The sun was shining in the cobalt blue sky and the wind was blowing just enough to make the trees bend and move. As the man surveyed everything around him, all seemed right in his life. He smiled when he thought about his family, his job and his plans for the coming days.

Suddenly, without warning, a huge and powerful lightning bolt struck from the sky. At first, the man was stunned, and then he began to run blindly trying to escape the lightning and the burns. He ran without thinking, looking, or listening. When, at last, he became aware of his surroundings, he realized he was lost . . . lost in a deep forest, a strange and uninviting place. For a while he sat still, dazed and numb. As he tried to think, he could think of nothing other than the lightning. He was aware that he was lost, but this seemed unimportant compared to his pain. The lightning had been so sudden and so powerful that his wounds were still raw, but he was so numb that he felt little pain.

As the numbness wore away and the pain became more noticeable and intense, the man realized the importance of finding his way out of the woods, and he began to run. As the man ran, he noticed a shack by the side of the path. An old man in a rocking chair sat on the porch and waved to the man as he went by. He hardly noticed the old man or gave him a thought. He just kept running and running. Soon he saw another cabin on the side of the path with an old man similar to the one he had seen before. This man waved, as well, but again the man continued running without reacting. Because his mind was racing from the lightning and the burns, he ran faster than he had ever run before. Again and again he saw a cabin and an old man who waved, and each time he didn't talk, he didn't wave and he didn't acknowledge the greeting.

At some point, he became aware that the cabins looked very much alike. Then he realized that they weren't different cabins; he had been running by the same cabin and the same old man over and over again. The next time he passed the old man, he heard a voice inviting him to stop and visit. The runner yelled back that he couldn't stop, even for water or food. Although the

19

runner realized he was going around in a big circle and was getting nowhere, he didn't seem to be able to stop himself. He continued running and running.

Each time he ran a lap, the greetings of the old man became clearer in his mind. He was sure that if he did stop, the man would ask him why he was running in circles and he would have to talk about the lightning. The runner realized that talking about the lightning would force him to focus on how badly he was burned, causing the pain of these burns to become very intense. "I can handle this myself," he said, "I'll just keep running and running and I'll find my way out." He refused to acknowledge to himself that an endless circle has no exit.

The old man seemed to tire of waving to the runner without getting a response. He left his rocking chair and walked to the side of the path. Upon seeing the old man, the runner stopped for a moment. Then he ran on, taking another lap, trying to outrun the pain that had begun to surface as he stopped. When the runner rounded the circle again, the old man was blocking his way. Although afraid, the runner stopped. With a puzzled look, the old man inquired, "Why are you running around and around this path? Don't you realize you're getting nowhere? You're only wearing yourself out."

Having been a logical man before the lightning struck him, the runner realized this was true. But he seemed disconnected from logic so he ran another lap. The old man was there when he passed his way again. "I know you're lost," he said to the runner. "Tell me what happened and I'll help you find your way out of these woods."
"There is nothing you can do to help me," the runner exclaimed. "I have to do it myself." And he ran yet another lap.

The next time the runner passed in front of the old man, he stood on the edge of the path, allowing the runner take several more laps. Then, for a second time, the old man stood in the middle of the path. "Have you convinced yourself that running around and around is getting you nowhere?" he asked the runner. "You'll never get out of these woods and find medicine for those burns unless you stop running in a circle."

The words of the old man began to penetrate the logical side of the runner. He was hungry and thirsty and getting nowhere. So he stopped and sat with the old man. He described the lightning, even though talking about it made him aware of his painful burns.

The old man listened and then explained what happens when lightning hits so suddenly. He talked to the runner about burns, and about running in circles. At that point, the conversation focused on how the runner could find his way out of the woods. "I can tell you things that will help move you in the right direction," the old man said. "If that is not enough, remember that throughout your life, you have been a very innovative and motivated man. Use these strengths now to find everything else you need to heal your burns and move out of these woods."

As they talked, the runner realized that when he ran in circles he became numb so the pain wasn't noticeable. But being a logical man, he knew he didn't want to continue to be lost, running in circles. Logic told him to ask directions from this old man, overruling the general "male rule" about finding one's own way at any cost. **

So the runner walked the path in the way the old man had advised. As his burns began to ache, he remembered he had heard that berries have special healing qualities. So he began to pick different berries from the woods, first one kind and then another. He continued his search until he found just the right combination to heal his wounds as quickly and completely as possible.

After using the berries on his wounds, the runner continued to move along the new path. He began to notice the trees and plants lining the pathway. Then the light at the end of the path became visible — an indication that he would soon be out of the woods.

When he emerged from the woods, his family, friends and co-workers were waiting to greet him. "You really scared us," they told him. "We realized that you were lost, but we didn't know how to help you." To celebrate his return, everyone accompanied the runner back to his home for a picnic. The runner sat on a picnic table, telling everyone about the lightning and the burns. He told them about running in circles and about the old man. He emphasized the details of finding his way out of the woods and looking for berries to heal his burns. As the runner continued to talk about his journey, everyone listened with their heart. Even though many of the listeners had never been struck by lightening, the story told by the runner left a distinct memory in each of them so that they would have a map to help them find their way if lightening or burns caused them to lose their way.

©1995
Nancy Davis, Ph.D.

**From: Tannen,(1991)

The Sports Car and the Alarm

Problem(s) Addressed:

Symptoms of Post Traumatic Stress Disorder, specifically the speeded-up cognitive functioning, inability to concentrate, hyperactivity, hypervigilance and lack of feeling safe. Treatment of these symptoms with Eyemovement Desensitization and Reprogramming (Foa, et. al., 1995; Shapiro, 1995).

Appropriate for:

Ages 6 through adults. Males tend to be more interested in cars than females, but the metaphor of the story will be understood by both sexes.

Message:

The moving of the eyes from left to right and from right to left while reviewing a traumatic memory helps to process this memory and can reduce or eliminate many symptoms experienced as a result of trauma (Shapiro, 1995). This technique is a critical part of EMDR and is also found in MTP, a fast treatment for trauma recently described by the author.

Symbols and Metaphors:

Flood: any traumatic experience

Mud & sand in engine: the stress hormones which alter the functioning of the brain

Speeded-up electrical system: the speeded-up electrical firing of cells in the brain that have been found to be a result of experiencing trauma

Running off the road: poor concentration

Alarm going off when there is no danger: hypervigilance and paranoid behavior common to those in PTSD

Moving of head lights back and forth: the eyemovement used to process memories of trauma

Elements of the Story That Can be Changed:

Other symptoms can be added, but they must be a metaphor that fits with a car. The type of sports car can be changed to mirror someone's preference in cars.

Note:

This story was designed for a ten-year-old male who had been repeatedly raped by a 15-year-old male in the neighborhood. The parents did not know this teenager, and did not understand what was happening to their child for at least a year after the abuse began. Consequently, his symptoms of PTSD increased dramatically. When this boy was brought to therapy, he was in such a chronic and severe state of PTSD that he was afraid to allow any therapeutic technique to be used in session. He screamed to leave and called me names. For three sessions, I sat in front of the door so he could not leave (with the parent's permission) and read therapeutic stories (without any explanation). The boy began to calm down at the end of the third session. In order to do EMDR, I had to demonstrate the technique by using it on his mother. This is not uncommon, since trust is an issue in those with PTSD. With the combination of stories, EMDR and three minute endless tapes, the boy significantly improved.

The three minute endless tape can be purchased at Radio Shack; it is an answering machine tape. Direct positive suggestions to control his behavior were recorded on a tape of this type (reflecting the boy's symptoms). When the boy felt himself becoming out of control at school, he would hold up a red card and the teacher would allow him to go to the teacher's lounge where he listened to the tape until he calmed down and could return to class under control. This story had two purposes: further acceptance of the EMDR technique and a directive to his unconscious to find a way to process the traumatic memories on it's own.

The script for the three minute tape is as follows:

You are feeling better and better about yourself every day. Every minute you are doing better and better in school. Every minute of every day you are finding a way to get yourself more and more under control, becoming more and more calm, feeling better and better about who you are. You are changing your behavior so that you have more and more friends, because you are discovering just what you need to do to have friends, just what you need to say to have friends and how to act to have friends and you are doing all of these things. As you get yourself more and more under control and use all the techniques you are learning to make friends, you are feeling better and better about yourself, more and more confident in your ability to control your behavior, to turn down your anger and to calm yourself. You are remaining calm, even when someone says something to you that is hurtful or mean. You are able to ignore any mean statements and concentrate on doing your school work.

You are reading better and better every day and you are paying attention to the teacher and to doing your work. You are able to do your work, and do it well. Each day you are improving so that you can concentrate better and better each day. You are especially remaining calm when you are with your family. You are wanting to do your reading writing and math assignments and all of your other assignments. You are slowing down your mind and your thoughts, remaining calm and concentrating as you complete your work. You are getting better and better grades. You are finding ways to be responsible in school so that your teacher is rewarding you for your behavior and you are able to tell yourself more and more positive things. When you feel yourself starting to become upset, you are able to get yourself under control, you are able to calm yourself down, and your mind is figuring out just how to do this and you are doing it—at home, at school and with your friends.

As you sleep, your mind is giving you very positive dreams and helping you to feel better and better about yourself. Your dreams are helping you to know that you are in control of yourself and to feel safe. You are changing, you are becoming more and more positive in all the statements you make to yourself. You are able to remain calm and to act in a way where you really like yourself and you are doing this because you want to do it. Every day you are feeling better and better about yourself, doing better and better in school and liking yourself more and more each day.

The Sports Car and the Alarm

Once upon a time there was a white Porche with leather seats and a powerful engine. It was a very rare and expensive sports car. In order to protect his car from thieves, the owner installed the best car alarm money could buy. Even though the Porche was a car, it seemed to sense that it was powerful and fast. The car to find pride in knowing that many boys dreamed of owning a Porche when they grew up. When the Porche was parked along the street or in a parking lot, many people would walk up to the Porche, saying very complimentary things. The Porche understood that these admirers were harmless, therefore, it made sure that the car alarm never went off. The sports car liked being admired and hearing boys and girls remark, "When I grow up, I want a Porsche just like that one."

Now, every once in a while one of these people admiring the Porsche would be destructive or aggressive. They would kick his tires or scratch the paint with a key. Even the sports car understood the difference between admiration and abuse, so he would quickly sound the car alarm. The car alarm would scream, "Get away from the car, you are hurting it." The person who had been hurting the car was quickly scared away.

The Porsche could not have designed a better life for himself. Every weekend his owner would drive him to a race track where there were no speed limits. Then the Porsche would drive over 100 miles per hour. He loved to drive as fast as he could. Sometimes the Porsche joined parades where he was decorated and admired even more than usual.

As happens in the lives of most people and cars at one time or another, tragedy befell the Porsche. It rained and rained for days. The river that ran near where the Porsche was parked, rose suddenly over its banks. As the water rose higher and higher, the Porsche soon disappeared under a sea of mud. Water, mud and sand settled in the engine.

When the flood was over and the water ran once again between the banks of the river, the owner of the Porsche attempted to rescue his car. He washed it, dried it and polished it, but

27

he did not understand the damage that the flood had caused to the engine. The mud and sand from the water had settled in the electrical system, causing it to run much too fast.

Believing that driving the car would work out any problems from the flood, the owner took the Porsche for a drive. When he stepped on the gas, however, rather than accelerating and running smoothly as the sports car had done before the flood, it ran off the road. It made strange noises and ran very differently from the Porsche the owner was used to. Sometimes the Porsche would run other cars off the road believing that these cars were trying to take his space on the road or cause him to have an accident.

When the Porsche was parked and admirers approached it as they had before, the car alarm would go off. Sometimes it would even go off when people were walking down the street paying no interest to the Porsche at all. The car alarm would yell, "Get away from the car, get away from the car."

The owner did not know how to fix the Porsche by himself, although at first he tried to repair it. The owner took the car to several car mechanics, but the Porsche seemed afraid to allow the mechanics to work on him. When his hood was opened, the alarm would go off screaming "Get away from the car, get away from the car." Several mechanics tried to repair the Porsche. One put new oil and fluids in the engine. Another changed the battery and added a water pump. Still another changed the spark plugs and adjusted the carburetor. Nothing seemed to work, and the alarm of the Porsche continued to sound even when there was no danger at all.

One day, the owner noticed a newspaper article about a mechanic who specialized in repairing cars that had been damaged by floods. One satisfied customer remarked that the mechanic was so good his car was running better than it had before being covered with water and mud. Wanting very much for his Porsche to function as it had before the storms, the owner took his Porsche to the mechanic mentioned in the news. The owner explained that the Porsche had been covered with water, mud and sand. Then the owner added, "The alarm keeps going off when there is no danger. Furthermore, my car runs other cars off the road. Sometimes it goes too fast and at other times it goes too slow. I have had my car to many mechanics, but no one seems to know how to fix it. This is an extremely valuable car and it is very important that it is repaired. I plan to keep this car forever. It is the best car I have ever had."

At first, the Porsche sounded his alarm when the new mechanic approached him. This mechanic was different from the other ones that had tried and failed to repair the Porsche. He understood how floods can change the way an engine functions and what needs to be done so the engine can began to work in a normal way again.

"I have worked on many cars that have been through floods," the mechanic told the owner. These cars need to be repaired in a very different way than cars that break down because of normal use. The flood has caused the electrical system in the engine to go too fast. Although this may seem very strange, it can be repaired by using the headlights.

At that, the mechanic brought out a headlight adjusting mechanism and turned on the headlights of the Porsche. Then he touched the car and acted like he was going to kick the tires as he moved the beams of the headlight back and forth. Then the mechanic rubbed the mud and sand from the flood on the engine, and again moved the headlights back and forth. "When you are reminded of the flood," the mechanic told the Porsche. "Find a way to move your headlights back and forth until it seems as if the flood happened a long time ago. Soon you will find yourself staying on the road, running the way you are directed to run, and only sounding your alarm when there is real danger."

The owner watched this mechanic moving the headlights and talking to his car. He wondered if he had made a mistake by bringing his treasured car to this repair shop. The mechanic directed the owner to take his car home and allow it to return to maximum functioning without pushing it too hard. Figuring he had nothing to lose since no one else had repaired his car, the owner drove his Porsche home.

Soon, to the surprise of the owner, the Porsche was running much the way it used to run. When he drove the Porsche on the road, his car responded exactly as it was designed to do. When parked, the alarm of the Porsche only activated when someone started to kick the car, tried to steal it or hurt it in some way. Then the owner drove the Porsche to the racetrack for its final test. The sports car drove over 100 miles per hour; it stayed on the track and the engine purred as a car does when it believes it is the best car ever made. It wasn't long before the Porsche was running better than it had before the flood, because as all car buffs know, a great car gets better with age.

In the days that followed, when the owner noticed other cars that had been damaged by the flood, he made sure to tell their owner about the car mechanic who used head lights to repair the damage from the flood.

©1995
Nancy Davis, Ph.D.

The House and the Hurricane

Problem(s) Addressed:

The withdrawal and numbing symptoms of Post Traumatic Stress Disorder while in the avoidance stage (Foa, et. al., 1995; Riggs, et. al., 1995).

Appropriate for:

Anyone from age 6 years to adult level who is withdrawing. Young children in this stage can look and test retarded. Their withdrawal and "closing off" often is chronic, if the trauma was long-term.

Message:

You can protect yourself and find ways to feel safe while relating to those around you and join in the activities of the world.

Symbols and Metaphors:

Hurricane: any traumatic experience
Boarding up the windows: withdrawing and closing off perceptions and interest in the outside world

Elements of the Story That Can be Changed:

Sex of the main character, the events that the main character misses by withdrawing can be personalized.

Note:

This story was designed for a seven-year-old boy who was very withdrawn. His IQ tested in the 70's. He had been in foster care all of his life after being born to a drug- addicted mother. He was also stealing, could not sleep and had nightmares. This story, along with "The Hunger that Wouldn't Go Away," "The Dark Sunglasses," "The Hole in the Heart" and "The Boy Who Got Rid of His Nightmares" were all written for him. He listened to them nightly along with "The

32

The House and the Hurricane

Once upon a time there was a little town located by the ocean. Most of the time, living in this town near the ocean was a relaxing and happy experience. At times, however, storms would appear and the ocean would churn, appearing dark and scary. Hurricanes were the most damaging of the storms. The townspeople had learned that the winds of a hurricane blew with such force that they often broke the glass of the windows. When that happened, broken glass would fly through their houses, causing even more damage. Long ago, as the townspeople repaired the broken glass in their homes following a hurricane, they figured out a way to keep this from happening again. When a hurricane was forecast, everybody in the town boarded up the windows on their houses and stores.

The summer days came and went with hardly a storm. Then one day the weatherman said, "There's a hurricane coming this way. You need to board up your windows." So everybody in town boarded up their windows.

In this town there was one little house where the windows were boarded up very, very tightly because it didn't want to be hurt by the hurricane. Soon after the boards were secured, the winds of the hurricane began to blow. It wasn't long before the wind blew harder and with greater force. As the winds became more fierce, tree branches battered the house as did all kinds of other flying objects. Although these flying objects made a couple of dents in the roof, the windows did not break because the windows were all boarded up.

After the hurricane had blown over the little house looked like a mess on the outside. Some of the roofing tiles were curled, the paint had peeled a bit and there were some holes in the siding. The owner of the house saw that the hurricane had caused some damage but also realized that without the boards on the windows, more of the house would have been destroyed. "I don't like my house to be hurt." the owner said to himself. "I think I'll just leave these boards on the windows all the time in case a hurricane or a storm comes unexpectedly. Then, in the future I won't have to worry about the windows ever being broken."

The owner paid a price for leaving up the boards. Every room inside the house stayed dark and he could no longer see out the windows. "Although I would like to be able to see out of my windows", the owner said to himself, "feeling safe is better than seeing. Keeping up these boards is worth the price I pay, since no hurricane can come unexpectedly and blow my whole house apart and break all the windows. Perhaps I can drill tiny holes in the boards so I can see enough out of my windows to know what is happening around me. In that way, my house will be protected but I'll know if anyone is outside."

So that is what he did. He continued to have a house that was very dark inside and had small holes in the boards on the windows so he could see out when he wanted to. However, he still couldn't see very much because when he looked out of the holes the only view he had was directly in front of him. He couldn't see anything on either side, so he missed most of what would have been visible from a window. He couldn't see the ocean, he couldn't see the birds flying and he couldn't see the blue sky.

On days when the weather man forecast storms, the owner would say to himself, "I'm so smart to keep my windows boarded up all the time because I don't have to put up the boards every time a storm is forecast. Who knows, a little storm might turn into a hurricane without warning. I don't have to worry about storms because my windows are completely closed; they are boarded up and I'm protected."

Fierce storms and hurricanes didn't come often to the little town, perhaps once a year. This left 364 days when the weather was pleasant and only one when it wasn't. So for the 364 days when the weather was nice, the owner sat in his dark house without seeing very much.

One day a circus came to town and marched down the street where the house was boarded up, and invited everyone to come and have fun at the circus. However, the windows of the house were boarded up, so the owner didn't see the circus on his street, so he didn't go.

On another day, some of his friends came to town to go to the beach. Usually they stayed at his house, but this time they drove by the house and noticed the boards. "It looks like nobody is home because the windows are all boarded up," they said to each other. "It seems our friend moved away." So they went to the beach without him. Because the owner did not look through his tiny holes very often, he didn't see his friends and missed having fun.

A neighborhood picnic was held on another summer day, with everyone but the man attending. Those at the picnic barbecued ribs and hot dogs and everyone played games. The owner loved picnics but wasn't able to see that there was a picnic going on because his windows remained boarded up and he stayed in his house.

On one of the rare occasions that the owner left his house, the own saw his neighbor trimming his bushes and walked over in his yard for a chat. "This place isn't any fun at all," the owner commented. "It's really boring to live here."

"What do you mean it's boring?" his neighbor replied in amazement. "Lots of things have been happening lately. Last week the circus came to town, we had a picnic recently and just the other day your friends came to visit."

"They did?" the owner responded, "I didn't see them." His neighbor remarked, "Well, no wonder you didn't see them. You keep your windows all boarded up. You can't see much of anything. You miss almost everything that happens out here because of the boards on your windows."

"But I need to keep them boarded up because of storms that might come," the owner replied with hesitation.

His neighbor looked at him with concern, announcing, "There aren't many storms in your life, and you're missing a lot by keeping those boards up. Why don't you try taking the boards down and see what happens?"

The owner considered removing the boards. Even though he was very afraid of storms, he decided that the neighbor was right; storms do not come very often. He could listen to the weather report and if a storm was coming, he could put the boards back up. So he pulled the boards off his windows and he let light in to every area of the house. He went inside his house and discovered it was now easy to see out his windows. This house had great big windows. He even cleaned the glass so he could see more clearly.

The next day there was a party in the neighborhood. The owner was looking out of his window and he noticed it. So he made some cookies and took them to the party. The owner had so much fun.

Then, on another day, some children fell off their bikes near his yard. Because the owner was now able to see out his windows, he realized that they were hurt and ran out to help them.

Before long, his friends returned and seeing that the boards were no longer on the windows, said to each other, "Our friend must be home now. Let's go visit him." So they knocked on the door. He was very happy to see them, and they spent the day talking and laughing and doing things all friends like to do when they're together.

That night the owner was watching the news on television and saw that there was a hurricane in another part of the world. The news program showed pictures of everybody boarding up their windows. So the owner spoke to the people on the television, as if they could hear. "Hey, you people boarding up those windows. Remember to take those boards off when the hurricane is gone. If you don't, you will miss a lot of things in life that are fun and that make you happy and help you to grow." Then he smiled because he realized he was talking to himself. The owner had learned that windows are a very important part of life and boards can be a prison as well as a protector.

©1995
Nancy Davis, Ph.D.

The Closet

Problem(s) Addressed:

Withdrawal from the world because of trauma, the avoidance, the numbing stage of PTSD, This story is also appropriate for those who close down because of lack of being loved and nurtured when they were a child.

Appropriate for:

Ages 5 to adult

Message:

Although the way you dealt with trauma was appropriate in the past, it is time to re-join the world and to "let go" of the withdrawal, the numbing, and the depression.

Symbols and Metaphors:

The tornado: any trauma

Locking the doors and getting into the closet: withdrawal and rejection of the world in order to protect oneself

The window and the light: opening up perceptions

Unlocking the locks which are different: finding the power within one's self to leave the symptoms of trauma behind

Teacher calling: a reference to the child's difficulty with learning because of withdrawal due to trauma

Elements of the Story That Can be Changed:

Name and sex of the child, the type of trauma from which the child hides, what the child does when he/she leaves the closet.

The Closet

Once upon a time there was a girl named Mary who lived in a big house. Now this house was very nice and had many rooms. In fact, it had so many rooms that Mary hadn't been in all of them. There were big rooms and small rooms. There were rooms that were shaped like squares and some that were shaped like triangles. The house even had rooms that were shaped like circles. There were rooms with other kinds of shapes as well. There were rooms that had big windows in them and rooms with lots of lights. There were rooms with soft carpet and other rooms with shiny floors. All in all, this house had rooms of all colors, sizes, shapes and textures.

One day a tornado tore through the neighborhood where Mary lived. She had learned at school that the safest place to be during a tornado is in a protected place in the center of the house. When Mary heard about the tornado, she was playing outside. Her friend yelled, "There is a tornado coming. You need to go in the center of your house, go in the closet and close the door because that's where you'll be the safest." So Mary ran in the front door and locked it. Then she ran through some more doors in the house and locked them. Mary kept locking and locking doors until she got to a closet in the very center of the house. Then Mary opened the door of the closet, walked in and locked the door. She sat on the floor with her arms wrapped around her.

Although Mary did not like the dark of the closet, at least she felt safe. She didn't have to think about the tornado as she hid in her closet. Mary was locked so deeply into the center of the house, that she couldn't hear the tornado, nor could she feel the strong and damaging winds. Mary felt safe, deep inside the middle of the house in this closet.

The tornado came and went. When the tornado moved over Mary's house, it blew roofing shingles off the house, bent some of the siding and even broke a couple of windows. But these were things that could be easily fixed. Because Mary was inside the closet, she didn't know if the tornado had come or gone. Mary stayed in the closet, and she even stopped listening to find out what was happening. While she was in the closet, Mary didn't think about much. She just sat in the corner of the closet with the door shut, not able to see or hear and hardly able to think. Her friends became very worried about her because she never came out of her house to play. After a while, however, they thought that maybe she had moved away. But she hadn't moved away, she was still in the closet. She sat there for a long time getting older and older.

One day, someone from the local school knocked on the door of Mary's house. They had heard a girl lived behind the doors. But Mary was in the closet and she couldn't hear the knock because she was so deep inside the house. The school officials looked up Mary's phone number and dialed her number. Mary's phone began to ring and ring. Mary heard the phone and decided to answer it. So Mary opened up the closet door and listened to the ringing phone. Then Mary found the phone by opening many doors. "Hello," said Mary. The teacher from the school said, "It's time for you to go to school. It's time for you to learn. It's time for you to grow up and know what the world is all about, so you need to come out of the house and come to school."

Well, Mary had been in the closet for so long she wasn't sure that she remembered how to get out of the house. She told this to the teacher, who replied, "It's important that you open up all the rooms in your house so that you can use them and visit them and, especially, so you can let in the light that you need in your house." So Mary began to open each door.

Many of the doors were locked in very different ways. Sometimes Mary had to listen to the sounds on a lock to figure out how to unlock it. Other doors were very heavy, and the rooms in which they were located were very dark. Mary would feel the door and the shape of the lock and then she would be able to open the door. Other doors were easier to unlock, and she could figure out how to unlock them by simply looking at them. Mary started out slowly opening doors but she got faster and faster as she moved through the house. It wasn't long before Mary had opened every closed door in that entire house. The light came in the windows and Mary was able to see what was outside her house. She discovered many children waiting to play with her and walk her to school.

Mary found the front door of her house and ran out asking the waiting children, "Where is the school because I'm ready to learn. I've missed a lot of things while I was in that closet and it's time for me to learn. I've got to hurry up and learn everything I missed while I was in the closet." So the other children showed her the way to school. Mary recognized the voice of the teacher who had called her and said, "Thank you for calling me on the phone. I don't know if I'd have ever gotten out of that closet if you hadn't decided it was time for me to come to school and learn."

This teacher, and all the other teachers Mary had, taught her many things. She learned from the school, from her friends and from playing, reading and watching TV. She learned from other adults in her life, as well. Mary caught up with the other students in learning and then moved to advanced classes.

As Mary grew, she learned much about the world. She also learned that she never again wanted to be shut away in a closet. Mary became a weatherwoman who not only reported how to get in closets when tornados arrive but how and when to get out of them as well.

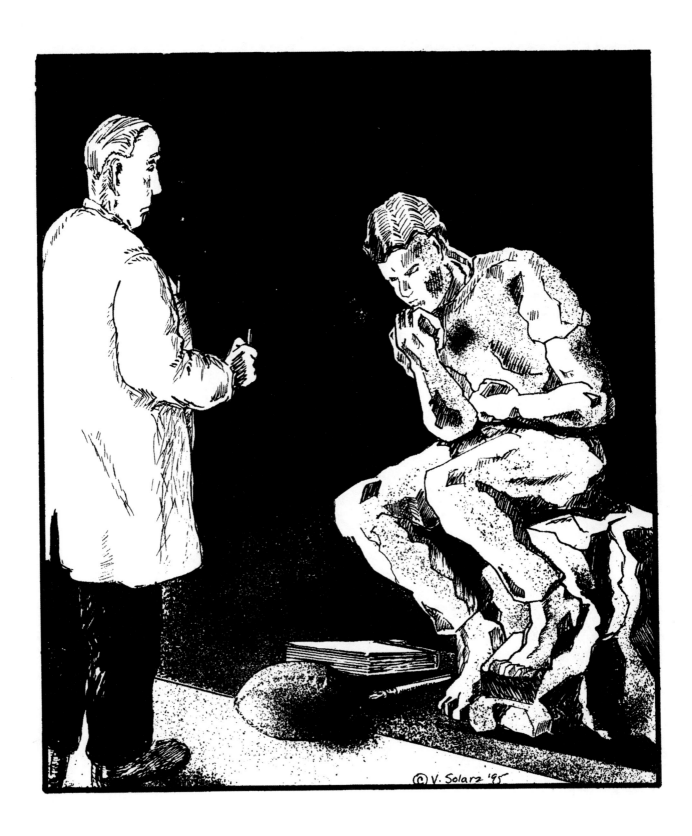

The Boy Who Turned to Stone

Problem(s) Addressed:

The numbing and withdrawal stage of Post Traumatic Stress Disorder.

Appropriate for:

Ages 6 - 16

Message:

You can find the power within yourself to come out of your withdrawal and rejoin the world.

Symbols and Metaphors:

Spell: the symptoms of Post Traumatic Stress Disorder

Couldn't see his gifts: low self esteem

Witch: anyone who causes PTSD in a child

Turned to stone: withdrawal to the point of having no affect and refusal to relate meaningfully to the world

Elements of the Story That Can be Changed:

The sex of the main character, the symptoms, what the main character says to himself, the family constellation.

Note:

This story was written for a 12-year-old boy whose angry withdrawal from the world kept him in a prison of unhappiness. It was created before I understood the withdrawal and numbing stage of PTSD could cause these type of symptoms. It is important that the abuse be a thing of the past when telling this story since a child cannot heal if the abuse is on-going.

The Boy Who Turned to Stone

Once upon a time a boy was born with many gifts. He was given the gift of intelligence. He was given the gift of artistic ability. He was given the gift of good looks and he was given the gift of a joyful laugh. His mother named him Shawn. At the time of Shawn's birth, there was an old witch who lived near Shawn's mother who was very jealous of her and thus put a spell on Shawn so he wouldn't know he had these gifts.

As the witch cast her spell, she said to herself laughing, "As that baby grows, he will not realize that he has gifts. He will be a behavior problem in school and he won't have any friends. He'll be very sad." Because this witch was mean, the thought that Shawn would have gifts with no awareness of them made her laugh to herself, "Ha, ha, ha."

Just as the old witch predicted, as Shawn grew, he was unaware of his gifts. When he looked in the mirror, he thought he was ugly. When he went to school, he did no work and the teachers wondered what was inside of Shawn. He didn't use his gift of drawing except to draw the same thing again and again. Shawn was unable to use his smile or laugh with joy because, after all, he had lost his gifts.

Shawn grew taller and older. Soon he was as tall as his mother and yet, he still had no idea of the gifts he possessed. Shawn had to go to school like everyone else but he would sit still for hours at a time, doing nothing. In fact, Shawn sat still for so long that eventually he turned to stone. Shawn couldn't move and he couldn't think. He couldn't talk and he couldn't smile. He was frozen with his hand on his face and the other arm around his stomach. He couldn't play sports and he couldn't have friends because he had turned to stone.

Shawn's teachers and principal were very concerned when they noticed what had happened to him. They called Shawn's mother to come quickly to school. When Shawn's mother saw him, she began to cry because she had no idea how to help him. An ambulance was called to take Shawn to the hospital. As Shawn was being carried out of school to the waiting ambulance, everyone noticed that Shawn's face had also turned to stone, just like his body. Stone statues cannot smile nor can they laugh. The face of a statue is frozen in one expression forever.

When Shawn arrived at the hospital, no one could understand how he had turned to stone. Many doctors and medical students examined Shawn, but none could cure him because they were unaware of the jealous witch's spell. They sat Shawn in a chair, where he remained waiting for someone to understand what he needed.

Shawn's mind was still thinking even though his outside was stone. "This is what I deserve because I'm such a terrible, ugly stupid person. I'm so worthless I don't deserve to be real."

When the neighbors heard about Shawn, they were concerned. Many sent food and flowers to Shawn's mother. The witch, however, laughed and talked to herself about the spell that had turned Shawn to stone. One neighbor heard the witch laughing and confronted her. "Take your spell off Shawn," she demanded, "or I will pour water all over you."

Because pouring water on a witch makes her disappear, the witch was not laughing any more. She tried threatening the neighbor, but the neighbor refused to back down. "Take the spell off of Shawn and I mean now," she yelled at the witch.

"Okay," said the wicked old witch. "I'll remove the spell but you must help by putting these special drops in his eyes." The witch handed the neighbor a small bottle.

The neighbor took the drops to the hospital and found Shawn still looking like a statue made of stone. Taking a mirror, the neighbor held it in front of Shawn. Then she dropped several drops in each of his eyes. The drops enabled Shawn to see himself in a new way and to reclaim his stolen gifts. First Shawn's eyes began to move. Then his hand reached to hug the neighbor who had brought the special drops. Soon Shawn was laughing and talking and flirting with all the girls in the halls. Very quickly Shawn was ready to return to school.

"I could not see my gifts when I was frozen by the spell," Shawn told the neighbor.
"That's true," she said, "but you can see them now."

©1995
Nancy Davis, Ph.D.

46

The Storm

Problem(s) Addressed:

Traumatic experiences. Giving up hope when trauma is encountered.

Appropriate for:

Ages 9 - adult

Message:

Life has many traumas. You can recover from trauma, regain your optimism and heal your wounds.

Symbols and Metaphors:

Tree: a person

Storms: any trauma

Forest ranger: any one who cares enough to help someone to heal

Some branches were broken beyond repair: trauma causes many changes and some permanent losses

Elements of the Story That Can be Changed:

Sex of forest ranger

Note:

This is another story written for victims and rescue workers of the Oklahoma Bombing disaster.

47

48

The Storm

Once upon a time somewhere away from big cities, grew a forest filled with trees of many kinds. There were big, tall trees, and there were small, short trees. There were trees that had been in the forest for many years and others had sprouted just days before. Among the many trees, an oak tree stood on a hill, almost as if it were watching over the forest. Because of the size of the oak, many believed it was the oldest tree in the forest. The government had declared these trees a part of a national forest, meaning that they were protected from loggers and developers.

Many visitors came to admire the trees, to get away from the busy city or to vacation with their families. Sometimes these people camped or had picnics. Many visitors enjoyed sitting quietly under the trees and admiring the most majestic among them.

Although being in a national park protects a tree from being cut down for lumber, it cannot protect the trees from the elements of nature. One dark day, a tremendous storm hit the forest. It was a storm with raging winds. The hail was the size of golf balls. The winds blew with such force that the leaves and branches on many of the trees were damaged or torn away. Some of the tops of the taller trees toppled with the force of the wind.

Because the oak tree grew high above most of the other trees, it was especially exposed to the fierce destruction of the storm. The winds and the hail tore away the leaves, broke the branches and tore away much of the bark.

When the storm had moved away, and the sun returned, so did the visitors who had frequented the forest in days past. They gazed at the damaged trees with much sadness. Children asked questions of their parents:

"Why are there storms in the world?"

"How hard did the wind have to blow to hurt this tree so much?"

"Will these trees grow back?"

"Is this tree going to die?"

"Why did the oak tree lose branches and other trees weren't hurt?"

Many of their questions had no answer.

The visitors asked a park ranger if there was a way they could help to restore the forest. This park ranger had worked around trees all her life; her father had been a forest ranger. She understood that a storm can destroy some trees, but it also makes some trees stronger and more determined to survive. She also understood that often it wasn't the damage of the storm that determined if a tree recovered and thrived. Experience taught the park ranger that it is the care a tree receives after a storm and the life force within the tree that often determines it's future.

The huge oak tree high on the hill had always been the favorite of the park ranger. It had a huge trunk and its branches had reached far out and up from the tree. The park ranger understood that the oak tree had lived for many years and had weathered many storms. Artists also found this oak tree a favorite to sketch.

As she viewed the tree after the storm, the park ranger overheard visitors making comments such as, "This tree will never make it!" But the park ranger did not view the world with such pessimism. It wasn't that she refused to see how extensively the oak tree was damaged. She understood that this tree would need special care to survive and grow and she was willing to provide this.

To begin, she cut off the branches that were broken beyond repair, understanding that the tree could sprout new growth and replace these branches. The tree was so big that pruning the branches took most of the day. The ranger smeared salve made especially for tree wounds on the biggest holes in the trunk to keep the insects from invading the tree. She used tree bandages to wrap the trunk with loving care, covering up any wood exposed to the elements.

Because the ranger had always thought of the trees as being her friends, she talked to the tree, encouraging it to heal. "You are going to make it," the ranger told the tree with encouragement, as if a tree could hear. "In fact, you are going to grow to be even more majestic than you were before the storm." She reminded the oak again and again that bark which regrows on a damaged trunk is even stronger than the original bark.

Perhaps because the ranger believed in the ability of the tree to heal itself, the tree somehow absorbed her optimism. It began to heal. The leaves began to sprout and the branches sent out new growth. For a while, the tree seemed to use its strength to replace everything that was lost. Then the strength turned toward new growth, which resulted in a tree even more magnificent than it had been before the storm.

The next summer, visitors returned to the national forest to admire the trees. Most of these people were unaware of the damaging storm. But the park ranger remembered and the tree

50

remembered. The park ranger used the storm to help her to understand how trees grow and how trees mend when they are damaged. The tree learned that bark which grows over wounds can be stronger than the bark that was torn away. They both learned that storms can be very devastating and learning how to heal from these storms is a valuable part of life.

The Tape Player

Problem(s) Addressed:

Problems with concentration, memory and academics commonly seen in those with chronic PTSD; this includes victims of child abuse (Browne, et. al., 1986; Friedrich, et. al., 1987).

Appropriate for:

Ages 6 to adult

Message:

You can find a way to heal your mind and allow your brain to function normally.

Symbols and Metaphors:

Tape Player: mind, memory
Only play a little bit of music: loss of memory; inability to use brain functioning
Repair man: wisdom of the unconscious

Elements of the Story That Can be Changed:

Sex of the main character; sex of the repair person.

Note:

Many children have academic problems because of undiagnosed PTSD. Since adults who have experienced trauma often have problems with reading, writing, math, and memory, a child who has never learned these skills would have much more difficulty. It is important to look for trauma in a child's background when he or she is having learning and/or behavior problems in school.

The Tape Player

Once upon a time there was a boy named Chris who saved up his money to buy a tape player. Chris loved music and he had been given many tapes by friends and relatives. Because Chris didn't have a job, he couldn't afford a new tape player, so he decided to buy a used one at a pawn shop. When Chris had enough money saved, he bought just the tape player he wanted. He couldn't wait to get it home and listen to music.

When Chris put a tape of his favorite songs in the tape player for the first time, all he could hear were parts of the songs. "What is happening here?" Chris asked himself. "Maybe I have a damaged tape." So he tried another one of his tapes. Again, just little parts of the songs on the tape could be heard. The tape player would skip over most of the song and only play a little bit of music every now and then. "What is wrong with this tape player?" Chris wanted to know. To make sure that it was his tape player that was having a problem, Chris took his tapes to a friend's house. When he tried his tapes in his friend's tape player, they played perfectly.

Chris began to get angry. He knew that the pawn shop had a no-money-back policy, so he was stuck with a tape player that wouldn't work. "What is wrong with this tape player?", Chris yelled. He shook the tape player but that didn't help. It still skipped over most of the music on a tape. In fact, the madder Chris got at the tape player, the worse it played. When he kicked the tape player, he couldn't hear a thing although the tape was turning in the player.

Chris decided that he had to do something. It didn't make sense to keep a broken tape player and he didn't know how to fix it. Chris remembered that a man in his neighborhood knew a great deal about electronics. This man knew how to fix all kinds of things so that they worked as good as new. So Chris took his tape player to the man's house. "Can you help me?" he asked the man. Then Chris described what was happening when he tried to play a tape.

"That's a very common problem," the man told Chris. "I see that problem in tape players that have been dropped or banged around a lot. Sometimes tape players with this problem have been left outside in freezing temperatures or no one has owned them and taken care of them."

55

Then the man removed the back of the tape player, opened it up and showed Chris the problem. "This tape player has had so much bad treatment that the little parts that touch the tape and read the music are pulled away and shut off and shut down. I can fix this but after I do, you are going to have to treat this tape player very well."

"I promise, I promise," Chris declared.

So the man moved the parts of the tape player that had pulled away from playing the tape. He made sure that he adjusted these parts so that they would have the benefit of touching all of the places necessary to play beautiful music. Then he replaced the back and returned it to Chris.

"Let's try a tape," Chris said. So he popped a tape in the tape player and it played the entire song. "This is really neat," Chris announced happily. "Thank you, thank you so very much." Chris played his tape player all the way home. He played happy songs, he played sad songs, he played dancing songs and he played rock and rap songs.

As Chris played these songs, he talked to his tape player. "You can always play music for me. You don't have to pull away because I'm not going to mistreat you. Music can help you to feel happy and it can also teach you many things. If you had continued to be so disconnected, you might have ended up in the garbage or with some street person who couldn't hear very well."

The tape player, even though it wasn't alive, seemed to listen to Chris and understand. Because Chris knew how to treat a tape player, it stayed on track and connected to the tapes that were playing. Each day Chris thought the tape player sounded even better. One day Chris had a visit from a friend carrying a tape player. "This tape player skips a lot of music," the friend said.

"I know what's wrong," Chris told him. "My tape player used to skip music on tapes, but the problem is completely gone."

The tape player seemed to smile as Chris told his friend how to get the broken tape player repaired.

©1995
Nancy Davis, Ph.D.

The Dog and the Hurricane

Problem(s) Addressed:

Fear and withdrawal that is a result of exposure to a traumatic event (van der Kolk, 1995)..

Appropriate for:

Ages 5 - 12

Message:

You are safe and can 'let go' of your fear.

Symbols and Metaphors:

Hurricane: any traumatic experience that is over

Cave: withdrawal, shutting down, depression

Filling up the entrance to the cave: finding a way to keep from withdrawing

Didn't know the hurricane was coming: sudden trauma or a child's innocence in not understanding about sexual abuse

Elements of the Story That Can be Changed:

The sex of the main character. Symptoms displayed because of the fear of the hurricane.

Note:

This story was created for a six-year-old boy whose relative entered the bathroom while he was taking a bath and sexually assaulted him. He became withdrawn and could not talk about the event. He also had problems in school. This story can be used for any type of trauma in which the child's withdrawal becomes a problem.

58

The Dog and the Hurricane

Once upon a time there lived a furry, energetic dog named Mack. Because he lived on the ocean, he loved to run up and down the beach, jumping in the waves and chasing crabs. He was so full of joy that he made friends with all the dogs and cats that lived along the beach.

One day a hurricane hit the beach. Mack didn't know the hurricane was coming; dogs do not listen to weather reports or read newspapers. At first, when the big waves hit the beach, Mack ran right into them. As the waves got bigger and the wind blew harder, however, Mack got scared. The hurricane was so powerful that he couldn't outrun it, so Mack did the only thing he could think of to protect himself — he found a place to hide. Mack knew of a cave that went deep into the ground, but he had never been in it because it seemed so dark and scary. Mack decided that the darkness of the cave was not as frightening as the winds and force of the hurricane. So Mack ran deep into the cave and hid in order to protect himself from the powerful hurricane.

The wind blew, and blew. Houses were torn apart and streets were flooded. After what seemed like forever to Mack, but was really a short time, the hurricane was over. Soon the sun came out and Mack's friends started looking for him. When they discovered him hiding in the cave, they called for their friend to come out and play. But Mack would not come out; he was scared.

The cats he had befriended and the other dogs that lived along the beach tried to get Mack to join them on the beach. Eventually Mack came out for a little while, but he was easily scared and spent most of the day hiding in the cave. Mack no longer chased waves or crabs.

"What is wrong with you?" asked one of the dogs that had been his friend for a long time. "Not only have you stopped playing, but you seem to have stopped learning as well. What did that hurricane do to you? Why are you so scared?"

Mack hung his head and didn't answer. He wasn't sure why the hurricane had done things to him, or what had happened to him. Mack just knew he didn't feel very good inside and he wanted to run back in the cave again.

One day, Mack's friend stood in front of the cave, blocking the way so Mack couldn't hide. "Mack," he said, "if you keep running in that cave, you'll never be able to do anything you used to do before the hurricane came. You're hiding when you are supposed to be learning. I'm going to help you. Let's cover up the hole to the cave so you can't run back in it anymore."

Mack wasn't quite sure that he wanted to cover up the cave. It scared him to think he might not have a cave to run into. But Mack realized his friend was right — he shouldn't be hiding inside that cave all the time. So his friend got all the other dogs on the beach to help. They dug and dug with their paws until they had totally covered up the entrance to the cave. Now Mack would have to find another way to face his fear.

After that, Mack had many dreams that helped him let go of his fear so he could play, learn and laugh. It wasn't long before Mack was again chasing waves, crabs and butterflies. He learned many new things from his friends and he made new friends with the cats and dogs who had just moved to the beach. Mack had learned something very important from the cave and his friends: there's no need to hide from a hurricane that's already gone.

The Big Furnace

Problem(s) Addressed:

The explosive anger and irritation common in those experiencing both acute and chronic PTSD (Marcey, 1995).

Appropriate for:

Ages 6 - adult

Message:

You can find a way to turn down the hyperstimulation in your brain and decrease your anger to an average level. Your problem with anger is related to your traumatic experience.

Symbols and Metaphors:

House: person

Lightening & storms: any trauma

Damaged the control of the furnace: stress hormones changed the functioning of the brain

Repair the controls: find a way to regulate the brain

Elements of the Story That Can be Changed:

The way the anger is expressed.

Note:

Many individuals who experience trauma find that the symptoms include irritability and anger that moves instantly from non-existent to rage. We have found that these symptoms are reduced following treatment with techniques which focus on the right brain (Eyemovement Desensitization & Reprocessing; Multi-Sensory Trauma Processing); the area of the brain which imaging indicates is over-stimulated during PTSD (van der Kolk, 1995).

The Big Furnace

Once upon a time there was a house in the woods — a very special house. It had thick walls, a sturdy roof and many windows. The inside of the house was furnished with love and care. All in all, it was a very appealing house, until one stormy day when a bolt of lightning hit the roof of the house. The bolt was so powerful, that it burned a hole through the roof and struck the furnace.

Before the lightning and the storm came, the house was always at just the right temperature for comfort. The lightning, however, damaged the furnance controls causing it to constantly overheat. After the storm, the basement of the house was hot, the attic was hot and the living area was especially hot. The heat from the house was so intense that it would reach out and burn all the things that lived around it. Soon all around the house was bare and lonely. No one would visit the house and no plants grew near the house as they had before. The furnace in the house even burned itself, causing the inside to be dark and charred and burned. Obviously, no one was able to live in this house comfortably.

One day a family walking through the woods came upon the overheated house. The family noticed that, as they walked closer to the house, the air seemed to become hotter and hotter. The burned plants around the house caught their attention and they observed that the house was abandoned by animals and people.

"Why is this house out here in the woods?" one child asked.
"Why is everything so burned around it?" the mother wondered.
The father decided to find out. He was a very good mechanic and quickly discovered the source of the problem. "The furnace in this house is burning too intensely," he said. "The thermostat is stuck so that the furnance can't cool off."

As he continued to study the furnace, the burns from the lightning bolt became apparent. "A lightning bolt has damaged the furnace. The furnace is burning itself up and its fire is so destructive that everything around it is being destroyed," he informed his family. At that, the man turned the furnace off. Then he found a way to repair the controls so that the furnace could again regulate itself. He adjusted the furnace until he was satisfied that the furnace was in control. He then observed the furnace as it began to heat the house in just the right way, so that it was once again comfortable and inviting.

After the repairs were complete, the family found the house very appealing. So they cleaned and decorated the inside of the house and replanted trees and flowers on the outside. Soon grass began to grow around the house and the yard began to look green and alive. Birds returned to sit on the roof. Animals reappeared in the yard, delighted again to be near the house. The house was very happy that the family had discovered why the furnace was so hot and realized that just because something breaks does not mean it can't be fixed.

©1995
Nancy Davis, Ph.D.

The Angry Red Ball

Problem(s) Addressed:

Expressing emotions directly by talking about what is bothering you rather than indirectly through behavior.

Appropriate for:

Ages 3 - 6

Message:

Talking about the things that bother you will help your angry feelings to go away.

Symbols:

Red Ball: feeling of anger or sadness or rejection

Magic Lady: therapist or teacher

Out through your mouth: talking about feelings

Elements of the Story Which Can be Changed:

Sex of the main character; the behavior the child displays when angry; the events that caused the anger; the person who talks to the child to get them to express feelings.

Note:

This story was written for a four-year-old who was having problems talking in the therapy session. It is very simple and appropriate for young children who need to learn to express feelings. It is important not to promise that the parents will discontinue their behavior just because the child expresses his/her displeasure to them.

The Angry Red Ball

Once upon a time there was a boy named Mark. Mark lived in a family where he played and played all day. Then some things happened in the family that made Mark feel very funny inside. When Mark felt those funny feelings, a big angry red ball seemed to appear inside of him with sharp points that hurt his tummy. When the angry, red ball was in his tummy, it seemed to make Mark do things he didn't want to do. He hurt the cat and threw things across the room. He broke his toys and wrote on the wall. When Mark acted like this, he got in big trouble and his family became angry with him. Mark got mad at himself but he didn't know what to do because that big, painful, red ball was still inside him. Sometimes the ball burned and this made Mark feel sad.

One day Mark said to himself, "I don't want to have that red ball inside me anymore. I am tired of this." So Mark went to talk to a special lady who knew all about getting rid of red balls. He said, "Will you get rid of this angry red ball inside of me, magic lady?"

"I can help you, Mark, but you must talk to me and tell me what's bothering you. The ball will come out with your words as you talk about things that make you feel funny inside."

"Okay," said Mark, "I thought talking about the funny feeling would make it worse, but I will tell you about it and see if that helps." Mark talked and talked about everything that had been bothering him. The magic lady helped Mark think of ideas that would make the funny feelings go away. Mark tried the new ideas when he returned home.

Soon Mark was talking more and more. He told his family about the funny feelings. Then he told them about others things that had been bothering him. One day, Mark noticed with surprise that the ball was gone. He stopped breaking his toys and hurting the cat. He used pencils to write on paper, rather than the wall. He laughed with his family and rarely got in trouble.

After that, any time that Mark felt a red ball forming in his tummy, he made sure he talked to people about it, so that any angry red balls that were forming in his tummy could disappear. When his parents asked Mark what he wanted for his birthday, he told them a red ball. Mark wanted to remind himself that red balls are to throw and play with and they do not belong in your tummy.

The Incredible Car

Problem(s) Addressed:

Sudden trauma

Appropriate for:

Ages 6 - adult

Message:

You can find a way to heal from the trauma you have experienced and to rebuild your dreams. You can find a way to be optimistic, despite the fact that life is not fair, nor has it ever been.

Symbols and Metaphors:

The Car: any dream

Vandals: any trauma, especially those purposely caused by humans

Elements of the Story That Can be Changed:

The sex of the main character; characteristics of the car

Note:

This story was written for victims of the Oklahoma City Bombing disaster in 1995. It was used with the families and children of rescue workers, as well. "The Incredible Car" was one of the many stories recorded on an audio tape given to those touched by this disaster. Many of the rescue workers continued to have symptoms of PTSD months after the disaster experience. In my experience working with these individuals, it was the memory of the children that caused the most troubling flashbacks.

70

The Incredible Car

Once upon a time there lived a boy who, from a very young age, dreamed of building a magnificent car. When he was young, he played with toy cars. Then, as he grew from a boy to a man, he spent all of his spare time looking at cars and learning about cars. He loved Porsches and Mazdas and Corvettes. He admired Ferraris and Mustangs and Miratas. He looked carefully at the differences in the bodies and engines of each car. He was always asking questions about engines to anyone who would listen. Each day as he grew, he told himself, "I am going to build a car of my very own and it will have the best of every car I have ever admired."

Every night while he slept, his mind designed his car. It added parts and details into his dream so that as he became an adult, he had a clear picture in his mind of the perfect car. He knew exactly how it would look and could imagine the way it would drive. He sensed how powerfully his car would move from zero to sixty and how it would feel to shift the gears and hug the road as it went around corners. He could even smell the leather of the seats. There was never a doubt in his mind that he would someday build the car of his dreams.

Because he realized that attaining his dream required more than luck or magic, he attended schools that taught engine repair and body design. After graduating and finding a job, he devoted every spare minute of his time and all extra money he earned to building his car. He rented a garage and he spent hours and hours building this car. Because the car of his dreams was very complicated, it took months to perfect it. He made sure that the engine worked in the most efficient way. The body was sleek and different from any other car. He sprayed bright red paint on the body of the car until it was smooth and shiny.

At last, the day came when the car he created matched the car in his dream. It was time to show his dream to the world. Even his license plate said, **MY DREAM.** As he drove his car for the first time, the motor seemed to purr as it idled at stoplights.

As the red car moved from street to street, people stopped to admire his car. It was unlike any other car on the road. As word of his car spread, representatives from all the major car

71

manufacturers arrived to look it over. It was apparent to all the representatives that this man had talent. They offered him jobs designing cars for their companies.

However, not everyone in the town admired his car. A group of angry teenagers were jealous that the car was not theirs and they had not designed or built it. Rather than approaching the owner and finding a way to learn from him, they found out that the car was left in a garage at night, unattended. Then, intending to take their anger out on the magnificent car, they broke into the garage. Using hammers and baseball bats, the teenagers beat the car until it was dented from bumper to bumper. Not satisfied with damaging only the body, they ripped the seats and upholstery with knives and then poured syrup into the engine. Content that they had damaged the car beyond repair, they laughed as they ran from the garage.

As the owner of the car entered the garage the next morning, he stopped in shock as he viewed his dream. As reality replaced shock, feelings of sadness and grief rose within him. The car of his dreams was a mess. "Why," he asked himself, "would someone destroy my car, the car that I have spent a lifetime designing and building?"

The grief and anger at losing his dream overwhelmed him, shutting down the energy and vision that he had used to create his car. He stopped dreaming about cars. His dreams of cars were replaced with thoughts of catching the people who had vandalized his car. Soon he began skipping work.

"Well, that's that," he muttered to himself one night. "I've spent all my life dreaming about this car and now my dream is dead."

Each night as he sadly fell asleep, he had nightmares that he was driving his car through fires or hurricanes or floods. The car would, of course, be almost a total wreck from the battles in his dreams, but as the nightmare ended, his car would be restored and he would wake up.

It took time before the message of the nightmares became clear: "I can handle this," he said to himself firmly, "my dream is only dead if I allow it to be. If I give up, then the vandals win; their anger will not destroy my dream." So he searched within himself for the part that had motivated him to pursue his dream in the beginning and used this force to motivate himself again.

First he applied to the insurance company to pay him for the damages. When they paid him, he used that money to make his dream car even better than it was before. He bought leather to reupholster the seats. Because of recent improvements in leather, the new seats were even more comfortable and stain resistant than before. Then he hammered out all the dents and repainted the car. The new paint was incredibly durable, shiny and fade-resistant. He drained the syrup out of the engine and cleaned it. He was even able to improve the engine so it would run more efficiently than the old engine. Although it took a lot of work, this car was again a mirror of his dreams.

Now, instead of using the car on special occasions, he drove it every day. The people of his town continued to admire his creation. He received many job offers and a picture of his car was even on the cover of a national automotive magazine.

Because he was a man who learned from the past, he moved his remodeled car to a new garage that was secure. He installed locks and alarms to keep out vandals and thieves. He even bought a watch dog to sleep with the car so that anyone who tried to bother his car would have to deal with the dog.

In the years following, the man built more cars and had other dreams. He had learned that it is important to hold on to your dreams even when life tries to take them away from you.

©1995
Nancy Davis, Ph.D.

The Tadpoles Who Became Frogs

Problem(s) Addressed:

Frozen developmental growth caused by traumatic experiences. Emotional and social growth is especially affected. Although common in individuals who have been abused as children, this stunting of growth happens in other types of traumatic experiences such as the sudden and/or violent loss of a family member (Marcey, 1995) or even in life experiences typically not regarded as traumatic by many professionals, such as when the parents of a young child divorce.

Appropriate for:

Any child or adult where growth in some area is stunted or delayed.

Message:

You can find a way to move the traumatic experience into your past and grow all parts of you to your chronological age.

Symbols and Metaphors:

Tadpoles: childhood

Frogs: late adolescence and adulthood

Toxic Waste: any traumatic experience which affects growth

Memory of the toxic waste moved far into the past: the challenge to put the memories into the past, rather than keep them in the present, as is typical of PTSD

Elements of the Story That Can be Changed:

Individualizing some of the symptoms or behaviors characteristic of the person being told the story.

Note:

Many individuals become developmentally frozen; this frozen development occurs in social, emotional, intellectual and even physical areas when trauma is experienced (Downs, 1993; Perry, 1993; Rosen and Fields, 1988). Others have growth which is inappropriate such as becoming sexually active or developing breasts at a young age. It is important that the therapist use as many techniques as necessary to "unstick" the frozen development.

This story was written for a fourteen-year-old boy whose father had been murdered when he was seven. He was still in PTSD when entering therapy (although he had been to other therapists) and seemed emotionally and socially much more like a seven-year-old than a teenager. He especially liked the endless tapes that gave positive directives for his thinking and behavior. His mother turned the tape on in the middle of the night, allowing it to play for two hours. Later, she put the tape on a timer of the type that is used to turn lights off and on when on vacation. It wasn't long before the teenager was creating his own tapes, with some direction from the therapist. His behavior, and his developmental growth changed dramatically.

The Tadpoles Who Became Frogs

Once upon a time a frog laid her eggs in a bubbling brook. The water of the brook wove its way through a lush green forest, where many animals gathered along its banks to drink. The eggs hooked on a submerged branch, where the tiny black spots in the center of the clear jell began to grow.

Soon the tiny tadpoles emerged from the clear covering of the eggs. They swam here and there, weaving their tails back and forth as they moved through the water. It wasn't long before small legs began to grow on the front and back of their underbellies as they began the transformation from tadpole to frog. Things went smoothly for a while as the sun warmed the water to just the right temperature for the tadpoles to grow.

Then somewhere upstream, a factory began to dump toxic chemicals into the stream that ran beside its building. Soon the poison drifted down the brook until it reached the tadpoles. Some tadpoles became very ill from the toxic waste. Others were swimming in grass close to the edge of the stream, so they were less affected by the poison than those in the middle. As time passed, the toxic waste dumping was discovered and stopped, and the stream returned to being clear and clean. Many of the tadpoles, however, had taken in the chemicals in such a way that their growth was stunted and changed.

When it became time for the tadpoles to leave the water and hop on the land as frogs, problems of many kinds arose. Some tadpoles found a way to thrive despite the toxic waste and quickly hopped out of the water, with no sign that they had encountered any problems in their growth. Others had many characteristics of a frog, but when they left the water, they had problems. Some had difficulty breathing air or hopping. Others had difficulty giving up the ways of a tadpole and adapting to the ways of a frog.

Some of the tadpoles refused to leave the water, even though they had many characteristics of a frog. They did not feel safe hopping by themselves on land, preferring to remain in the confines of the familiar. Thus, these tadpoles were unable to move and develop as nature had intended them to do.

Those tadpoles that refused to leave the water and the frogs that had trouble adapting to land seemed to sense the natural order of change and growth was being interrupted, but they did not know what to do. So some frogs were out of place on land not seeming to fit in with more developed frogs. And some tadpoles were out of place in the water since they had many characteristics of a frog.

One day, two scientists from the state laboratory came to the stream to determine how the toxic waste of the factory had affected the plants and animals living there. These scientists noticed the poorly-developed tadpoles still living in the water. Looking on land, the scientists found that some frogs seemed to have developed normally despite exposure to the poison. Others, however, looked like their development had been frozen and stunted.

Because the scientists understood that exposure to toxic waste was harmful, they had brought with them solutions to reverse trauma caused by the chemical plant. First they mixed clean, clear water with the solution. Then they scooped up all of the tadpoles from the stream and washed each of them in the solution. "Nature has intended you to grow into frogs and hop away from the restriction of the water," one of the scientists remarked as he washed the small creature. "Find a way for all parts of you to grow and develop and become what nature intended you to be."

Then the scientists found all of the frogs whose growth had been changed by the toxic chemicals. They washed each one in the solution, as well. "Find a way to release all the toxic chemicals that you took in," the other scientist said as she gently washed each frog. "You can find a way for all parts of you to grow quickly to the age nature intended you to be."

After returning the tadpoles to the water and the frogs to land, the two scientists moved on, looking for other plants and animals they could help.

It wasn't long before the solution began to work. Soon the tadpoles had turned into frogs and hopped away from the water as they were designed to do. Frogs that had been stunted in their development, grew quickly into normal frogs. The memory of the toxic waste also moved far away into the past, as memories are designed to do.

Soon the frogs could be heard croaking in what seemed to be a musical harmony as they celebrated their understanding that nature provides ways to heal from even the most traumatic of experiences.

©1996
Nancy Davis, Ph.D.

The Flower that Froze

Problem(s) Addressed:

The impact of fear on developmental growth. Caretakers who do not understand the healing value of love and encouragement for victims of trauma.

Appropriate for:

Ages 5 - adult

Message:

Find the power to 'let go' of your fear and grow as nature has intended. Giving love and encouragement to a victim of trauma can help them to heal.

Symbols and Metaphors:

Storm: any kind of unexpected trauma

Frozen growth: the impact of trauma on developmental growth

Berries into jelly: the message that love and attention to others has its own rewards in returning nurturing to the caregiver

Elements of the Story That Can be Changed:

Sex of the scouts; the message given to the plant.

Note:

This story can have a dual purpose. If it is taped for a child to listen to it at bedtime, the caretakers are bound to listen to the story, at least on an unconscious level. They will hear the message as well. Their unconscious can then hear the messages that encouragement and love are the best ways to heal a traumatized child and perhaps change their behavior, if necessary.

The Flower That Froze

Once upon a time a plant began to grow from a seed. It was a very strong plant — its leaves were healthy, its branches sturdy and it grew tall and straight.

One spring day, a late winter storm suddenly turned the sky grey, dropping snow and sleet. The sleet hit the plant with a hard force, tearing the leaves and injuring the branches and stem. Because this storm was unexpected, the plant was not prepared for it.

Even after the storm was over and the spring sun returned, the plant remained damaged. As the days changed to summer, the other plants in the area recovered from the storm, growing and changing. But this plant had problems recovering. It still had torn leaves and broken stems and branches. The storm had been so sudden and scary that the plant seemed to freeze as if it were a silk plant rather than a living plant. The other plants grew tall, shading this plant from the sunlight it needed to grow.

One day a group of boy scouts, looking for rare and unique plants to earn a badge, came trooping through the area where the frozen plant was hidden. These boys looked here and there searching for plants. One of the scouts, who was very curious and determined, looked under logs, between trees and behind bushes hoping to discover unusual plants. In doing this, he pushed aside the plants which had been hiding the frozen plant. The scout looked carefully at the leaves of the plant. Pulling a book on plants out of his pack, the scout found a picture of the plant he had discovered. Seeing that this plant was rare, he called to the scout master, "I have discovered a very rare plant, but something has happened to it. It does not seem to be growing. By this time of the summer, it should be tall and have many berries."
"Well," the scout master responded, "perhaps we can change that."

The scouts did not dig up unique plants, believing that they should remain in the wild. Instead, they cut away all the weeds from around the plant. They watered it and fertilized it.

81

Then the scouts spoke words of encouragement to the plant. "You are a unique plant. Find the power to grow and be magnificent as you were intended to be."

The plant somehow understood the words of the boy scouts, but seemed frozen with fear. The scouts did not give up. They continued to visit the plant. They brought pictures of similar plants bearing red flowers or berries. "The plants in these pictures have grown as nature intended them to," one scout said to the frozen plant.

The enthusiasm of the scouts moved into the deepest core of the plant, seeming to wake it up from the sleep which had frozen it in time.

Soon, the plant began to grow. The scouts returned each week and were wonderfully surprised to find the plant grew stronger and taller each time they visited. The broken leaves fell off, the torn stems mended and the main branch of the plant came together. Soon there was little sign that the plant had ever been through a storm at all. The plant, however, remembered the storm and grew very strong just in case it had to face another storm in the future.

One day when the scouts visited the plant, they discovered it was forming flowers. Each week they watched it flower, and soon the flowers turned to berries. Even though the scouts did not dig up unique plants, picking berries was something else. So they made a campfire near the plant and used the berries to make a tasty jelly, earning themselves yet another badge. While the jelly was still warm, they ate it on biscuits brought along just for that purpose. The scouts told themselves how lucky they had been to discover the unique plant among the weeds that surrounded it. They talked about the badges they had earned while working with the plant.

The plant realized it was really the lucky one. The scouts had helped the plant understand it was unique and special. Because of this knowledge, the plant discovered that summer is no time to stay frozen, and love and attention can help you to grow.

©1995
Nancy Davis, Ph.D.

The Gerbil in the Cage

Problem(s) Addressed:

Symptoms of PTSD which keep a child "stuck" with a need to control. This type of child does not progress in therapy and is always trying to control the therapy session and everything else in his/her life. It is their way of trying to protect themselves and feel safe.

Appropriate for:

Ages 6 - adult.

Message:

It is time to find a way out of your circular thinking, and leave the prison which your need to control has created. (Note that the tenses change in the story in an unusual way, but this is a way of getting the unconscious to pay attention).

Symbols and Metaphors:

The door was locked from the inside: the message that the person in the cage has the power to find a way out

Running on exercise wheel: the circular thinking and being "stuck" characteristic of PTSD

Found a way to unlock the door: the challenge to the unconscious to find other ways to cope and to feel safe

The cage: the isolation of withdrawing from others which is also characteristic of PTSD

Elements of the Story Which Can be Changed:

Sex of the child, behaviors that accompany the isolation and need to control.

Note:

This story was written for an eight-year-old boy whose police-officer father had been killed in the line of duty when the child was only four. The boy was able to talk constantly about his father's death, but remained in PTSD. He had sleep difficulties, especially when sleeping in a strange place. He had been through years of therapy with various therapists, and was in a class

83

for children with emotional disturbances. In our office, he tried to control the therapy session, refusing to allow the therapist[1] to do Eyemovement Desensitization and Reprogramming (EMDR). He rejected three minute endless tapes which are designed to repeat direct suggestions for removal of symptoms in a positive way, i.e., "you are finding ways to feel more and more safe each day; you are sleeping a deep and restful sleep with positive dreams which help you to feel better and better each day." The mother was directed to play the tapes when he went to bed at night. This did not work, so she tried playing the tapes after he had been sleeping for hours since this had worked for her other child. This boy awoke, however, and destroyed the tape.

When the mother was given a script to read to him as he slept, he also awoke and demanded to know what she was saying. The therapist tried having our office manager call into her office during the session; the therapist took the call telling the boy it was an emergency and pretended to talk to another therapist who was treating a child with a similar problem.[2] This ·· .n works since the therapist can talk directly about the child's problem, using some disgui· ., such as changing the sex and age of the child (Rossi, 1983). For example, this ther· .. said, "Katie has a need to control everything to feel safe. She won't let anyone help ier. She needs to recognize that she must give up the need to control in order to really find safety and peace." Following the telephone conference, the therapist continues the therapy without commenting on the phone conversation. This did not work with this child, although it has worked well with other children and their parents.

The story which follows was given to the mother to read to her child, directing that she say that she had found it somewhere. The therapist and the child also made up a similar story in therapy, with the child having input into the story (thus helping him to feel in control). The mother also realized that listening to the radio all night in his room exposed her son to news of violence on an unconscious level and might be the cause of some of his fears. He avoided listening to the news during the day, because it scared him.

After the therapist made up a Gerbil Story with the boy, the mother left it on the car seat. He found the following story on the seat of the car, riding home from therapy. The mother indicated that she had found it at the elementary school where she volunteered. He read it, commenting that it reminded him of the story he had helped to design in the therapy session. The mother also changed the radio playing at night to taped, soothing music. She called very excited several days later to report that her son had been sleeping through the night and his mood was much improved.

---

[1]Marcella Marcey, Ph.D. was the therapist for the boy and Nancy Davis, Ph.D. was the mother's therapist.

[2]In the spirit of Erickson,1976; Rosen, 1982)

If this had not worked, I would have suggested that she get permission from her medical doctor to give her son medication which would help him to sleep[3] and read this story while he slept. Medication, at this point, would have been the last resort, since everything else that had been tried by many therapists had failed.

---

[3]Dr. Everly (1994) has seen many individuals with sleep problems related to PTSD that use Benadryl or Drixoral as a way to self-medicate for sleep. He finds it diagnostically significant when clients indicate that they take these medications because they cannot sleep.

The Gerbil in the Cage

Once upon a time there was a gerbil who lived in a cage. The door of this cage was locked from the inside. This gerbil spent all of his time running on his exercise wheel. He ran and ran and ran, but he never got anywhere and he wasn't happy. One day the gerbil decided that he was tired of being in a cage and running and running without getting anywhere. He found a way to unlock the door and get out of the prison where he had kept himself. He felt free and confident that it is time to unlock the door, leave your cage, and find that leaving is an adventure. He discovered that he has all the skills he needs to feel safe.

CHAPTER TWO

Stories That Empower and Treat the Symptoms of Child Abuse

Child abuse often causes permanent changes the body, brain and functioning of a victim. The symptoms seem to be more severe when the abuse was sexual, the victim was young, it occurred over a long period of time and/or combined with physical and emotional abuse (Briere and Runtz, 1993; Browne and Finkelhor, 1986; Conte and Schuerman, 1987; Finkelhor, 1984; Putnam, 1996; Trickett and Putnam, 1993.) Many abused children are in a Post Traumatic Stress Disorder as a result of their experiences; symptoms of PTSD usually affect all areas of a child's functioning. School work and learning are constricted. Social relationships, ability to control feelings, memory, speech, and a multitude of skills necessary to develop into a healthy functioning adult are impaired. In addition, self image typically becomes negative, often accompanied by intense shame as the victim assumes responsibility for his/her abuse (Downs, 1993).

These stories are appropriate for children, adolescents and adults. The unconscious will interpret the metaphors in these stories in a personalized manner, allowing their use for a wide variety of traumatic experiences. Changing them so that the story line more closely matches the life experiences of the abused person to which they are being read also seems to make the stories more powerful.

The Hunger That Wouldn't Go Away

Problem(s) Addressed:

Lack of nurturing, stealing (because of Post Traumatic Stress or deprivation in background), poor problem solving skills, eating disorders related to abuse.

Appropriate for:

Ages 5 to adult

Message:

You can fill the emptiness in your heart and thus give up stealing and problems with eating. You can find a way to solve the problems you have which are related to feeling un-nurtured.

Symbols and Metaphors:

Stealing food: trying to nurture one's heart and soul

Elements of the Story That Can be Changed:

Name and sex of the child; types of food taken and the occasions when this occurs; types of problem situations at school

Note:

This story was written for a six-year-old foster child who stole food obsessively. He also stole other things, storing them under his bed. In addition, he had symptoms of Post Traumatic Stress Disorder in that he could not sleep at night and had problems learning. This story, along with others on the tape, enabled him to totally give up stealing. It should be noted that he was rewarded with food when he did not steal, thus teaching him that he could find a way to earn nurturance and be responsible.

The Hunger that Wouldn't Go Away

Once upon a time there lived a boy named Cliff. When Cliff was a little baby, he went through some very tough times. There were times when he did not have enough to eat or enough milk to drink. There were also times when he was very cold, scared, sad and lonely.

Sometimes when a tummy is empty for a long period of time and when a heart gets really scared and hurt, then even when things get better, a hunger seems to remain. This is what happened to Cliff. He moved to a new home where there was always food for breakfast and lunch and dinner. In this home he was even given snacks for school. However, Cliff had the hunger in his heart that he had brought with him from the times when he was so empty. So Cliff tried to fill this hunger by eating everything he could. He would eat dinner and then have seconds when there was extra food. Often when he finished, Cliff was still hungry. At school, Cliff would eat food other students didn't eat at lunch. Then, because he still felt hunger, Cliff would eat food from garbage cans and steal food from lunch boxes.

In his new home, candy dishes sat in the living room. His new mom told Cliff, "Don't touch that candy unless I give you permission." Cliff wanted to obey, but something in him got so hungry he just couldn't stand it. Then he would fill his mouth and pockets with candy. Taking candy got Cliff in big trouble, but the more he got in trouble, the more hungry he became. When Cliff looked inside himself, there seemed to be a battle going on. One part of Cliff declared, "I am full after I eat," but another part cried, "I need food to heal my heart and to feel safe." Although Cliff knew about the battle, at first he didn't know what to do about it.

His new parents talked to Cliff and punished him when he was caught stealing food. He was sent to the principal at school. His school counselor created a reward chart for him. But Cliff continued to be hungry and to take food.

Cliff liked his new home and he didn't like having people mad at him all the time. He wanted to figure out how to stop the battle inside himself. So one night as Cliff lay down on his bed to sleep, he said to himself, "I need for my dreams to figure out how to solve this problem so that my heart stops hurting and my tummy stops being hungry all the time and I stop taking things. I need to stop stealing food and taking things out of garbage cans because I don't need them anymore. I get plenty to eat now and plenty to drink, and things are much better than they were when I was younger. It's time for my heart to heal and my tummy to heal because this hunger is causing me a lot of problems. I'm always getting in trouble and I don't like getting in trouble because it makes my heart hurt. Getting in trouble makes me even hungrier, so taking food has not solved my problem."

Well, the very deepest part of Cliff's mind, which creates dreams and can figure out how to solve problems, heard Cliff ask for help. That night, while he was sleeping, his mind and his heart and his tummy worked together in a dream and figured out a way to solve his problem. In the morning, as Cliff got out of bed, he remembered that he had asked for a problem-solving dream. At first Cliff was upset. "I don't remember having any dreams last night," he whispered to himself.

So Cliff took a shower and sat down in the kitchen to eat breakfast. After breakfast, to Cliff's surprise, he did not feel hungry or empty. Then Cliff spent the day at school. He ate lunch and had snacks and, again, Cliff didn't feel empty like he used to. At school he noticed food in the trash can like some he had taken in the past, but he was able to talk himself out of eating food that he found in the garbage.

Cliff was surprised. "Maybe I am changing. I think my brain is figuring out how to solve my problem." However, Cliff was afraid to believe that his problem was solved because he had been let down before by all kinds of people. That night, Cliff ate a huge dinner and he even had seconds and dessert. In the past, even when he ate that much, Cliff would still take candy. This time, however, even though Cliff wanted the candy, a voice in him announced, "You're okay, you can go to bed without that candy. Don't take that candy because it's going to get you in trouble." So Cliff did not take the candy.

That night as Cliff went to bed, he was happy. But Cliff understood that he would need to continue to work on his problem with hunger. So he talked to his mind again, "Thanks for helping me today. You did a good job last night but I need some more help. After all, I've been feeling hungry for as long as I can remember. I need for my mind to continue working on this problem while I sleep tonight and every night until I have stopped stealing food and feeling hungry, even when I have eaten. I want my tummy and my heart to work on this problem so that while I sleep, I will learn even more about how to help myself." That night, Cliff's mind and his heart and his tummy heard him ask for help, so they worked again to help him solve his problem.

The next day Cliff had a great day. He had lots to eat at breakfast, lunch and dinner and Cliff didn't take anything else. He even did well in school. Cliff started talking more in school and he started making lots of friends. Because Cliff liked the new ways he was acting, every night Cliff would ask for more problem-solving dreams until the day came that he didn't want to take things anymore. Cliff had made stealing a thing of the past and was very proud of himself. His new parents rewarded him and the school counselor gave Cliff certificates for his wall. He didn't get sent to the principal anymore and he found that he liked going to school and learning.

Cliff was very proud of himself because he had figured out how to solve his own problems. He knew that when other problems arose in his life he would not give up until he had discovered how to solve them. Each night he went to sleep feeling better and better about himself and surprisingly smarter when he awoke. When Cliff grew up, he decided that because he loved food, he would be a great cook. So he attended cooking school and, after graduating, worked in one restaurant after another until he became the chief chef at the best restaurant in town. People came from miles around to eat the food that Cliff cooked. One day an article about Cliff and his cooking appeared in the newspaper. The article said Cliff served the best food in town, adding that no one ever left Cliff's restaurant hungry.

©1995
Nancy Davis, Ph.D.

The Dark Sunglasses

Problem(s) Addressed:

Abuse and PTSD which results in a victim shutting down perceptions of the world in order to feel safe (Friedrich and Reams, 1987; Holaday, et al., 1994; van der Kolk, 1989 and 1996).

Appropriate for:

Ages 6 - 12

Message:

You can find the power to give up the distorted perceptions that helped you to feel safe in the past. Safety is in seeing the world the way that it is and using this knowledge to develop effective techniques to protect yourself.

Symbols and Metaphors:

The Witch: any abuser

Sunglasses: the shutting down and/or distortion of perceptions

The sunglasses affected his mind so he couldn't think: distortion of perception also causes academic difficulties since the child is distorting and blocking academics

Elements of the Story That Can be Changed:

Sex of the child; the behavior and sex of the abuser; the way the child behaves because of the distortions.

Note:

Many victims distort the way they see the world. This provides safety during the abuse, but is destructive when the child is out of the abusive situation and grows older. Perceptual distortion affects all aspects of a victim's life from academics and social relationships to self esteem. It is imperative that therapists and teachers help children to "let go" of their distortions of the world so that they have the opportunity to reach their potential.

The Dark Sunglasses

Once upon a time a boy named Rick was born. Although many children have loving moms and dads, this boy was unlucky because he lived with a witch. At times this witch was nice, but most of the time the witch was really mean, as witches often are. The witch would hit and kick and scream when she was mean. Rick didn't know what to do; he couldn't get away. He wanted to crawl out the windows but they were too high. He wanted to run out the door but it was locked. He tried hiding under the bed but the witch always found him. As Rick became more and more afraid, he realized he had to do something; the witch was scaring him so badly he couldn't even think.

One day Rick found a pair of very dark sunglasses and he tried them on. Most people do not like to wear dark sunglasses all the time because they keep eyes from seeing the world in a clear way. But Rick really liked them. When the sunglasses were on and he looked at the witch, he could not see her clearly. When he looked at the door, he couldn't tell it was locked. When he looked at the windows, he couldn't tell they were high. The sunglasses kept him from being scared. Rick did not like being afraid, so he began to wear the glasses more and more until they became a part of him — he never took them off.

In the town where Rick lived, there were soldiers who had heard there was a witch in his house. One day they knocked down the door and they found Rick wearing the dark sunglasses. They rescued him and took him to a new home. In this new home, there were no witches but Rick wouldn't take his sunglasses off. The sunglasses had made him feel safe in the past so he was afraid to take them off.

Rick could not see very well in school because of the sunglasses but he still refused to take them off. The teacher would ask, "What's wrong with you? Why don't you take your sunglasses off?" Rick didn't answer her because he didn't know what to say. He even wore his sunglasses to bed because he didn't want to have scary dreams about the witch. He felt as if the sunglasses would protect him from thinking about her.

One day, shortly before his birthday, Rick went to the toy store to decide what to ask for as presents.. His sunglasses made the toys seem to run together, so he couldn't make a decision. At school, other students talked about toys, but Rick didn't listen. Sometimes the sunglasses affected his mind so he couldn't think.

On the night before his birthday, Rick went to sleep hoping to get a special gift. Rick began to dream. In his dream, a Birthday Angel appeared. She said, "Rick, I'm going to give you the best gift of all for your birthday. I'm going to take your sunglasses off."
Rick cried, "No, you can't take off my sunglasses. I'll die or I'll get sick or something bad will happen to me."
"It's time to take them off, Rick," she said gently. "If you continue to wear the sunglasses, you won't be able to see where you're going. You won't be able to see your school work or your friends. The sunglasses will keep you forever in the dark." Then the Birthday Angel gave Rick the gift of understanding so he felt safe enough to give her the sunglasses.

The rest of the night, Rick dreamed about very happy things and it was amazing because he could see everything clearly in his dream. The next morning when Rick brushed his teeth, he noticed that he was smiling. That day, his new family gave Rick a birthday party and got lots of new toys. Because Rick no longer wore his sunglasses, Rick could see his toys clearly. Rick told himself, "Life without sunglasses is really great." He went to school without his sunglasses and found that his clear vision improved his grades more and more. Rick wanted new friends, so he closely watched and listened to the students who had many friends. Soon Rick understood how to make friends. He also noticed things on the TV he had never noticed before and he thought about things in very different ways, ways that made sense. Rick realized that many things were different and he liked the way his life had changed.

One day, a new student named Matt entered Rick's class. Matt had sunglasses on. Rick sat by him at lunch and said, "You really need to give up those sunglasses." The new student firmly replied, "No, I'm scared." Rick understood Matt's fear; he remembered feeling the same way. So day after day Rick talked to Matt until Matt finally gave up his sunglasses. After that, Rick and Matt became the best of friends because both understood you can do yourself harm if you refuse to give up what needs to be thrown away.

The Kittens Who Looked But Didn't See

Problem(s) Addressed:

Distortions in perception caused by trauma; distortions in perception can also be taught by families.

Appropriate for:

Ages 5 - 10, but may be appropriate for anyone who distorts their perceptions

Message:

You can find a way to clear up distortions and see the world clearly.

Symbols and Metaphors:

Tom Cat: any abuser

Look, but do not see: even though the eyes can sometimes describe the objects seen, their meaning is often distorted. At other times there is a closing down so that objects in the environment are not noticed

Magic Fairy: wisdom of the unconscious

Elements of the Story That Can be Changed:

The type of change agent can be from a fairy to something else, like a wise teacher or counselor; symptoms can be individualized.

Note:

It is common in families to distort perceptions; the more dysfunctional families distort perceptions even more than healthy ones. For example:

Distortion of Vision: Mom comes in drunk. Child says, "Mommy has been drinking." Dad replies, "No she hasn't, she's just tired."

Distortion of body sensation: Child: "Daddy, that hurts." Dad: "No it doesn't."

Distortion of hearing: Child: "I heard you and daddy fighting last night," Mom: "No you didn't. You must have been dreaming."

Distortion of judgement: Child: "My teacher is really mean. She's always putting everyone down and hurting everyone's feelings." Dad: "That's not true, your teacher is nice."

In abuse, it is understandable why a child would learn to "look but not see." For example, a child who sees her mother beaten by her father, might change what is happening in her (or his) perceptions. She needs the mother to be able to protect her, so she refuses to see that the mother can't even protect herself. Children who learn to 'look but not see' often grow-up and marry abusive mates. When their children are being sexually abused, they do not notice. This explains why some victims do not pick up the symptoms of abuse in their children or note signs that a prospective mate may become abusive.

One of the symptoms of Post Traumatic Stress Disorder is the inability to remember part or all of the trauma (Williams, 1992 and 1994). PTSD may account for some of these distortions. Many, however, are taught by families as is demonstrated in the examples listed previously.

The Kittens Who Looked But Didn't See

Once upon a time there were kittens that were born to a fuzzy mommy kitty. At first everything was very nice for the kittens. The mamma kitty licked their fur and fed them and she even purred when they were around. But after a while, the daddy kitty left and another old Tom cat came around. The Tom cat had claws and he was mean and he bit really hard. The little kitties were afraid all the time. They were scared in the morning and at night. They were scared while they were asleep and while they were awake. Life for the kittens was very unhappy. Because they had so much fear, it affected their eyes. Their mamma would say, "Kitties, would you go catch that mouse," and one of the kittens would reply, "What mouse?" When other kittens who lived nearby would chase blowing leaves, the kittens wouldn't even notice. There were times when the kittens didn't seem to even see each other. This seemed strange to anyone who watched the kittens play. Their eyes stopped seeing because they were so afraid of being scratched and bitten by the mamma kitty and her new Tom cat.

After a while, things got better for the kittens. They moved to a new home where no one hurt them. The new home was a happy and warm place with plenty of food and a nice comfortable place to sleep. But the kittens still had problems seeing. When someone would say to them, "Here is some delicious food for dinner," the kittens would reply, "What food?" This would happen even when the food was right in front of their noses. When a mouse would scamper in front of them, they wouldn't even notice. After realizing that not being able to see was causing them big problems, the kittens announced one day, "We need some help with this."

That night, when they were sleeping all snuggled up together purring, a very special magic fairy came to visit them. The fairy told the kittens, "You have problems with your eyes because of things that happened in the past. You didn't want to see things that would hurt you because it scared you too much, so something inside you made a decision that it was better to not see. You are safe now but you still act as if you're not. You look, but do not see." The fairy reached for her magic wand, letting the kittens know they would soon be able to see everything around them. One kitty got scared and said, "It's going to hurt if you touch my eyes with the magic wand." So the fairy reassured them. "I'm not going to touch your eyes, I'll just wave the magic wand over them and they will change so you can see." After the dream, the kittens continued to sleep.

In the morning when the kittens awoke, they discovered that they all had the same dream. Although this seemed very strange, they did feel better. "It's a beautiful day, look at that sun and those birds," one kitten said. Another exclaimed, "Look at those leaves blowing through the grass." Then all the kittens noticed bugs and spiders crawling around them. They were surprised and happy at all the new things they could see because they had never noticed those things before.

In the days that followed, each of the kittens could see more and more. They had learned how to open their eyes so that never again would they look and not see.

©1995
Nancy Davis, Ph.D.

The Boy Who Became a Fireman

Problem(s) Addressed:

The symptoms of Post Traumatic Stress Disorder caused by trauma and child abuse

Appropriate for:

Ages 5 - 18

Message:

You can find a way to reach out to people who can help you and use this knowledge to heal yourself.

Symbols and Metaphors:

Touched him in ways that made him feel sick or ashamed: sexual and/or physical abuse

Fireman: any adult that can help a child to heal through attention, love, encouraging the child to talk about their trauma and encouraging the child to find ways to heal

Elements of the Story Which Can be Changed:

Sex of the fireman; sex of the main character; symptoms of trauma.

Note:

This story was written for a foster child who had been abused and almost killed by his mother. He listened to it many times, declaring that it was his favorite story.

The Boy Who Became a Fireman

Once upon a time there was a boy named Leon. His family lived in an inner city neighborhood where everyone was very poor. There were often fights on the street in front of Leon's house. Sometimes Leon heard gunshots at night. Many people around Leon chose to use drugs, bringing even more problems. Cockroaches and rats ran across the floor at night, scaring him to the point that he was afraid to sleep. The people in Leon's house sometimes fought and hit him. No one hugged Leon or tucked him into bed at night.

Leon grew up feeling afraid much of the time. As he grew older, things got even harder. Frequently, Leon didn't have enough to eat and people were especially mean to him. Sometimes people touched him in ways that made him feel ashamed and sick. After this happened, Leon couldn't sleep. He couldn't get his mind to think. He often couldn't remember the things he needed to remember. Leon even had trouble playing with his friends because often when a child is very scared and sad, they forget how to be a friend. At night, Leon would try to sleep, but his mind wouldn't go to sleep even though his body was really tired. Sometimes in his dreams Leon would relive all the scary things he had experienced. This made him afraid to sleep. So Leon would lay down at night and then get up, lay down and get up all night. When morning came and he had to go to school, Leon was not rested.

Then Leon moved to a new place where he was safe and had enough to eat. In this new home, the people loved Leon and he had lots of toys. But Leon continued to feel just as he had when he was being hurt — he couldn't sleep, he couldn't read and he especially couldn't make friends.

One day when Leon was at school, a fireman came to his class for a talk. At first, the fireman talked about fires and smoke. Then he talked about burns. Next he began to tell the class what can happen when a person sees very scary things. The fireman told the class how fear could affect their sleep. Leon began to listen carefully, although it was difficult because he

107

had trouble concentrating. The fireman told the class that seeing scary things can cause scary nightmares. Leon listened even more closely. "He must be talking about me," Leon whispered to himself. Then the fireman told the class that seeing awful things could keep a student from learning how to read or do math problems. He added that living through awful experiences could cause someone to get angry easily and punch people. Leon thought, "He must have come to this class to help me."

The fireman let the class know that he knew all of these things from personal experience because a burning building had collapsed on him as he was inside trying to put out the fire. "After I was rescued," he told the class "I couldn't sleep or read or think very well. I yelled at my friends and no one wanted to be around me."

After the fireman completed his talk and all the other students were going to recess, Leon stayed behind. "Can I talk to you?" Leon asked the fireman. "Sure," the fireman replied. "Have a seat." So Leon started to tell the fireman all the terrible things that had happened to him. He told the fireman that he couldn't sleep, couldn't think and had bad dreams. Leon talked about how his mind felt like it was racing. The more Leon talked, the better he felt. Leon described how he punched other students and had trouble in school. Leon said, "Sometimes I try not to think about anything because that makes me think I am going to be better — but it doesn't work."

Firemen are usually people who like to help other people and this fireman was no different. He could see that Leon had gone through a lot of trauma. "You can change all of those problems. You can sleep and you can read. There are ways to do that. Your mind has a way to figure out just what you need to get rid of the problems caused by the bad things you have lived through. Perhaps your mind will tell you to get help from someone else; perhaps it will find a solution without help."

Leon and the fireman sat and talked for a long time. Leon asked questions and the fireman answered. The fireman explained to Leon how he had found a way to heal all the problems caused by being caught in a burning building.

Leon decided that every night when he went to bed, he would tell himself again and again to find a way to slow down his mind and heal the part of him that been injured by his past. Leon made sure he got many ideas from the fireman about ways to help himself. When the other students began to return to the class, the fireman gave Leon his card so that Leon could call him whenever he needed to talk.

Leon learned to talk to himself as he went to sleep. He found a counselor who could help him. He began to read books and get ideas from many places to solve his problems. Leon even called the fireman several times to ask him more questions. It wasn't long before Leon found that he could sleep and have dreams that helped him rather than scared him. Leon found he could figure out problems and he was reading more and more. Soon Leon was laughing and playing instead of punching everybody. Every day Leon improved more and more. He began to read so well that he was appointed to read stories to the kindergarten class.

Leon and the fireman remained friends as he grew up. When Leon graduated from high school, he decided to be a fireman, just like his friend. Leon attended the training academy and became a fireman who helped people put out their fires. Because Leon's heart remembered how pain from the past can hurt you in the present, he became very skilled at helping others who had been burned by fires.

©1995
Nancy Davis, Ph.D.

The Hole in the Heart

Problem(s) Addressed:

The symptoms caused by child abuse and lacking of nurturing.... particularly stealing, eating constantly, problems sleeping and academic difficulties.

Appropriate for:

Ages 5 - 16

Message:

You can find a way to heal the trauma of your abuse and 'let go" of your symptoms

Symbols:

Hole in the heart: the trauma caused by lack of love and nurturance
Heart doctor: any adult who can understand and aid in healing
Light: healing, knowledge, the opposite of darkness; opening up to knowledge in order to heal

Elements of the Story Which Can be Changed:

Sex of the main character; symptoms; sex of the doctor

Note:

This story was one of many stories created for a foster child that had trouble in stealing, especially food. He has now been adopted, is happy and rarely steals anything.

The Hole in the Heart

Once upon a time there was a boy named Chris. When Chris was a baby and a young boy, things didn't go well in his life. Because things didn't go very well in his life, Chris got a big hole in his heart. Love is the food your heart needs to operate and to grow. Since Chris didn't have much love to feed his heart, he developed a big hole that caused him to often be in pain.

When Chris got a little older, he moved to a very nice place, but things still didn't go very well because he brought the hole in his heart with him. Chris sensed that the hole needed to be filled, so he constantly tried to fill it. He would take things and keep them. He would hide things. He would even take food and try to feed his heart in that way — but the food Chris needed to fill his heart was love. So even though Chris took a lot of things, these things didn't fill the hole in his heart. The hole in Chris's heart continued to hurt, and Chris kept trying to fill it up to make the pain go away.

Some days the hole would hurt and the pain would mess up the way Chris was thinking. Other days the hole would hurt and the pain would mess up the way Chris talked. Sometimes the pain was so bad, Chris couldn't sleep. Then the hole in his heart gave Chris nightmares so he was both in pain and also afraid.

The hole in Chris's heart caused him so much trouble that one day he loudly announced, "I'm tired of this hole in my heart. It's time to get this thing fixed." So he talked to his foster mother, telling her, "I want to go to a doctor that can fix this hole in my heart." Chris's foster mother made him an appointment with a heart doctor. When Chris got to his appointment, he told the heart doctor, "I've got a hole in my heart and I want you to fix it because it's getting me in big trouble. It makes me take things and then I get punished. It makes my thinking all messed up and it makes my talking all messed up. The hole in my heart causes me have bad dreams and to have trouble sleeping. And that's not all, this hole makes me have problems at school and I've had it. I am tired of this hole in my heart and I want it to go away."

So the doctor took pictures of Chris's heart. But when he looked at the pictures, he couldn't see the hole. Chris didn't care whether the doctor saw pictures of the hole or not. "It's there, I'm telling you, it's there," he insisted.

"Well," the doctor remarked, "I think I know what's wrong. You have the kind of hole that doesn't show up on pictures. You have the kind of hole caused by not getting enough love or enough of the things your heart needs to grow in just the right way. I'll bet you have spent lots of time trying to fill up your heart and nothing has worked."

"You're right," Chris cried. "I'm always in trouble and that makes the hole in my heart hurt even more."
"I know how to fill up the hole in your heart," the doctor reassured Chris.

The doctor took Chris to a special treatment room where he got a ball of light out of a safe. The light looked like a small sun to Chris. The doctor told Chris, "Although many things can heal your heart, light is the way that works best for me." At that, the doctor put the ball of light in front of Chris's chest. When the doctor let go of the light, it floated like a balloon filled with helium and moved into Chris's heart. Chris thought the light was strange because he had never experienced this kind of medical treatment.

"This is weird. Is this an x-ray?" he asked.
The heart doctor replied, "No, it's not an x-ray, but the light goes into your body like an x-ray. This is my way of healing the kind of hole in a heart that you have." The doctor told Chris he could go home, but recommended that Chris to keep the ball of light in his heart so that the hole could continue to mend.

Chris wondered if the heart doctor knew what he was talking about but decided to trust him. This doctor was the first person Chris had met that recognized he had a hole in his heart and had some suggestions on how to get rid of it. So Chris returned home. Soon he noticed that he was feeling and behaving in new ways. Instead of taking things and hiding them in his room, Chris played with them and put them back. At meals, Chris no longer felt the need to eat everything on the table to fill himself up. At night, Chris began to sleep more and more. Chris was amazed. The light in his heart helped him to sleep so peacefully that he no longer had scary nightmares.

Each morning when Chris woke up, he felt even better. He started talking to his foster mother and his teachers, and he talked in a very different way. He said what he was thinking and what he was feeling. He used big words and long sentences. The adults asked him, "Are you sure you're Chris?"

Chris replied proudly, "Yes, I'm Chris."

114

Chris replied proudly, "Yes, I'm Chris."

"What happened to you?" his teachers and foster mother asked. "You have really changed. You are doing your work and talking so much better."

Chris didn't say anything, he just smiled. He decided to keep the knowledge about the light to himself. So Chris left the light in his heart so it could continue to heal the hole in his heart even more. Every day Chris got better and better. He slept more and more peacefully, and he did better and better in school. He talked more and more and began to make good friends.

One day he completely stopped taking things that weren't his and putting them under his bed or in his pocket. Chris smiled on the day this happened. "I am so glad that hole in my heart is gone because I didn't really want to take all those things anyway," he said to himself. "I was just trying to fill my heart up, but taking things never worked."

Chris got better and better and did so well in school, everybody was amazed. He even amazed himself. Then one day a new boy came to live in his foster home. Chris noticed that he took things and hid them. So Chris put his arm around the boy and said, "I know what's wrong with you. You've got a hole in your heart and I know just the doctor that can help you to heal."

©1995
Nancy Davis, Ph.D.

The Bird Who Was Afraid of Dragons

Problem(s) Addressed:

Fear that is triggered by a particular thing, and similar things; poor problem-solving skills.

Appropriate for:

Ages 3 - 10

Message:

You can find a way to deal with your fear.

Symbols and Metaphors:

Dragon: a physical or emotional abuser; any scary adult or thing which incites fear
Fire: abusive words
Bears and foxes: any object in which fear diffuses
Eagle: wisdom of the unconscious
Flying Higher than bears or foxes: any technique which keeps the child safe

Elements of the Story That Can be Changed:

Sex of the main character; what the dragon does or says

Note:

Therapeutic stories can often decrease and eliminate phobias and excessive fears. Have the child listen to a tape with a variety of stories nightly and have the parent note the behavior of the child to see if the fear is decreasing. EMDR (Shapiro, 1995) and MTP (Davis, 2002) are also helpful with these types of problems.

The Bird Who Was Afraid of Dragons

Once upon a time there was a colorful little bird who flew up and down through the air having so much fun. This bird flew high and flew low. It could often be heard singing as it perched in trees. Life for this bird was happy and pleasant.

Then one very dark day, things changed. As the little bird was flying and diving through the air, it happened to glide past a dragon. Just when the little bird was closest to it, the dragon roared, spit fire and said some mean and cruel things. Flying by the dragon almost scared the little bird out of her feathers. After the experience with the dragon, the little bird became more and more hesitant to fly.

The little bird couldn't stop thinking about the dragon, even when she perched on a limb. When the little bird pictured the dragon in her mind, the dragon seemed so real. This scared the little bird even more. Soon the little bird stopped singing so she would be sure to hear if the dragon was approaching. Most of the time the dragon was no where around, but the little bird continued to sit on a branch and quietly listen for the dragon. She wanted to be sure that she would avoid the dragon's roar, fire and the mean face and words. All in all, the fear of the dragon started to ruin the little bird's life.

The little bird began to realize how unhappy she had become and how her fear was paralyzing her. So one day she told herself in a loud voice, "I don't have to take this anymore." She was talking to anyone who was listening, but mostly she was giving herself courage.

"I'm going to fly away so that I can be in a place where there aren't any dragons," the little bird decided. She didn't want to spend the rest of her life being afraid. So she began to fly, going as fast as her little wings would go. Soon she passed a bear. The bear was in a particularly grouchy mood and was roaring. The little bird, remembering the dragon, started to shake. She was having trouble telling the difference between a dragon and a bear. Just hearing the bear roar ruined the rest of the little bird's day.

119

So, rather than continue her flight, the little bird spent the night perched on a tree. Gaining courage the next morning, she continued on her journey. Soon, she flew directly over a red fox. As the little bird looked down and listened, she heard the fox barking just like a dog. She noticed that the fox looked very angry and scary.

"That fox reminds me of a dragon," the little bird said to herself with a quivering voice. She stopped at a nearby tree, trying to hide in the leaves of a branch. When she tried to fly the next morning, she was too afraid to even flap her wings. It wasn't very long before the little bird was afraid to leave the safety of the tree. She had started off afraid of dragons, and now she was afraid of bears and foxes, as well.

One day an eagle, who had been flying high in the air, happened to land in the tree where the little bird was hiding. Eagles are not only very strong and powerful birds, but they have exceedingly good eyesight. The eagle felt the branch of the tree shaking and then noticed the scared little bird. Puzzled, the eagle inquired, "Why are you shaking little bird?"

At first the little bird was afraid of the eagle, but the eagle kept asking what was wrong until the little bird quietly replied, "There are mean dragons everywhere and mean bears and foxes. I'm very scared."

"Hmm," said the eagle, "the only dragon I have ever observed lives far away from here; you're nowhere near a dragon."

"But there are brown bears that look like dragons and red foxes that sound like them, too."

The eagle considered the words and the fear of the little bird, thinking how to help her. "I believe that you have become so afraid of dragons that you see dragons everywhere," the eagle said softly. "It seems that you have convinced yourself that any animal who roars, barks or has an angry look on their face is a dragon. But they really aren't dragons. You can find a way to understand that dragons are very different from bears and foxes. A mean look and an angry face cannot make a fox or bear into a dragon."

"But I don't like it when an animal sounds angry like a dragon," the little bird said.

"You don't have to like it," the eagle responded. "But you can find a way to **Let Go** of your fear so you can fly right by a bear or fox without shaking at all."

"Are you sure?" the little bird asked, afraid to even think about not being afraid.

"Let me help you with your fear," said the eagle. "I'll fly with you today to help you see and hear things differently."

And thus it was that the eagle flew with the little bird that day over many areas of the forest. As they flew, a bear suddenly roared in anger at being chased by bees. The little bird started to shake and fly very close to the eagle.

The eagle started to fly up and down and all around the bear. The bear kept roaring. "We are flying so high that no bear can touch us," the eagle told the little bird. "That bear is just roaring to hear himself roar, anyway."

After several trips flying back and forth over the bear, the eagle said to the little bird, "Have you noticed how silly that roar seems coming out of the bear? As long as you stay in the air, he can't hurt you. Perhaps you haven't noticed the difference between a bear and a dragon. The bear is much smaller, doesn't have fire, and isn't nearly as big and mean."
"Oh," said the little bird, "I never noticed how different they really are."

At that point, the two of them flew over a fox. The fox was making a lot of noise, "Bark, bark, bark, bark."
"See that angry look on his face?" said the little bird. "He must be just like a dragon."
"An angry look on a face can't hurt you. How can you think that fox is a dragon. It doesn't even look like a dragon. It's small and red and it barks."
"Wow," the bird whispered to herself. "I never noticed just how different a fox is from a dragon."

Then the eagle flew to the top of a tree, with the little bird right beside him. The eagle talked to the little bird about anger and fear. They talked about the difference between a mean look and a mean touch. They talked about fire and dragons and bears and foxes. They talked about everything the little bird needed to learn. The eagle was a very good teacher. After their talk, the little bird had a new understanding of anger. She understood the difference between dragons and other animals. She understood that she could fly high above angry faces and roars, so they couldn't hurt her. Most of all, she understood that she would never allow fear to keep her from flying again.

One day the little bird accidentally flew above the roaring dragon as he was spitting fire and looking very mean. The little bird changed her flight. She flew so high that the dragon's anger and fire couldn't reach her.

"Gosh, I'm smarter than dragons," the little bird thought to herself. And she began to smile.

©1995
Nancy Davis, Ph.D.

121

The Animal Who Didn't Know Who She Was

Problem(s) Addressed:

The lack of a sense of self that evolves from being abused, neglected and/or unloved (Browne and Finkelhor, 1986; Downs, 1993; Trickett and Putnam, 1993; Putnam, 1996).

Appropriate for:

Ages 4 - 12

Message:

You have everything you need to heal from the trauma of the past.

Symbols and Metaphors:

Didn't know who she was: lack of a sense of self

Key: opening up understanding within the unconscious

Hole was filled with scary feelings: the energy required to survive child abuse often leaves no energy left for the development of healthy functioning

Drops in the eyes that cleared up the darkness: clearing up the distortions in perceptions caused by the abuse

Gifts of hearts, fur: symbolic gifts that create the understanding of healing in the unconscious

Elements of the Story Which Can be Changed:

Sex of the main character

Note:

Many abused children have problems in developing a sense of self. Thus, many problems in functioning occur. (This story helps the unconscious to began to develop this sense of who they are and what they want to be.)

The Animal Who Didn't Know What She Was

Once upon a time there was a little animal that didn't know what she was. She didn't know whether she was a bunny, a fox or a kangaroo. When she looked inside of herself, she couldn't find anything but a big, empty hole.

The little animal would ask other animals around her who she was. Sometimes these animals would make up a story to tell her. At other times, these animals would reply, "I don't know who are you." No one seemed able to give her the answer she needed to find out who she was. So the empty hole within her got bigger and bigger.

One day the little animal was walking along a path when she met a wise owl. Since she was so used to asking everyone the same question, the little animal asked the owl. "Can you help me? I don't know who I am. I don't know what kind of animal I am and I have a big hole in me."

For once, the little animal found someone who responded with a positive answer. "Let's have a talk," the owl said to the little animal. "I'll sit here on the branch of this tree and you sit on the soft grass growing under it."

After the little animal was comfortable, the owl began to talk. "Remember when you were much smaller?", the owl asked.
"Yes", the little animal replied.

"Remember all those bad things that happened to you?", the owl asked.
"How can I forget?," the little animal replied, starting to get sad.

"Well, those bad things happened during the time of your life when you were supposed to figure out what kind of an animal you are. Because of all those bad things, you didn't have a chance to figure out who you were. You were so busy trying to run away, to feel safe and not be scared that you didn't have time for anything else. Instead of the hole being filled with the knowledge of who you are, it got filled with scared feelings. And now that you don't have to be scared anymore, there's nothing left."

Hearing these words, the little animal started to cry.

The wise owl continued to talk. "I know that you feel like crying, but soon you will feel better. I have gifts for you that can fill the empty hole".

"What kinds of gifts?" the little animal asked, beginning to feel a sense of hope.

"Follow me," the owl said. So the owl flew above the little animal to a tree with a large opening. The owl went into the hole and came out with a golden heart. "This heart will help you to love yourself," the owl explained as she handed it to the little animal. Then the owl gave the little animal a soft piece of fur and said, "This is to help you to open your heart to love." More gifts from the owl followed, gifts that helped her to open up her mind, to motivate her and to help her to understand how to act in order to have friends. The owl continued to pull gifts out of the tree. "Here are some special drops for your eyes," the owl explained. Put them into your eyes to clear up any darkness which keeps you from seeing the world in a clear way." Then the owl handed the little animal a key. "Use this key to open up every part of you which has been locked away", the owl instructed. "Your heart will understand how to use this key".

After the little animal had received all the gifts, the owl found food for them to share. The owl continued to talk to the little animal about life and love and empty spaces. Then the little animal fell asleep surrounded by the gifts from her new friend. As she slept, her mind found a way to understand the meaning of the gifts she had received and to use this understanding to fill all the empty holes that came from another time and another place.

When she awoke, the little animal hopped down to the river for a drink of water. For the first time, she observed her reflection in the water, realizing that she was a soft, furry rabbit. Then she noticed that the rabbit in the reflection had begun to smile. "I'm a rabbit", she said to herself. "Isn't interested that I have come to this river many times for water and never before noticed my reflection in the water."

As she hopped away from the river, the rabbit noticed other rabbits eating clover and hopping through the grass. As she approached them, the rabbit didn't ask anyone what kind of animal she was because she knew. Soon she had many friends and noticed that the empty hole was filled with a sense of who she was and what she wanted to be. One day an animal approached the bunny and asked, "I don't know who I am, can you help me?"

"Yes!", the rabbit replied and began to smile.

The Boy With the Chip on His Shoulder

Problem(s) Addressed:

The anger that comes from lack of love and/or abuse. This anger interferes with finding love and satisfaction from life that would heal the hurt from past rejection and abuse. "Loss of ability to regulate the intensity of feelings and impulses is possibly the most far reaching effect of trauma and neglect" (van der Kolk and Fisher, 1994)

Appropriate for:

Ages 6 - 16

Message:

You can find a way to "let go" of your anger and change your behavior and thinking to ways that make life a rewarding experience.

Symbols and Metaphors:

Chip on the shoulder: anger and the behavior that results.

Elements of the Story Which Can be Changed:

Sex of the main character; behavior and thinking that are problems; the person who helps the main character to change; the new behaviors that result from changed thinking.

Note:

This story was written for the same child that inspired "Problem Child." The teachers reported a change in his behavior as he heard these stories again and again. He was adopted by a loving family and his angry behavior appears to be a thing of the past.

The Boy With the Chip on His Shoulder

Once upon a time there was a boy named Chuck who, for many years, had a very difficult life. People who were supposed to love him disappeared. And when these people left, a big chip appeared on Chuck's shoulder. Chuck found another home but the people who were supposed to take care of him hurt him instead. When this happened, Chuck got an even bigger chip on his shoulder. Now, it's hard to imagine what a chip on your shoulder might look like, but for Chuck it was something very heavy that weighted him down.

When Chuck's teachers got mad at him, the chip on his shoulder would get bigger. Chuck realized he was not getting the love he needed to grow and this made the chip grow even more. One day Chuck found out things about his family he didn't want to believe, and the chip got so big that when Chuck walked, he couldn't stand up straight.

Chuck became very tired of having to carry the chip on his shoulder everywhere he went. The chip made him feel angry all the time. When kids would try to talk to Chuck, he would kick them or fight with them. Chuck had come to believe that if he kicked or punched other people, the chip would go away — but it only made the chip grow bigger. Each time Chuck got into trouble at school for fighting, the chip became heavier. Each time Chuck's behavior got him into trouble with his family and his neighbors, the chip grew bigger. As the chip on his shoulder became enormous, Chuck was so weighed down that he didn't know if he was going to be able to walk anymore.

Because Chuck had learned to solve problems in school, he decided to use these problem-solving skills on himself. "I've got to get rid of this chip," Chuck said to himself one night as he lay on his bed. "I'm tired of being worn out from carrying this heavy load on my shoulders all the time. I need to find a way to get this chip off my shoulder."

Chuck asked his family what to do, but no one had an answer. Then Chuck asked his teacher, but she didn't know how to get rid of the chip either. In fact, his teacher frowned when Chuck asked her what to do about the chip on his shoulder and remarked, "What are you talking about? I don't see any chip on your shoulder."

At first, Chuck started to give up. "I don't know what I'm going to do," he said sadly. "No one is ever going to be able to help me." Then Chuck realized that he had only asked two people and there were hundreds of people left that he could question. It would only take one of them to give him a solution that would work.

So Chuck continued to ask for advice — he asked the kids in his class, the clerk at the store and the mailman — but none of them could help him. Chuck, however, would not let himself give up. "There is someone out there who can help me," he said with determination.

Then Chuck asked his school counselor. The school counselor had a long mirror in her office and she asked Chuck to stand in front of the mirror. "Look at this chip on your shoulder," she said.
"Thank you for seeing this chip," replied Chuck. "You're the first person that has been able to see my chip. It is so heavy that it makes my back hurt. How am I supposed to get rid of this?"
"You have the power to get rid of the chip yourself," the counselor told Chuck. "If you change the way you're thinking, feeling and acting, it will go away. You can make a decision within yourself to not let that all the bad things that happened to you keep you from being happy, having friends and doing great in school. You can li the chip off yourself."

Chuck looked at the counselor in disbelief. "I don't know if I can do that. It sounds too difficult."
"It will be hard, but it's not as difficult as keeping the heavy chip on your shoulder," the counselor told him. "I will help you."

So Chuck and the counselor talked and talked about new ways of thinking and changing his behavior. They talked about letting go of things that happened in the past and changing his behavior in the future. Then the counselor told Chuck that he could come to see her on a regular basis.

Chuck started to practice new thinking. It was hard, but Chuck began to catch the thoughts that had given him the chip on his shoulder. He thought about how his behavior was making the chip on his shoulder grow bigger and bigger. As he practiced new ways of dealing with problems, the chip on his shoulder began to shrink. When a kid at school talked to Chuck in a mean way, Chuck stopped himself from punching him. Instead, he found a way to talk to

130

the kid and soon they were friends instead of enemies. When this happened, even more of the chip disappeared. The chip on his shoulder continued to get lighter and smaller as Chuck talked to the counselor on many different days about the sad and painful things from his past.

One night Chuck had a dream which helped him find the power to 'let go' of the remaining chip on his shoulder. The dream also helped Chuck to behave in new ways, to like himself and to be happy. Chuck seemed so different from the boy he had been when he had a chip on his shoulder that many people did not even recognize him.

Soon Chuck began directing all of the energy he had used in the past to carry the chip on his shoulder into becoming a track star. Chuck ran and ran. He found that running made him feel better about himself. Soon he was running in races and winning awards as he came in first more and more.

One day, the coach told the track team that "Chuck runs like the wind." As he heard these words, Chuck began to smile; he realized that he could never have run like the wind if he were still carrying a heavy chip on his shoulder.

The Scorpion Bunny and the Dog

Problem(s) Addressed:

Withdrawal, anger and the lack of feeling safe that are characteristic of Post Traumatic Stress Disorder. In this case, the withdrawal relates to being abused.

Appropriate for:

Ages 6 - 12

Message:

You can find a way to feel safe without withdrawing and isolating yourself. You can find a way to establish meaningful relationships.

Symbols and Metaphors:

Scorpion Shell: Withdrawal from relationships
Stinger: the rage reactions typical of PTSD symptoms or as a response to abuse

Elements of the Story That Can be Changed:

Sex of main character; sex of dog; symptoms

Note:

Those in PTSD often find that their anger moves from nonexistent to rage in an instant. Difficulty controlling anger is a common symptom and is a result of brain changes caused by the stress hormones produced during the traumatic event(s) (Everly, 1994; van der Kolk, 1995 and 1996). Rage reactions may decrease or disappear when PTSD is treated through techniques which focus on the right brain -- which is where symbolic, metaphoric, emotion and vision are processed (Mills and Crowley, 1986)

133

The Scorpion Bunny and the Dog

Once upon a time in a forest not so far away a baby bunny was born. Bunnies are very soft and furry animals and they have few defenses against their enemies. Many other animals have defenses that help them to feel safe. Skunks have a stinky smell, porcupines have sharp needles, and bears and foxes have sharp teeth and claws. The bunny has none of these. When threatened or faced with danger, a bunny has only two choices: run very fast or hide.

Although bunnies have many enemies, such as bears, foxes, mountain lions and eagles, this bunny was most threatened by the bunnies around him — the ones who should have protected him. Life was very hard for the young bunny and he often was hurt. He did not feel loved or wanted by the bunnies around him because they were always mean and angry.

Because of the way he was treated, the bunny did not get the love he needed to grow and develop. A heart needs to be filled with love to grow and develop; this bunny's heart was filled with something far different..... his heart was filled with anger. The anger grew and grew until he began to develop a hard shell on the outside.

One day the bunny saw a scorpion sting and paralyze an opponent. "I wish I could be like that," the bunny remarked. So he approached the stinging thing and asked, "Who are you?"
"I am a scorpion and you had better keep away from me," the creature replied in a nasty way. "I don't care about anyone and no one cares about me and I like it that way. I have a hard shell and a stinger that can kill." At that, the scorpion dragged away his prey, leaving the bunny to think about what he had observed.

"I want to be a scorpion," the bunny said to himself. "If I were a scorpion bunny, life would be easier and I wouldn't have all these sad feelings inside. If I were a scorpion bunny, when I felt afraid, instead of running away, I could just sting anyone who scares me."

So the bunny found a way to use his anger and sadness to change into a scorpion bunny. Even though scorpions have no friends and are cold and hard on the outside, the bunny liked the idea of being mean and hurting others in the same way he had been hurt. He didn't really feel like he had a choice because life had been so hard for him; he believed that attacking others was a way to protect himself.

Being a scorpion bunny in a bunny world created lots of problems. Other rabbits yelled at him even more because he always seemed to be doing something wrong. "You're not acting right," they said. "What's wrong with you?" When the scorpion bunny heard these words, he would feel sad. Then that sadness made his shell harder and his stinger more pointed.

The scorpion bunny paid a big price for having a shell and a stinger because he was very lonely. He had wanted to be a scorpion so he would not feel. But even with the hard shell on the outside, he was still a bunny on the inside and his pain grew and grew. The more he hurt, the thicker his shell became. Then he responded to his own pain by attacking others and hurting them with his sharp, poisonous stinger.

One day the scorpion bunny was sitting alone on a rock when a dog happened to wander by. Most dogs chase rabbits, but this dog was unique. He had been raised with rabbits on a farm and because of this, noticed that this scorpion bunny was very unusual. "What's wrong with you? Why are you so different?" the dog asked the scorpion bunny.

"Get away or I'll sting you," answered the scorpion bunny, lifting his stinger high in the air. He was sure that the dog was wanting to eat him for dinner.
"I'm not going to hurt you," the dog said, backing up a little. "Why do you have a stinger like a scorpion?"

"I am a scorpion," the bunny responded as firmly as he could.
The dog began to smile, and talked to the scorpion bunny. "I'd like to be your friend. I know that most bunnies don't have dogs for friends, but you look like you could really use a friend."

"Go away," said the bunny. "I don't need a friend, I don't want a friend. I'm just fine."
"You're not fine," replied the dog. "You're not even close to fine. The hard shell and stinger mixed with your soft fur is proof to me that you are not fine."

Hearing these words, the scorpion bunny began to cry. There were so many tears in his heart that he couldn't hold onto them any more. As he continued to cry, all the sadness that had been in his heart from a lifetime of pain and fear began to be released in big tears.

"I don't know what else to do," sobbed the bunny. "I don't know any other way to protect myself. There is so much in this world that hurts and causes pain."

"Let me be your friend," said the dog, "and I'll help you get rid of that shell."

"How will I sting people if I don't have the shell?" the bunny wanted to know.

"You won't need to sting those around you when you feel safe," the dog replied. "You'll be able to let them know how you feel and to protect yourself in other ways."

The scorpion bunny was afraid to give up his shell and his stinger. He had gotten used to being a prisoner in a hard shell, even though he had been very lonely. As he thought and thought about what to do, the part of him that had hope and needed love found a voice and urged him to give up his shell and his stinger. This part let the bunny know that finding love is worth taking chances and getting hurt. So with the help of the dog, the scorpion bunny gave up his shell and his stinger and returned to being a bunny once more, but he kept them near just in case he needed them again.

At first, the bunny felt exposed and unprotected without his shell. The dog had promised to be his friend, and so he became the bunny's constant companion, helping the bunny to feel safe. At first, the bunny would hold the shell in his hand, just in case he needed it. Or he would find his stinger and hold it. But the dog not only stayed with him, he demonstrated what to do when threatened or scared. He showed the bunny different ways to talk and behave so that he would no longer need his shell and stinger. Soon the bunny was able to throw away the scorpion parts forever.

Before long the bunny and the dog were best friends. The bunny found he wanted the dog around not just to guard and teach him, but just because he liked him. The friendship and love from his friend, the dog, began to mend the pain in his heart and fill it with love. It wasn't long before the other rabbits noticed a change in the bunny. He discovered how to talk to the other bunnies in ways that helped him get even more love and to feel safe. He began to learn and to listen and to enjoy being a bunny.

Then the bunny introduced his friend, the dog, to all the other bunnies in the forest. They made a strange pair, the bunny and the dog. Their friendship was held together by the knowledge that love and trust are the bonds of friendship, and a good friend can help you recover from even the worst of traumas.

©1995
Nancy Davis, Ph.D.

The Fireman Who Put Out Fires That Weren't There

Problem(s) Addressed:

Distorted perceptions particularly in failing to observe abusive or dangerous situations (Briere and Runtz, 1993).

Appropriate for:

Ages 6 - 16

Message:

You can learn to see danger and protect yourself from it. You can recognize the abusive people in your family and be honest with yourself in assessing whether they are dangerous and how to stay away from them.

Symbols and Metaphors:

Fires: abusive situations, abusive people

Couldn't see the fires: refusal to acknowledge the dangerousness of an abusive family member

Didn't see the fire and got burned: being hurt or abused by the abusive family member because of the inability to recognize danger

Recognize the fire through feelings: the directive to use emotional reactions or the intuitive side to warn of dangerous situations

Elements of the Story That Can be Changed:

Sex of fire fighters.

Note:

This story was designed for a nine-year-old boy in foster care. His mother had beaten him severely when he was eight years old; on one occasion he was hospitalized following a particularly brutal beating and removed from her care because of this abuse. Social service

139

allowed the mother to see her son in the therapists office. She was angry and appeared disturbed and dangerous; she refused therapy or drug testing. The child continued to maintain that he wanted to live with his mother, ignoring the signs that she was still as dangerous as she was when she abused him. This story and others allowed him to see his mother more realistically in order to protect himself.

The Fireman Who Put Out Fires That Weren't There

Once upon a time a man named Eric joined the fire department. Although there are many reasons to be a fireman, Eric joined the fire department because there had been numerous fires in his life and he wanted to learn how to extinguish them. Eric believed that putting out fires would help him feel good about himself. Eric knew that as a fireman he could save people's lives, save people's homes and drive a fire engine all around town with the siren blaring. Eric liked the idea of cars stopping to let the fire engine pass. "Being a fireman is going to be great," Eric whispered to himself. "I will be in control. I will be putting out fires. I will feel safe if I am in control of putting out fires."

To be a fireman, Eric attended the fire department training school where he learned everything possible about putting out fires and saving victims. Among other things, he learned how to drive fire trucks and give first aide and CPR.

Although Eric graduated first in his training class, he had a lot of problems when he became a real fireman. When the fire alarm rang, all of the firemen would jump on the fire truck and ride to the scene of the fire. Arriving at the fire, all the firemen would run to put out the fire except for Eric; he would grab a hose and run in the opposite direction, squirting a house that wasn't on fire. Eric wouldn't even notice the house that was really burning. It was the strangest thing. All the other firemen would look at Eric thinking he was weird. One of the other firemen said to him, "What are you doing?"

Eric didn't seem to know what he was talking about. He replied, "I'm putting out this fire over here. Didn't you hear the siren go off? The house is on fire."
"There's not a fire in that house," the other fireman responded.

Eric would look directly at the house he was squirting maintaining, "Yes there is, I see it. Don't you see it right there?"
"There's not a fire in that house", the firemen began yelling at him impatiently. "Look! The fire is over here."

"No, it's not," Eric declared. "I don't see any fire over there. The fire is over here in this house."

As you might imagine, Eric's problem in seeing fires continued day after day. One evening as the fire engine arrived at a big warehouse blaze, Eric again did not see the fire. Because he couldn't see it, Eric, the fireman, walked into the fire and got burned. His co-workers treated his burns at the scene, then he rode to the hospital in an ambulance from his unit so that his injuries could be treated. The emergency room doctor bandaged up Eric's burns as she remarked, "I understand that you walked into a fire."

"You're right, I did," Eric answered. "It's the strangest thing, I didn't see the fire in the warehouse, but I sure felt it burn me."

"Maybe you're not looking at fires in just the right way," the doctor remarked. "You need to look at fires by feeling that they are going to burn you; then your eyes will start getting use to that feeling. Soon your eyes will learn to see fires just as your body can feel them."

As the doctor continued to bandage his burns, Eric talked to her about fires and how to know where the fires were. Eric was smart and understood that he would lose his job if he couldn't learn to see fires. He also realized he might get burned again. So the next time the fire alarm rang and he rode the fire engine to the fire, instead of looking to see where the fire was, Eric let his feelings guide him to the fire. He could sense just how hot the fire was and Eric also smelled the smoke from the fire. Following his feelings to the fire, Eric looked carefully. His eyes began to see the fire in the same way that his body could sense it, as Eric urged his eyes to look and to see.

Because he had seen the fire, Eric was able to help the other fire fighters put it out. They slapped him on the back in congratulations, saying, "Wow, it looks like you figured out how to fight fires."

After that, Eric got better and better at seeing fires and putting them out. One day as Eric responded to a house fire, the neighbors yelled that children were trapped in the burning house. Eric had taught himself to see exactly where the fire was most dangerous in a way that allowed him to rush into the burning house, find the children and rescue them. The morning paper had a front page story and picture of Eric rescuing the children from the burning house. To reward Eric for his bravery, the fire department gave him a medal of honor.

Eric kept the medal on his locker so that he would be sure and see it day after day. It was a reminder that fires can be dangerous, unless you learn to see them and put them out.

©1995
Nancy Davis, Ph.D.

CHAPTER THREE

Stories that Develop Healthy Emotional Reactions, Thinking, Perceptions, Beliefs, Self-Image and Social Skills

The stories in this chapter combine metaphor with cognitive therapy, Ericksonian techniques, and important concepts that children, adolescents and adults must learn to function in an emotionally healthy manner. Some stories were created for children who had been abused or traumatized, but many were designed children and adolescents with other common problems.

Several of the stories in this chapter deal with problem solving skills. Many, if not most, therapy patients seem to have limited problem solving skills. This can be the result of trauma, being in a family where parents had poor problem solving skills, and/or being depressed or pessimistic. Individuals who have limited ability to solve problems give up when confronted with problems. They attempt one or two solutions and when these don't work, convince themselves there is no solution to their problems. Lack of problem solving skills and pessimism are often the roots of depression in adolescence and adult life (Seligman, 1995) The stories in this chapter which deal with problem solving skills allow the unconscious to understand that there are many solutions to problems and the most important element of solving a problem is the refusal to give up.

The Oyster

Problem(s) Addressed:
Low self esteem; distorted self image; inability to see strengths; trauma negatively impacting on self image

Appropriate for:
Any age female

Message:
Find your strengths and build on them. Find a way to take something positive from a traumatic experience.

Symbols and Metaphors:
Oyster: the self, as viewed by those with low self esteem or creating self image through negative belief systems
Pearl: the positive experience or strength that can be gained from trauma

Elements of the Story That Can be Changed:
This story seems more fitted for females since females tend to be the sex that wears pearls. The Oyster can be read to males as it is, trusting their unconscious will understand the message and personalize it.

Note:
The last stages in healing from trauma involve the ability to learn something from a horrible experience and to give something positive to the world because of it. John Walsh, who started The Center for Missing and Exploited Children and the television program "America's Most Wanted," after his five-year-old son was murdered, is an example of this principle. The loss of a child through violence is never completely healed in a parent (Marcey, 1995), but the ability to help others because of the loss can make the experience more bearable.

145

The Oyster

Once upon a time an oyster lay on the bottom of the bay. Oysters are very rough on the outside and not very colorful. The shell of an oyster is often ground up into small pieces and used to make roads. People and vehicles ride and walk all over roads made out of oyster shells.

This oyster was no different. "I am designed to allow people to walk all over me because I'm just a yucky, ugly oyster," the oyster told herself day after day. "I was created for people to walk on me." The oyster had also heard that people sometimes became poisoned from eating oysters. So she told herself, "I'm really worthless; all I do is make people sick."

Often when oysters are served at restaurants, people remark, "Yuck, oysters are slimy, they're yucky. Why would anyone want such a repulsive thing?" So the oyster would say to herself, "they're right, I'm not worth anything, I'm slimy, people hate me, and I am worthless."

It was not surprising that the oyster was always feeling sad. "Why couldn't I have been something different? Why couldn't I have been a diamond or ruby? Why couldn't I have been a sand dollar or have a shell that could be made into earrings? Why, why, why?" the oyster asked, as she thought a lot about what she wasn't. She told herself over and over that she was ugly and awful and slimy and made many people sick.

One day a fisherman threw a net into the bay and caught this oyster in his net. The oyster was even more upset and cried out, "This is exactly what I was afraid of. Now I'm caught and everyone is going to discover just how ugly and repulsive I really am."

The fisherman had a different way of looking at things than the oyster. Finding the oyster in his net, he opened the shell with a knife. From deep within the shell, he pulled out an exquisite white pearl. This discovery surprised the oyster. She had paid no attention to the hard pearl as it grew within her. "Isn't it amazing that you can have something so valuable within you and not even realize it? How could this be?" asked the oyster. "How could I have this beautiful pearl inside me when I am so ugly?"

147

Because the fisherman had spent his life on the sea, he sensed the oyster didn't understand how a pearl is formed and he began to talk to her. "Long ago, when you were very little, there were things in your life that were very irritating and scary and sad and painful. To deal with this, you began to build a covering around your feelings. You wrapped and wrapped all your pain and sadness to protect yourself. This was really helpful when you were young and the pain was very real. What you did not realize and now can see, is that you changed this awful pain into a valuable pearl. You found a way to take your pain and sadness, crystallize it and change it into something exquisite. This pearl was within, just waiting to be discovered."

"Wow," cried the oyster, "that's very surprising." Then the fisherman broke away the shell from the outside of the oyster because she didn't need that anymore. He removed the yucky, slimy part because she didn't need that anymore either. Then he polished the pearl allowing the beauty and luster to shine through. The fisherman gave the pearl to his daughter. She wore it on a necklace of gold and prized it dearly.

"Isn't it amazing?" the little pearl remarked to herself. "I never realized that I am special. I was unaware that deep within there was a pearl waiting to shine like a jewel." As the pearl continued to think about life, she realized that the most valuable jewels are often buried and are just waiting to be discovered and polished.

©1995
Nancy Davis, Ph.D.

The Girl Who Loved Applause

Problem(s) Addressed:

Basing self image and self value on the opinions of others. This, of course, means that emotions are on a constant roller coaster since no one can have the approval of everyone, or of one person at all times (Ellis and Harper, 1974). People who base their self value on external factors, such as the approval of others, rather than on self love or personal power.

Appropriate for:

Ages 8 and above; also appropriate for adolescents and adults

Message:

Self love and personal power come from an inner acceptance and belief in oneself, from optimism and repeating positive statements that are motivating. Happiness comes from building on one's strengths and finding value in who you are.

Symbols and Metaphors:

This story is straight forward, with little symbolism. It uses the example of being a rock star because so many children and adolescents believe that they will be happy and like themselves if they become rock stars or sports heros.

Elements of the Story That Can be Changed:

This story can be changed to male form

Note:

This story is an appropriate one for many students who have come to believe that self value comes from the cost of one's shoes or coat. It can be read to classes or groups as is and used for discussion of values.

150

The Girl Who Loved Applause

Once upon a time there lived a girl named April who didn't like herself very well. She didn't value who she was because she had not been taught to like herself. Those around April didn't like themselves either, so they were poor teachers. As she grew, rather than saying positive things to her, the people around April constantly criticized everything she did.

Because the statements from others around her did not seem to reflect love and acceptance, April did not learn to like herself. She constantly told herself, "Nobody likes me." When she looked at herself in the mirror, April didn't like her appearance. She never felt her grades were high enough or her schoolwork perfect enough. Even with friends around her, April didn't believe that she was liked. Her clothes embarrassed her because she had to buy them at a discount store and they did not have designer labels. Of course, no one really wants to be filled with self-hate, so April searched for ways to feel better.

As she was watching TV one night, a popular rock star sang her latest hit song. At the end of her song, everybody clapped, threw roses and wanted their picture taken with her. Watching this singer had a great influence on April. "I'm going to be a singer because if I become a singer then everybody will like me and I will be happy," she whispered to herself.

It is very hard to become a popular singer, but April had a good voice and she knew that with lots of hard work and practice she would have a great voice. When people applauded her singing, she told herself "I'm going to make it! I'm going to be a famous rock star and then I'll be happy because everybody will like me."

April had some good breaks, met the right people and did become a famous rock singer. She sang on TV and gave concerts in big stadiums where thousands of people came to see her. A picture of her latest concert appearance was on the cover of a rock magazine when she sold her first gold album.

One night when April was alone, she sat in her dressing room looking at her awards and her gold discs. "Why am I not happy?" she asked as if there were someone with her who could provide an answer. "I'm on the cover of magazines. Fans constantly ask for my autograph. I'm selling hundreds of tapes and albums. I'm making as much money as I could possibly ever spend, but I'm not happy. I thought if I had all these things, I would be happy." As she asked herself these questions, a tear rolled from each of her eyes.

As she was trying to understand what had gone wrong, a cleaning lady entered the dressing room singing, laughing and seeming to enjoy life. April watched the cleaning lady for a while. She noticed that the lady was wearing old, torn clothes and her shoes had holes in them. It was obvious that this woman cut her own hair, probably because she could not afford the luxury of having it cut at a salon.

Soon April and the cleaning lady were having a conversation. As they talked, April realized that the cleaning lady really felt good about herself. To confirm her observation, April asked, "Do you like yourself? Are you happy?" The cleaning lady looked at April strangely. "Well, of course I like myself. Why wouldn't I like myself?"

April responded in amazement, "But you're not rich, and you don't have a big car, and people don't clap for you when you perform and you don't even get paid much for what you do."

Now it was the cleaning lady's turn to be amazed. "Those things don't have anything to do with liking yourself. Liking yourself is something that's inside you, it's what you learn when you learn to be friends with yourself. When you are friends with yourself, you give yourself applause, you tell yourself you are a worthwhile person and you learn from your mistakes rather than putting yourself down because you aren't perfect. When you are friends with yourself, the things that make you happy come from inside you, not from money or an expensive car."

The words of the cleaning lady amazed April. She had spent her whole life trying to be famous and rich in her search for happiness. That night April had a dream about what she would really like to do with her life. She was tired of people asking her for autographs all the time, she was tired of agents telling her what to do, she was tired of having to travel around so much to give concerts and never being able to spend much time in her own house. She was also tired of the reporters following her around with cameras, trying to catch her in unflattering poses or printing lies about her in the tabloids.

In her dream, April saw herself as a teacher. She had always wanted to teach first grade so that she would be the first one to help a child learn to read and write. April wanted to have children bring her wildflowers from the playground, and she wanted to be there to hug them when they cried. The dream somehow gave April's heart an important message. When she awoke in the morning, she realized that she wasn't doing what she wanted to do at all.

That morning, April, the famous rock star, held a news conference to announce that she was leaving the music business. No one wanted to believe her. Her fans declared, "If I were her, I'd be happy." They also believed that money and nice clothes and having people clap for them would make them happy. But April had been there, and she had learned that happiness does not come from fame or money. Many of the rock stars that she had worked with were on drugs; others had killed themselves. Even her friends and agent advised her not to leave the music business. "What are you doing?" they asked, "You're crazy to give all this up."

April had stopped letting the approval of others direct her life; she was now being directed from a voice within her heart who knew exactly what she needed to be happy and to like herself. So April went back to school and became a teacher. After graduating, she moved to a small town to teach first grade. In this town, everyone knew April. The children thought they had the most wonderful first-grade teacher in the world. April taught her students to love learning and she also taught them how to be friends to themselves.

April often sang when she was invited to dances or county fairs. At the end of each song, the audience would cheer and applaud. Then April would smile as she remembered the cleaning lady who had helped her to learn that applause can never substitute for a heart which cannot applaud itself.

©1995
Nancy Davis, Ph.D.

153

The Rabbit and the Turtle

Problem(s) Addressed:

Rigidity; refusal to try new behaviors; the numbing and withdrawal symptoms of Post Traumatic Stress Disorder; parents who do not understand that it is the job of a parent to teach their children to do things they do not feel like doing.

Appropriate for:

Any age

Message:

Withdrawal from relationships is no solution for problems; trying new behaviors can be surprisingly rewarding; people often learn to love what they initially resist doing.

Symbols and Metaphors:

Turtle: Withdrawal; refusal to try new things
Turning the turtle over: any inducement to change (note that the turning over of the turtle does not injure or hurt the turtle, he just doesn't like it)

Elements of the Story That Can be Changed:

The sex of the characters

Note:

This story was designed many years ago for a child who had been abused in every way imaginable. Her mother and the mother's boyfriend were sentenced to three life sentences because of their crimes against this child and her siblings. She was afraid to try new behaviors because of her trauma. This child inspired more therapeutic stories than any other child I have treated. She listened to them time and time again. She has been adopted by an emotionally healthy family, her tested IQ increased from 80, at age five, to 131 when tested at age nine. She is now in gifted classes, has friends and is emotionally healthy. She is an inspiration to any victim since she had demonstrated that healing from extreme trauma is possible.

The Rabbit and the Turtle

Once upon a time, deep in the woods, a small turtle wandered through the forest searching for food. Turtles are very interesting animals because they carry their house with them; they don't have to find a cave or hole to call their home. When a turtle is afraid, it doesn't have to run; a turtle pulls into its shell to feel safe. This turtle was often afraid, so having a hard shell in which to withdraw seemed perfect. When the rains brought lightning, he pulled into his shell. When foxes were looking for food, he pulled into his shell. When lightning bugs reminded him of lightning, rather than investigate the light, he retreated into the safety and darkness of his shell. It wasn't long until he was staying in his shell all the time, afraid to come out for food or water. He was very much alone because it was impossible to make friends and withdraw at the same time.

One spring day, a rabbit hopped along the path and spied the turtle, who was, of course, in his shell. The rabbit knocked on the top of the shell, calling out, "Mr. Turtle, Mr. Turtle."

The turtle responded by yelling, "Go away."

"Mr. Turtle, Mr. Turtle, don't you want to race with me?" asked the rabbit.

The turtle repeated himself, "Nope, go away."

The rabbit was a very determined animal, and he tried everything he could think of to get the turtle to race him. He even tried to get the turtle mad at him, but the turtle wouldn't get mad. He just yelled from beneath his shell, "Go away."

This rabbit was not use to losing at anything, so, rather than give up, the rabbit flipped the turtle over on his back. When a turtle is upside down, it is in trouble because it is unable to flip itself over without help. The rabbit, of course, knew this. "You're on your back, ha, ha, ha. Now that you're on your back, are you feeling safe?"

The turtle was getting upset at this point, and began to yell, "Turn me back over."

"I'm not going to turn you back over until you race me," said the rabbit. "Will you race me?"

"No," the turtle said firmly.

"I'm going to leave you alone for a half hour, then I'll come back to see if you've changed your mind," the rabbit called over his shoulder as he hopped away.

Soon the rabbit was back, but the turtle still refused to race him. The rabbit was not accustomed to losing. "I'm going to leave you upside down all night, then we'll see how you are tomorrow." The rabbit then hopped away, leaving the turtle upside down in the middle of the path.

Turtles do not enjoy being upside down; they can't get water or food and it is very scary being helpless. So the next morning when the rabbit returned to ask, "Mr. Turtle, Mr. Turtle, are you ready to race me?", the turtle said, "Yes." He was afraid to race the rabbit, but he also did not want to be upside down for another minute.

All the other animals in the forest heard about the race and came to watch. As everyone knows, rabbits can run much faster than turtles. But the turtle and the rabbit started out at the same point with the animals of the forest yelling at the turtle to go faster. Of course, the rabbit won that race, but the turtle didn't really lose either, because he found out it was a lot of fun to walk as fast as he could and to have other animals cheering him on. In no time at all, he was racing other turtles and he was winning. The turtle noticed that with every race his fear got smaller and smaller. Soon the turtle only withdrew into his shell when he slept.

One day the turtle was walking along the path and he came upon some baby turtles, who immediately pulled into their shells in fear. The turtle stopped to teach the babies a lesson about real and imagined danger. He wanted to be sure that they learned that withdrawing in fear when there is no danger does not make fear go away, it only makes it stronger.

©1995
Nancy Davis, Ph.D.

The Bull and the Goat

Problem(s) Addressed:

Rigid attitudes; poor problem solving skills

Appropriate for:

Ages 5 - 9

Message:

Learn the difference between facts and beliefs; problems need much effort and many attempts to be solved; don't give up

Symbols and Metaphors:

Bull & the Goat: any difference which people use to make an enemy out of someone who could be a friend

Elements of the Story Which Can be Changed:

Sex of the main characters; the element of aggression and fighting could be introduced at the beginning of the story to teach children to see their peers in a more objective way

Note:

Conflict management is a main focus of many schools where violence has become a problem. Stories can help children to see these problems in a different way.

160

The Bull and the Goat

Once upon a time there was a farmer who had many animals. He had chickens and cows. He had rabbits and sheep. He had dogs and cats. He also had one goat. Each animal on the farm had a helping role. The cows gave milk. The sheep grew wool and ate the grass on the farm so it wouldn't have to be mowed. The chickens laid eggs and the rabbits helped eat the scrap vegetables. The dogs helped herd the sheep and cows and guard the farm. The cats kept the barn free from rats and mice so they wouldn't eat the farmer's hay. The goat gave milk and helped the sheep eat the grass.

Because the farmer didn't have a big farm, he often put different animals together in the same field. In one field there were a goat and a huge bull. Bulls are male cows and sometimes they can be very mean and aggressive. This bull tried to give the appearance of being mean, but deep inside he was as gentle as a teddy bear.

The goat missed having other goats on the farm, but he realized that he would probably stay the only goat on the farm. Since he was a problem solver, the goat decided to make friends with the bull. Using the direct approach, the goat walked up to the bull and asked, "How would you like to be my friend?"

The bull replied, "That's ridiculous. Who has ever heard of a bull being friends with a goat? That's not the way it is supposed to be. Aren't there rules that say bulls cannot be friends with goats? I'll bet we should even be enemies."

Well the goat thought that was pretty funny. He exclaimed, "Where in the world did you hear those rules? And why do you believe them?"

The bull avoided the question and replied, "That's the rule and that's the way it is going to be. You cannot change rules. You have to always follow a rule."

"Oh, don't be silly," the goat said. "Who made up that rule anyway? Tell me their name." The bull couldn't tell the goat the name because he didn't know. He had overheard the farmer telling his wife that bulls and goats cannot be friends and because the farmer had said it, the bull believed it to be true.

The goat, being a rebel, refused to give up. "You know we can be friends. You and I can talk and we can help each other. You must be very lonely in this field because you're the only bull."

The bull had been trying to act really tough as if he didn't care that he had no friends. But deep inside he did care and the more the goat talked to him, the more he realized that it was silly to create a rule where a rule did not exist. The bull decided he could be a little more flexible. Who would be hurt if he and the goat were friends?

Each day that the bull and the goat were together, they became better friends. They spent the summer eating grass and talking about things that were important and unimportant.

As the summer passed, there was little rain. Because grass needs water to grow, there was little grass. Since grass was the main course of their meals, the bull and the goat became more and more hungry. One morning the goat commented to his friend, the bull, "I'm starved."

"I'm pretty hungry too," the bull replied. "My stomach has been growling all night."
"Well, there is no grass around here," observed the goat, "I think we ate it all. If we don't figure out something, we are going to starve."

As they were talking, they looked around the field and noticed that there was a tall tree in the field with many leaves that they could eat. Both animals walked over to the tree but the bull couldn't reach the leaves and neither could the goat. So the two animals stood under the tree knowing that a good meal was just a few feet away. Motivated by their hunger, they talked about ways to reach the leaves. First the goat said wistfully "Maybe a storm will come and blow the leaves down."
"Don't bet on it," said the bull, "that's one of the reasons the grass hasn't grown. There haven't been any storms." So they continued to look longingly at the leaves while becoming more and more hungry.

Suddenly the goat had an idea. "How about if I jump up on your back and I'll get some leaves for both of us."
The bull was not convinced. "I don't know how you are going to get on my back. That's impossible."
The goat was a rebel who didn't believe anything was impossible. "When you say impossible, it just makes me try harder," he said.

At that, the goat started running and attempted to jump on the bull's back. The first few times, the goat fell right on his nose. But the goat was pretty determined and he was also very hungry. He kept trying, until all at once, after jumping on the bull's back and swaying back and forth, he was able to keep his balance. The goat could now reach all the leaves he wanted. He pulled off some branches, and chewed off other branches. When he had enough for both of them, the goat jumped back down. Soon the bull and the goat were feasting on the leaves.

"Remember when you didn't want to be my friend?" the goat asked the bull between bites.
"Yeah, that was pretty dumb, wasn't it?" replied the bull. "If I hadn't become your friend, we'd both be hungry right now."

The farmer, who had been watching the two animals, said loudly, "I thought bulls and goats weren't supposed to be friends." The bull and the goat looked at each other and smiled. They realized that it is important to understand the difference between a fact and an opinion.

©1995
Nancy Davis, Ph.D.

The Dump Truck

Problem(s) Addressed:

For people who help others but are unable to set limits and boundaries on their helpfulness. These people often rescue others when no one has asked for their help and are surprised when they are victimized by the very people they have tried to help. For a child who is taking care of the family, read "The Baggage Handler".

Appropriate for:

All ages

Message:

Taking care of others may make you feel bad about your own abilities and may not win friends or protectors.

Symbols and Metaphors:

Heavy load: the responsibilities that are taken on inappropriately
Criticism from the other trucks: the victimization of the person who helps but does not feel good enough about him or herself to set limits on this helpfulness

Elements of the Story That Can be Changed:

Who explains the lesson to the red truck; the age of the red truck can be increased

Note:

This story has been used successfully for children who have done school work for other children and adults who have moved homeless neighbors into their homes and then been robbed. It is about being able to say "no" and still feel good. I have never found that a helpful client stops helping others as a result of this story and therapy, but they learn that they have a choice and that they can say "no" at any time, even when a pattern has already been established.

The Dump Truck

Once upon a time there was a red dump truck. Now dump trucks are built to carry heavy loads and the red truck did this very well. Indeed, in the past, it would take on loads from some of the other trucks so they wouldn't have to work so hard. The dump truck would take some extra gravel from one truck or extra garbage from another and try to carry everything including its own load. The red truck wanted to help the other trucks and it wanted to make friends. "If I help them then they will like me and help me when I need help," it thought.

But the strangest thing happened. Rather than liking the red truck more, the other trucks often made fun of the helpful truck. "You're the slowest dump truck there is in the whole group," they would say. Then they would add, "You're always holding us up, you're always late for the job, you've had more accidents than anyone else and you need more repairs than anyone else." The other trucks were always blaming the red truck for getting into problems even though these problems were caused by the red truck's attempts to help others. Even while the other trucks were being mean, they still expected the red truck to help them with their loads. The red truck felt bad when it did not help the others or win their gratitude.

One day the red dump truck was going up a very steep hill which had a stop light at the top. A huge eighteen-wheeler pulled up beside the red truck. Eighteen-wheelers are able to carry much greater loads than dump trucks and know a lot about carrying things. The eighteen-wheeler looked over at the red truck asking, "Did you know that your engine is making all sorts of funny noises? I think you are being asked to carry too heavy a load. You should complain to someone. That's just not right, you'll be ruined if you're overloaded like that." The red truck explained that it always carried a heavy load because it was trying to help out all the other dump trucks so they wouldn't have to work so hard. The eighteen-wheeler asked the red dump truck to pull off the road so they could talk for a while.

The eighteen-wheeler understood what it was like to carry very heavy loads. It explained that each truck was made to carry a certain size load. Each truck needed to be very careful to carry only what it was made to carry. The eighteen-wheeler was amazed that the other trucks were always asking the red truck to do more than its share. The dump truck explained that it always offered to do more so it could feel good about itself. The big truck asked, "And do you feel good about yourself?"

The red truck had never really thought about that before. "Do I feel good about myself?" the red truck said out loud and was surprised to realize the answer was "no." The red truck realized that it didn't feel good at all. It remembered how the other trucks had grown to expect its help but never seemed to appreciate the help. The other trucks seemed to feel that they deserved the red truck's help and never had to give anything in return. The truck remembered the unkind things that the other trucks said. It didn't understand why the other trucks treated it this way when it was trying to be helpful, but it did understand that carrying everyone else's load was making it feel worse, not better.

At that moment, the red truck decided that it was time to carry just its own load, which was quite a bit. The next time that the dump trucks got loaded up, the other trucks moved on before their loads were completely put in, expecting the red truck to take what was left. "Not this time," the red truck thought. The other trucks looked very unhappy. They got angry. Some even talked about being afraid of trying to carry such a load by themselves. But the red truck remembered the words of the eighteen-wheeler and it didn't move a wheel. Finally each dump truck was loaded up with its own load, including the little red truck that had worked so hard.

As the trucks moved out to do their own work, the red truck felt lighter than it had ever felt before. It was doing its own job and trusting the other trucks to do theirs. For the first time, the red truck was able to get to the job on time, get everything done, and go to the job without any accidents or mechanical problems. All the other dump trucks did fine, too, because you see each one was given a load that they could carry on their own and they didn't need to share it with anyone. As time went on, the dump truck became better and better at the job that it needed to do because it no longer took on the loads of others. Being so outstanding at doing its own job brought respect from the other trucks. They felt better about themselves, too, because they now knew that they could carry their own loads without help.

©1996
By Marcella Marcey, Ph.D.

The Girl and the Rope

Problem(s) Addressed:

This story can be used early in therapy to explain and outline the tasks that the client will need to accomplish during therapy, i.e. build trust with the therapist, experiment with new ideas and behaviors even when it is scary, and finally 'let go' of old ways of coping and develop new ones. The story also outlines the role and commitment of the therapist. In addition, this is a useful story for children who believe that they must solve their problems without help from anyone.

Appropriate for:

All ages

Message:

Actions we take without thinking or that are adaptive at one time can become maladaptive later; we must drop maladaptive behaviors to move on move on.

Symbols and Metaphors:

Rope: problem

Holding the rope: a maladaptive way of coping with a problem based totally on feeling

Old woman: the therapist or the healthier part of the person

Wall: barrier that makes informed choice difficult to impossible

Other people who have stopped: others who have unsuccessfully tried to help before

Elements of the Story That Can be Changed:

Sex of the main character; sex of the helper if the therapist is a male

The Girl and the Rope

Once upon a time there was a girl who was walking down a street that had a wall running along one side. She had walked this street many times before and had been nervous about what might live on the other side of the wall. On this day, she saw a rope hanging over the wall. As she watched, she thought she saw the rope began to slowly slide back over the wall. Without thinking, she reached out and grabbed the end so it could not go back over the wall. But as soon as she took the rope into her hands, she felt a tug on the other end. She held tighter and began to pull back on the rope to prevent it from being pulled from her hands. As she increased her pull on the rope, the pull on the other end also increased. As she held on, her hands began to hurt but she believed that it was somehow important that she hold on and not let go. She stood for a long time holding on to that rope, refusing to let it go.

As time passed, many people stopped and asked her why she was holding on to a rope by a wall. Her friends found her and asked her to leave the rope and come and play, but she would not. Even her parents, who knew that she could be stubborn at times, began to become very angry with her because she would not drop the rope. No one understood why this task was so important to her. They didn't understand that the girl was afraid to let go. She had held on to that rope so long, given up so much, and invested so much energy into holding on that she believed that she could never let go. It wasn't safe to let go.

Many people came by asking questions, even offering to help the girl with her task. Many offered to help her pull on the rope and some offered to hold the rope while she took a break. The girl refused all offers of help and even seemed to become angry with those who tried to help her. What these people did not understand was that the girl was afraid, and she had learned that anger got rid of people quickly. Also it felt better to say that she did not want help rather than admit that she was afraid to accept anyone's help. Help from others in holding the rope might somehow be against the rules.

One day an old woman came down the street and stopped to talk to the girl. She began by asking many of the same questions that other passersby had asked. "Why are you holding on to that rope? Why don't you put it down? What is on the other end?" Unlike the others who had come to talk to the girl, the old woman stayed even when the girl explained that she could not answer these questions, but she knew that she must hold on or something terrible would happen.

"It looks like you've been holding that rope a long time," the woman said.

"Yes, I have. How could you tell?" the girl asked.

"Because you have scars on your hands and you look terrible. Anyone could see that you have been through tough times if they just took a good look at you. You know the rope is your problem. As long as you hold on to it, you can't move on. You've already stopped growing and you are alone a lot of the time. You can't learn and grow as long as you hold on to that."

"I've been here a long time but I have to hold this rope or something terrible will happen," said the girl. "When I first grabbed the rope, it just seemed like a good idea, but now I hurt all over. I don't know what will happen if I let go. I'm afraid to find out."

The old woman smiled kindly at the girl. "I know exactly what will happen if you let go of the rope. Your hands will heal, your back will straighten and you will grow, play and sleep as you were meant to."

The girl did not believe the woman at first. But the old lady said that she had plenty of time and did not want the girl to feel alone anymore with that rope. She stayed, helping the girl feel safe and supported.

Eventually the woman made a suggestion. "Why don't you let go for just a second and see what will happen? You could grab it back quickly if you needed to." The girl decided to try the experiment. To her surprise the rope just hung over the wall. Nothing bad happened and it felt so good to let go. The girl could hardly believe that it had been so simple to let go. The girl asked, "What is going to happen now?"

The woman took the girl's hands and said, "You will heal and you will be able to be with people and have fun. But you must remember this and learn. If you ever find that you are holding on to something too long and it is hurting you, you should let go and move on."

The girl knew she had learned a valuable lesson, one that she would always remember because she had learned it with her mind, heart and body.

©1995
Marcella Marcey, Ph.D.

The Sad Skunk

Problem(s) Addressed:

Rejection of children by peers because they are different or handicapped

Appropriate for:

Elementary school children

Message:

There is value in everyone; look for strengths, not weaknesses

Symbols and Metaphors:

Skunk: any problem that causes others to harass or degrade

Elements of the Story That Can be Changed:

Sex of the main characters

Note:

Children often attack and bully those who are different. Those working with children need to be constantly aware of this type of behavior and refuse to accept it as normal.

The Sad Skunk

Once upon a time there lived a lonely little skunk. He was lonely even though he lived in a forest where there were many kinds of animals. There were rabbits and raccoons, opossums and foxes, mice and bears. There were big birds and small birds, and many kinds of rodents. Even the streams had many fish.

The skunk had tried to make friends with every kind of animal in the forest. But whenever the little black and white creature wandered near other animals they yelled, "Here comes Stinky! Yuck! Run for your lives!" Then they would all run away, leaving the little skunk sad and alone.

"I just hate myself!" cried the skunk one day after the others had laughed and run away from him. "I didn't ask to be born a skunk. Why don't they understand that I would never spray my smell at my friends? They won't give me a chance to explain what I'm really like. I just want to be their friend!"

As he sat there alone and lonely, tears slowly rolled down his face. Time after time the little skunk tried to make friends, but no one would get close to him. None of the animals would give him a chance to explain that he wouldn't spray them with his stinky smell. Each time he approached them the other animals laughed and ran away. He got sadder and sadder. As time passed, the sadness became such a part of his life that he began to believe that part of being a skunk was being sad.

One day, as he was wandering through the woods sniffing for food, the unhappy skunk heard a fierce growl and frightened cries. Peeking through the underbrush, he spied a brown fox who had cornered three little bunnies and was planning to eat them for his dinner. Without a thought as to how mean the bunnies had been to him in the past, the skunk said to himself, "I think I can help them!" He ran into the clearing where the fox had cornered the little bunnies. Because the fox was so busy thinking about his tasty meal, he didn't even

175

notice the skunk moving in beside him. Getting very close to the fox, the skunk took careful aim and — whoosh! — shot his stinky spray right into the fox's eyes.

With a cry of surprise, the fox immediately forgot about dinner. He ran off into the forest, yelping and wiping his paws and face on the ground trying to get rid of the horrible smell.

After the fox was gone, the air was still heavy with the strong smell of the skunk. The bunnies looked around, saw the skunk and realized that he had saved their lives. They forgot all about making fun of him and running away. They ran quickly to the skunk, hugging him, thanking him and crying with relief all at the same time. Moving away from the bushes where the worst of the smell still filled the air, they apologized too for the way they had treated him in the past. They had discovered, from this experience, a new way to look at the skunk. "It's amazing," they said to each other, "how something that smells so bad can be good."

The bunnies and the skunk learned about friendship that day. The bunnies learned that friends can come in many different sizes, shapes and smells and the skunk had discovered that there are ways to get rid of sadness.

©1989
Nancy Davis, Ph.D.

The Red Car

Problem(s) Addressed:

Oppositional behavior that becomes self-destructive

Appropriate for:

Ages 5 - 16

Message:

You can find a way to use your oppositional tendencies to be assertive and to be co-operative and follow rules when either is appropriate

Symbols:

Red Car: any child whose personality style is to be oppositional or rebellious

Elements of the Story Which Can be Changed:

Sex of the car

Note:

Although rebels cause many problems for teachers, parents and for themselves, it is important to realize that rebels were the reason that this country is independent rather than a colony of England. Rebels need to learn to understand and use their rebellious nature in a positive rather than a destructive way.

177

CAR HELPS SAVE BOY

man
went
ed car
se the

e red
found
to the

e front

ecided
ar had
ecision
he was

d seen
the fire
to be a
d up the
red car

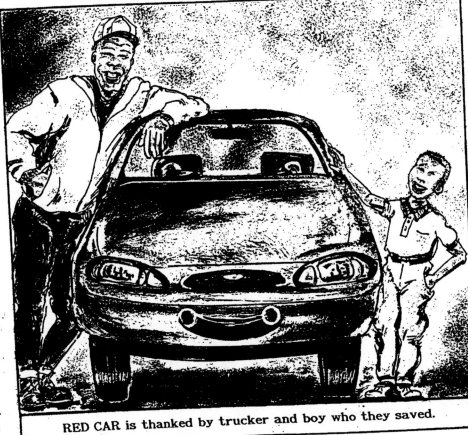

The re
put th
forwa
drove
red c

car v
you,'
hosp

pag

he
disc
that
sup

RED CAR is thanked by trucker and boy who they saved.

One day a boy was riding his bike near the sales lot where the red car
boy darted into traffic and was hit by a truck. The driver of the truck immediat
injured boy and put him in the back seat of the red car. He then jumped

The Red Car

Once upon a time a bright shiny red car sat on a sales lot with other cars. These cars were all waiting for someone to buy them. But the red car was unlike the other cars on the lot because when a customer tried to unlock the door, it locked. And when the customer tried to start the car, it stopped. When the gear was put in forward, the car went in reverse. It would even honk the horn when everyone wanted quiet. It was such an unusual car.

Even though customers were not happy with the red car, the red car was happy with itself. "This is the way to be in control," the red car said to himself. "I will do the opposite of whatever anybody tells me to do."

Many people came to the sales lot to buy cars, and the other cars on the lot quickly sold. Some customers liked the red car and he even liked some of them. Sometimes customers would try to take the red car for a test drive. However, when they put the gear shift into forward, the car went in reverse. This scared many people away. "I don't want this car," they told the salesman. "Show me something else."

The red car saw that no one wanted to buy him, but he didn't understand the connection between how he acted and their rejection. "I'm such an independent car," he muttered after driving away yet another buyer. "I think for myself. It shouldn't matter that I do the opposite of what everybody wants me to do." And he said to himself, "I don't care if anybody ever buys me." But in his heart he knew that wasn't true.

One day a boy was riding his bike near the sales lot where the red car was parked. The boy darted into traffic and was hit by a truck. The driver of the truck immediately picked up the injured boy and put him in the back seat of the red car. He then jumped into the red car exclaiming, "I have to get this boy to the hospital as quickly as possible."

The red car decided that this might be a time to stop being so stubborn. When the man put the key in the ignition, the car started. And when he put the gear shift into forward, it went forward. Then the driver pushed hard on the gas pedal to make the car go fast and the red car drove very fast. Soon they arrived at the hospital where the boy's life was saved because the red car had helped the driver get him quickly to the hospital.

When the boy's parents arrived to see him, they thanked the man who had driven the red car with their son to the hospital. The driver in turn thanked the red car. "I am so glad I found you," he told the red car. "Without you, I don't know if we could have gotten the boy to the hospital in time to save him."

If cars could smile, this red car would have smiled. A picture of the car was on the front page of the newspaper and the salesman even gave it a wax job.

Because of the publicity, many people wanted to buy the red car. The red car decided he was tired of being the only car in the sales lot that couldn't find an owner. The car had discovered the excitement of the world beyond the sales lot. He did, however, make a decision that he would have some say in who bought him. So he would go backwards when he was supposed to go forward only if he did not want the driver to become his owner.

One day a fire chief arrived at the lot to buy a car to use at the fire station. He had seen the red car on television, "I would very much like to use this car as my personal fire car," the fire chief told the salesman. "It would lead the fire engines to all the big fires. This car has to be a leader and be in perfect condition or I will have to pick another car."

The salesman remembered how the red car often did the opposite of what it was asked to do as he handed the chief the car keys. The chief jumped into the car for a test drive before the salesman could warn him. The red car had listened to the kind of car the chief wanted and decided being a fire car would be exciting. The red car thought about getting his own siren and racing down streets with regular cars having to stop when he was going to fires. He thought about leading big fire trucks and being around exciting events. "Wow," he told himself, "this would be even better than doing the opposite of what anybody wants me to do."

When the chief put the gear in forward, he went forward; when the chief put the gear in reverse, the red car went in reverse. And he did not honk his horn until the chief pushed the button on the steering wheel. He performed in every way like a car that deserved to lead fire trucks. The fire chief agreed and soon drove the red car back to the fire station.

Soon the red car had sirens and special emblems and red and blue flashing lights on the top. From that time on, when there was a big fire, the red car ran through the streets making sure that the other cars stopped and he quickly led the fire engines to the fire. As the red car sped past, people stopped and looked with admiration at him. The red car was now very proud of himself. He had realized there are all kinds of ways to be in control, and making a decision to cooperate can be one of them.

The Brown Leaves

Problem(s) Addressed:

Young children who delay and resist bowel movements

Appropriate for:

Ages 2-4

Message:

You can safely 'let go' when you go to the bathroom; it is safe to 'let go'

Symbols:

Tree: Child
Leaves: Feces

Elements of the Story Which Can be Changed:

Sex of the main character

Note:

Some young children delay and resist having bowel movements because they fear they are losing a part of themselves. This story, in very symbolic form, helps to change that belief.

The Brown Leaves

Once upon a time there was a little tree who was trying very hard to be a grown-up tree. In spring his leaves began to grow, and by summer he was covered all over with leaves. He thought he was handsome and very smart to have so many beautiful leaves all over him. Then autumn came and all of his leaves started to turn beautiful colors. He noticed that the leaves on the big trees turned pretty colors, too. Then all the leaves on every tree turned to brown, and he watched as the big trees let go of their brown leaves, letting them fall to the earth. The little tree didn't want to let go of his leaves even though he saw the big trees do it. He felt that the brown leaves were his very own that he had made himself. It made him mad and a little scared and maybe even a tiny bit sad to watch the wind and rain take the leaves away.

He thought, "What would I do with no leaves? The big trees can make lots of things — big shade to sit under, homes for little birds and squirrels. But I don't do all that — all I have is my leaves. I won't LET THEM GO, OH YES!"

Well, the wind came and tugged gently but he didn't LET GO, OH YES! And the rain came, plop, plop, plop, and he didn't LET GO, OH YES! My goodness, he was so tired with all that work. Pretty soon when he was so tired that he almost fell asleep, a furry kitty came by.

"Hello," said the little tree.
"Hello," replied the kitty. "My, you look so tired."
"I am," said the little tree. "I'm working very hard to not LET GO, OH YES of my leaves." The little kitty started to giggle. Then she started to laugh and she rolled all over the ground. This made the little tree mad! "Why are you laughing?" he asked.
"Because pretty soon you are going to look very silly if you don't LET GO of your leaves," she answered.
"Why?" asked the tree.
"Because when you get more leaves in the spring, where are you going to put them? There won't be any room," she giggled.
"Is that really true?" the little tree asked quietly.

185

"Of course," said the kitty. "Trees always grow new leaves in the spring and as they grow taller in the summer, the leaves get bigger and greener. Then fall comes and the leaves turn colors and drop to the ground. Then the trees sleep through the winter so that they can get ready to make new leaves in the spring."

"Gosh," remarked the little tree. "No one ever explained about leaves to me before." And all of a sudden, in just the right way, and in just the right place, plop, plop, plop, the little brown leaves came down.

"OH, YES," he said. And the little kitty smiled.

Karen Custer
©1987

The Smart Baby Eagle

Problem(s) Addressed:

Problem solving skills

Appropriate for:

Ages 3-5

Message:

You can figure out how to solve many of your own problems, all by yourself

Symbols:

Falling out of the nest: any problem which a child encounters that he/she must solve without the help of the parents

Elements of the Story Which Can be Changed:

Sex of the main character

Note:

This story is to help children for future problem solving or if they are too dependent for their age

The Smart Baby Eagle

Once upon a time there were two big eagles, a mommy and a daddy eagle. They built a big nest and soon they had two little eagles living with them. Since birds can't buy their food at grocery stores, they have to hunt for it. So these two little eagles would wait in the nest while their parents searched for food. They could not go with their parents because they had not yet learned to fly.

One cloudy day, one of the little eagles fell out of the nest. When the mommy and daddy eagle returned, they searched for him but they could not find him. He had fallen under a bush and they were not able to see him. "What am I going to do? How am I ever going to get back in that nest without mommy and daddy to help me?" the little eagle thought. He was scared and he didn't think he could get back in that nest all by himself. He could see his mommy and daddy flying above the nest, but they couldn't see him because he was hidden by the bush. "What am I going to do?" the eagle thought fearfully. "I must find a way to get back to that nest. I am just going to have to figure this out by myself," he said firmly.

The little eagle watched carefully as his parents flew over the nest. He watched other birds, too, as they flew from tree to tree. Then he copied the way they moved their wings and held their bodies. It wasn't long before he figured out how to fly all by himself. He moved his wings and body just the way he had seen the other birds do it. At first, he didn't fly as well as his mommy and daddy because he was just learning. But he flew well enough to get back to the nest.

That day when his parents returned to the nest with food, they were surprised see the little eagle sitting in the middle of the nest with his sister. "Where have you been?" they asked, fluttering their wings to show that they were happy.
"I fell out of the nest," the little eagle replied.
"We looked for you and we couldn't find you," his parents told him.
"I know you looked for me. I watched you and I figured out how to fly all by myself, and I flew back up in the nest," he said proudly.

"You are so smart," they told him. "You are one of the smartest eagles that any mommy and daddy could have, because you figured out how to fly by yourself."

The little eagle felt very good about that. It wasn't long before his mom and dad were taking him with them as they hunted for food. He flew high and low; the little eagle discovered that he loved to fly. Because he had learned to fly by himself, he grew up to be very brave. The little eagle had discovered that he was smarter than the average eagle and he could figure things out all by himself.

The Monster in the Mirror

Problem(s) Addressed:

A negative self image which is very evil, angry and or aggressive in form

Appropriate for:

Ages 5 - 14

Message:

You can find a way to see that you are a valuable and worthwhile person, to say positive and optimistic things to yourself, and to behave appropriately

Symbols:

Monster: a child who believes that he is worthless and horrible

Voice inside: the attitudes toward self which are constantly repeated

Elements of the Story Which Can be Changed:

Sex of the main character

Note:

This story was created for a boy who was aggressive and destructive. Combined with other stories and some behavior modification, his behavior became much more under control and his self image improved significantly.

192

The Monster in the Mirror

Once upon a time there lived a very special boy named Kevin who was getting taller every day. Many people told Kevin, "You are so handsome and smart." But, whenever Kevin looked in the mirror, he saw an alligator or a shark or an ugly monster.

"I'm not handsome at all. They must be saying that just to make me feel good. Why can't they see the way I really look?" Kevin whispered to himself. A voice within him constantly told Kevin that he was worthless and was a failure. This caused him to feel very bad about himself. He felt like being an alligator and biting people. He felt like being a monster and scaring people. He had a lot of anger in him just like a shark.

Kevin tried to get people around him to see the world the way he did. "I am not a handsome, smart person, I'm a monster," he said. Because no one would believe he was a monster, Kevin started acting like a monster. He growled, he hit, and he acted angry all the time. He attacked people and he did very mean or weird things.

Pretty soon, people were saying, "Why is such a smart, handsome boy acting like he has a monster inside him?" Then Kevin would smile because he was finally getting his point across — he was a monster. He just had to convince more people. So, Kevin did everything he could to make people think he was an ugly monster. It wasn't long before people said, "Kevin is really a monster!"

One day Kevin was sitting alone on the basketball court because no one would play with him. A little boy named John came up to him and said, "Hey, why do you want everyone to think you're a monster?"

Kevin growled, "Grrr, because I am a monster, that's why. Get away."

But John was very special, and he saw through all this growling and meanness, "Isn't it lonely trying to be a monster?" John asked.

Kevin had to admit, if he was honest with himself, that it was very lonely being a monster. It was also very lonely feeling like a monster and having everybody treat him like a monster. Kevin also had to admit to himself that the worst thing about being a monster was the mean things he said to himself.

"Are you ready to give up trying to be a monster?" John asked.

"I don't know how to give it up," replied Kevin.

"Let me take you to my mirror," John said. "It's a mirror that shows the truth."

"Okay, I'll go," said Kevin, feeling a little hopeful that maybe his life could be different. To his surprise, when he looked in this new mirror, that reflected truth, there wasn't a monster there at all. There was a very intelligent, handsome and well-built guy.

"So what if I don't look like a monster on the outside," Kevin sputtered. "I'm still a monster inside."

"You don't have to feel you are a monster inside much longer," John stated. "Why don't you ask for a special dream that can help you understand how to stop being a monster?"

So that night when Kevin was going to sleep, he decided to try it. "I need a very special dream to show me that I am not a monster," Kevin whispered to himself. Because he had decided that he wanted to change, a very wise person came in his sleep and talked to him for a long time. This wise person let Kevin know how special he was, how smart he was and how he was not a monster at all; it was only a trick his heart was playing on him. Then the part of Kevin that knew he was not a monster, a shark or an alligator became very strong and found a voice that talked to him all night. This voice said, "You are getting smarter every day. You are finding a way to make many good friends. You are doing better and better in school. You are remembering everything that you study and doing better and better on tests. You are liking yourself more and more each day. You are trying new things and discovering who you really are." [1]

When Kevin thought he was a monster, the voice inside him had said mean and negative things. This voice kept Kevin believing that things would always turn out wrong in his life and he would continue to feel like a monster forever. Now Kevin knew that voice would never be strong again. The part of Kevin with the positive statements had gained control and was directing Kevin to move in new and rewarding directions.

---

[1]This is reflective of messages in audio tapes which repeat positive messages again and again.

When Kevin woke up, the dream seemed so real; the positive voice was still talking to him. Then Kevin looked in the mirror and realized that he was different. In the days that followed, Kevin stopped acting like a monster. He stopped growling and hitting. He stopped hating himself and being angry like a monster.

It wasn't long before his life changed in many ways. He found ways to make friends and be a friend. The positive voice kept talking to him so that even when he made mistakes, he realized that was normal — it had nothing to do with being a monster. The more the voice told him that he could handle his anger, the better Kevin got at expressing anger appropriately.

One day when Kevin was walking down the hall at school, a first grader ran from the bathroom yelling, "There's a monster in there." Kevin smiled and hugged the shaking little boy. "There's no such thing as monsters," Kevin told him and when this happened, Kevin felt his heart smile.

©1995
Nancy Davis, Ph.D.

The Princess and the Pain

Problem(s) Addressed:

Poor self image related to judgmental and negative statements that are constantly repeated and become self abusive

Appropriate for:

Any age

Message:

You can find a way to change the negative things you say to yourself to positive statements, to like yourself, to set reasonable standards and to become optimistic

Symbols:

Pain in the leg: any emotional or physical pain or illness caused by self hate

Kicking her leg against the wall: the representation that saying mean, abusive statements to oneself causes much pain

Elements of the Story Which Can be Changed:

This story can be adapted for males, keeping the metaphor of kicking the leg against the wall while dreaming about being self abusive

Note:

This story helps individuals of many ages to find ways to be nice to themselves

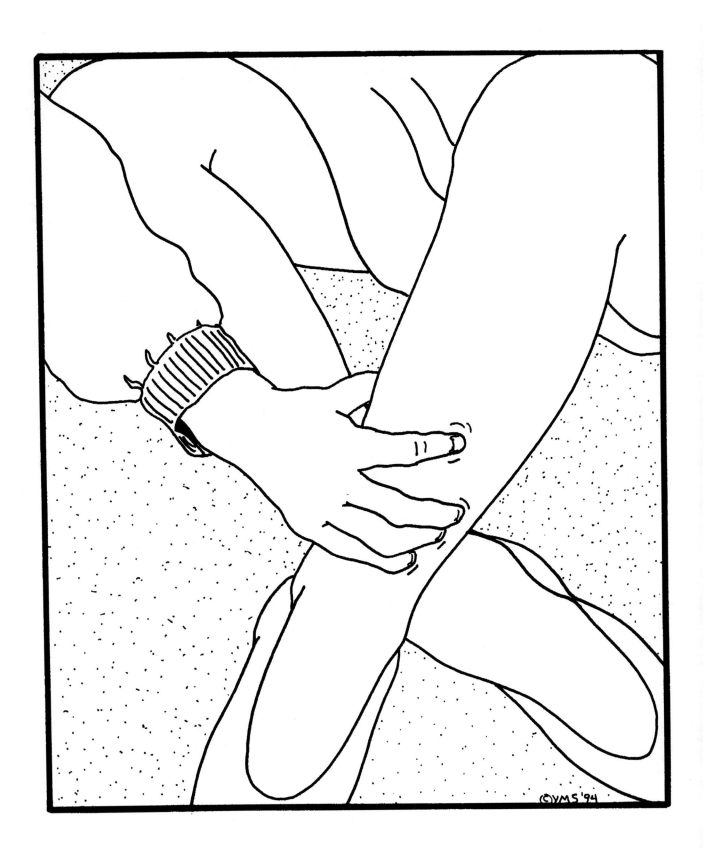

The Princess and the Pain

Once upon a time in a land not very far away lived a delightful, redheaded princess named Amy. She was the only person in her kingdom who had red hair and many people wanted red hair just like the princess. Although many of the girls in the kingdom envied Princess Amy and wanted to be like her, the princess was not very happy with herself. When Princess Amy wore a dress that she had made herself, people would say, "What a gorgeous dress." Rather than saying "thank you," Princess Amy would reply, "It's really not gorgeous. I should have sewn it better. Look at all the mistakes I made when sewing it."

Princess Amy got good grades in school. But even when she received an A on a paper, she would say to herself, "I don't deserve an A. This paper isn't good enough. I should have worked harder and the handwriting is messy.

Princess Amy was well liked and had many friends, but she felt they were not really friends. "They must be calling me because I'm a princess," she said to herself. "I don't think they really like me — I'm always making mistakes and acting stupid." When Princess Amy's family overheard her saying such negative things, they tried to convince her that she was wrong. Princess Amy refused to listen to them; she was certain that she was ugly, stupid, made too many mistakes and was disliked by all around her.

One morning as Princess Amy got out of bed she realized that her leg was hurting. She told her mom and dad about the pain in her leg. She was even limping a little as she walked. Her parents, the king and queen, told her that most pain does not last and her leg would soon be feeling fine. But the pain in her leg did not go away. The next morning when she got out of bed, the pain in her leg was worse. Princess Amy tried to remember if she had hurt her leg. She hadn't been jogging and she hadn't been working out in PE so she didn't understand why she was feeling such pain. The pain in her leg increased to the point that she had trouble walking, running and doing all the things she normally did.

Finally, Princess Amy's parents took her to the court doctor. He looked at her leg and remarked, "I can see that your leg is hurting but I don't know why." At that, Princess Amy began to cry. "You're a doctor and you should be able to help me," she sobbed. "Why can't you find out what is wrong with my leg? It hurts; I'm tired of having my leg hurt." So he called in other doctors and they did all kinds of tests on Princess Amy's leg, but no one could figure out why she was in pain.

In frustration, Princess Amy said to herself as she was laying down in her bed to sleep, "I need to figure out for myself why my leg is hurting. No one else seems able to help me so I'm going to have to help myself." As she slept that night, she began to dream.

First Princess Amy saw herself getting angry for making mistakes while sewing. Then she saw herself getting angry because her school work was not good enough. Then she watched as she told herself how stupid and unlikable she was when playing with her friends. At that moment, Princess Amy awoke with a start as she realized that she was kicking her leg against the wall with great force. At that, Princess Amy sat straight up in bed. She began to think about her dream and her leg. Then she realized what was happening. "Isn't that interesting," she said softly to herself. "Now what am I going to do about this?"

So Princess Amy laid back down on her pillow. "I could use another dream to help me understand how to solve this problem," she thought. After a while, Princess Amy drifted back to sleep and began to dream. In this dream, she was talking with a very wise teacher. They talked about liking yourself and judging yourself. They talked about wanting to be perfect and never being satisfied. They talked about learning and life. They talked about having friends and being a friend.

The next morning when she awoke, Princess Amy began to feel and think in new ways. It was hard at first. She was so used to putting herself down, saying mean things to herself and believing no one liked her. But she fought the old thoughts whenever they popped into her mind, until she was saying very positive and kind things to herself. Soon she was smiling when the teacher returned her tests or homework, even if the grades were not "A's." She told herself, "No one is perfect. I'm tired of trying to be something that is impossible. I am smart, I am learning and I am doing the best I can." When her friends called her, she smiled as she realized that she had many people who liked her.

Each day as Princess Amy became more positive and optimistic in the way she talked to herself, the pain in her leg decreased. One day the princess realized that she had changed most of the negative things she said to herself to positive ones. That was also the day that she noticed the pain in her leg was completely gone. That night when she went to bed, Princess Amy thought about her leg, and how much she had changed. She also realized that the pain in her leg had come with a lesson — sometimes pain is a message that you are hurting yourself.

©1995

Nancy Davis, Ph.D.

The Field of Wildflowers

Problem(s) Addressed:
Poor self esteem; being put down and degraded by peers

Appropriate for:
Any school age child who is scape goated by other children because of being different

Message:
Being different has nothing to do with self worth; you can find self worth even when others are degrading you

Symbols:
Flowers: an child who is different
Hiding under leaves: the tendency for a child with poor self esteem to hide their strengths, even from themself

Elements of the Story Which Can be Changed:
The types of comments made by other students can be individualized

Note:
This story was created for sisters from the Philippines. The children in their school were harassing them because of their skin color and the girls believed that they were ugly. This story helped to correct that self perception.

The Field of Wildflowers

Once upon a time there was a field filled with magnificent and brightly colored flowers. The flowers in this field were wild; no one had planted them; they sprouted and grew all by themselves. Some grew from seeds that blew in the wind. Others came from squirrels planting seeds for food and forgetting about them. Still more sprouted from seeds dropped by birds flying over the field. Small animals, with seeds hooked to their fur, also brought them to the field.

Because there were so many animals and birds around this field, and the strong winds often carried seeds as well, flowers of every color and variety grew as far as the eye could see. There were tall yellow Daisies and small purple flowers. There were Black-Eyed Susans and blue Forget-Me-Nots that grew along the creek which ran through the field. Anyone who passed the field would comment on its beauty.

One day, a bird flying from far away, dropped two seeds as she passed over the field. These seeds grew into two beautiful pink flowers which were unlike any other flowers in the whole field. Because they were unusual, the flowers began to say to themselves, "We're different. There aren't any other flowers like us anywhere in this field."

The other flowers noticed the difference, too. Soon they were taunting the pink flowers. "There is something wrong with you. You don't look like us," said one.
"You're the wrong color," said another.
"Your shape is different," said a third, "and your leaves are too green."

The two pink flowers did not like being rejected. Then the strangest thing happened...the pink flowers began to believe the mean things that the other flowers told them. Soon the pink flowers were repeating the mean taunts to themselves. "We're awful. We're not as good as those flowers. We're not as pretty. We're not as colorful and we don't smell as good." Believing that they were different and therefore ugly, the pink flowers hid so that no visitors to the field would see them.

One day, a teacher brought her science class to this field. Each student had an assignment to find flowers of many varieties. The students found Daisies, Irises and Forget-Me-Nots. They discovered Black-Eyed Susans and Bridal Wreaths.

Noticing the students as they searched, the pink flowers shook in fear. They were afraid that if they were discovered, the students would see just how ugly and different they were.

It just so happened that one student who was very curious searched very thoroughly for an unusual flower. Discovering the two pink flowers, she announced loudly, "Look what I found! Look what I found! I found some Lady Slippers. They're not supposed to grow around here. They are so rare and beautiful."

All the students in the class ran to see the newly discovered flowers. Everybody looked in amazement. "Wow, these flowers are so unusual," one student commented. "It's absolutely amazing that they would be growing here; they are such special flowers and so rare. Oh, I'm so glad you discovered them."

The teacher advised the students not to pick the rare pink flowers so they would produce seeds for more plants to grow. Many of the students took pictures of the beautiful pink flowers to show to their parents.

After the class had returned to school, the two pink flowers began to talk. "What did they say?" one asked.
"They said we were rare and valuable and we aren't supposed to be growing here," the other pink flower replied. "They said we're beautiful flowers and they even took pictures of us."

One of the other flowers around them, trying to make the pink Lady Slippers forget the students' compliments said, "I didn't hear anyone say that, you must have been mistaken." The pink flowers had very good ears, however, and they remembered and they learned.

Soon they were seeing themselves differently. The pink flowers no longer hid behind the other flowers. Because they saw themselves in a new way, the pink flowers grew very straight and produced more and more blossoms. Soon their blossoms were the most beautiful in the field. Visitors could tell by the way the pink flowers held themselves that they had come to understand that they were special. One day, one of the pink flowers commented to the other, "Isn't it amazing that we used to think we were worthless and ugly just because we're so different from the other flowers here. We are different from the other flowers only because a bird brought our seeds from far away."

After the visit from the science class, the pink flowers felt very good about themselves no matter what any of the other flowers said to them. When a new and very different flower sprouted the next spring, the pink flowers made sure that this new flower understood that being different has little to do with value.

Nancy Davis, Ph.D.

The Problem Solver

Problem(s) Addressed:

Poor problem solving skills

Appropriate for:

Ages 5 - 12

Message:

Keep trying until you figure out a solution

Symbols:

Locked out of the house: any problem

Elements of the Story Which Can be Changed:

Sex of the main character

Note:

Children who are optimistic and keep trying to solve problems tend to do much better in life than children who quickly give up (Seligman, 1995).

The Problem Solver

Once upon a time there was a boy named Brian. Because Brian's mom worked, Brian carried his house key on a chain that he wore around his neck so he could let himself in the house after school. One day when he arrived home, Brian realized that he had taken the chain with his house key off during PE and left it at school. Since Brian traveled to school by bus, he had no way to get back to school and find his house key.

Brian knew he had to find a way to get into his house without a key. First he tried to open the doors, but they were locked. Then he tried to open the windows on the first floor, but they were locked, too. "Well, I guess that's not going to work," said Brian with determination, "but there are other things I can try. I am going to figure out a way to get into this house." So Brian went next door and borrowed a ladder from a neighbor. He put the ladder against the house and climbed up to the second floor windows, but they were locked, too. "Well, I guess that's not going to work either," said Brian.

But he did not give up. "I can figure out how to get into my house," Brian told himself. He was smart, determined and a good problem solver so he knew he could figure out exactly what he needed to do. Next he called his mom at work from a neighbor's house to see if she could come and let him in. But she wasn't there; she was at a business meeting away from her office. "Well, we have a garage," he said to himself. "If I could find the garage door opener, I could get in that way." He checked the car that was parked in the driveway to see if it had a garage door opener, but the doors to the car were locked. "Well, I guess that won't work either," he said. Then he thought about breaking a window in the house, but said to himself, "No, that's the last thing I'll try. If I break the window, we'll have to fix it and that will be a problem." Next he looked to see if his mom had hidden any keys outside, under rocks or on ledges, but he found no keys.

So Brian sat down on his front steps for a minute to think and asked himself, "What else can I do? I know I can solve this problem." As he was sitting there, Brian saw a garden tool laying on the ground. He remembered that the lock on the front door had not been working well lately. "I bet I can figure out how to open the front door with this garden tool," he said. So he went to the front door and slid the garden tool into the side of the door by the lock. At first this didn't work, but Brian was determined. "I can do this," he said. "I'm smart, a good problem solver and I'm going to figure out how to get into this house." The more determined he got, the harder he tried until all at once "POP" the lock gave. He turned the handle of the door and was in. "Wow!" he exclaimed, "I knew I could solve this problem."

Brian went into the kitchen and got a snack. Then he sat at the kitchen table and said, "I don't ever want to get locked out of my house again. What if I were locked out in the winter when it was snowing, I'd freeze trying to find a way to get into the house. Then I'd have to break a window and let the cold air in the house. I'm going to figure out a way to not lose my key again," he said firmly.

He thought about asking his mom to get the rock that his grandmother had given him so he could hide a key outside, under the rock. However, Brian remembered his brothers. He knew his brothers would probably lose a key hidden under a rock or leave it in the house; then he would have the same problem again. He thought about keeping the garage door opener in his book bag, but realized it was too bulky to carry around all the time. Brian also realized that he didn't want to have to carry a garage door opener with him everywhere he went. He considered asking his mom for a cell phone so he could call her any time, but then he realized that was not a good solution either because cell phones are expensive.

As he was sitting at the table thinking about how to solve his problem, Brian looked at his book bag realizing he had homework to do. He began to notice the zipper on the outside of his book bag and noticed there was a big hole in the zipper handle. Suddenly, Brian knew exactly what he would do. He found an extra house key and hooked it onto the zipper handle of his book bag. "This way I will always have a key," Brian told himself, "because I always have my book bag. I always remember to bring my book bag home because it has my books, homework and other important things. The teacher always reminds us to bring our book bags home, so I won't forget it." Brian was extremely proud of himself for not only figuring out how to get into his house without a key, but for figuring out how to learn from this experience so it wouldn't happen again.

When his parents came home that evening, Brian told them everything he had done to get into their house. Then he added, "You better fix our front door. If I can get in it without a key, other people might figure it out too." Brian's parents were very proud of him and Brian was very proud of himself. He understood that he was a great problem solver. He tried several solutions and didn't give up until he found one that worked!

The Drive to the Beach

Problem(s) Addressed:

Rigid thinking; problem solving; believing that there is only one way to accomplish a goal.

Appropriate for:

All ages

Message:

There are many ways to solve problems, and the experience of finding solutions can be exciting and educational.

Symbols and Metaphors:

Drive to the beach: any routine way of solving problem

Map: A way of discovering other solutions and ideas

Other ways to go: different solutions

The drive: the idea that getting to a goal can be as satisfying as reaching the goal.

Elements of the Story That Can be Changed:

Family members; sex of the children; destination of vacation to match geographical areas.

Note:

Many people lead constricted lives because of their rigid thinking and inability to problem solve. This story is another way of challenging rigidity. Children like the idea that they can teach adults new behaviors.

The Drive to the Beach

Once upon a time there lived a family who drove to the beach every summer for a vacation. They owned a cabin at the seashore and spent two weeks there each year — swimming, playing in the sun, and relaxing. Each of the two children in the family always brought along a friend to keep them company and share in the fun. Because the family traveled the same road year after year, they knew exactly how much time their trip would take from the time they left the house until they arrived at their cabin.

On a bright summer day, this family started for their annual vacation in a van packed with food, beach towels, and children who could hardly contain themselves with excitement. The radio was playing as they laughed and planned their activities in the days ahead. Suddenly, a news bulletin interrupted the music on the radio to announce that a gasoline truck had overturned on a bridge to the beach. The announcer explained that the truck had exploded and caused extensive damage to the bridge. The bridge would be closed for many weeks until it could be repaired, he added.

Upon hearing this announcement, the family was in an uproar. "We will have to go home," the parents stated sadly. "We always take that bridge to get to the beach and the announcer said it would be closed for weeks." Three of the children began to cry loudly in disappointment. One child, who was invited as a guest, saw things in a different way than the parents in the car. "Do you have a map?" he asked.

"I don't understand maps," replied the father.

"They confuse me," added the mother.

"I understand maps," the child announced. "We need to look at a map to find other ways to get to the beach."

"We don't have a map!" the father stated firmly.

"There is only one way to get to the beach," the mother responded. "Our vacation is ruined. We have to turn around and go home."

The friend, however, came from a family that did not give up easily. "Stop at this service station " he requested, pointing to the side of the road, "and get a map. Let me prove to you there are many ways to get where we're going. Some routes take longer than others and are more complicated, some have more appealing scenery, and others have different traffic patterns. There are many ways to get where you are going; you just need to look for them."

So, the parents stopped at a service station and purchased a map, muttering to themselves that they knew better than any kid. Because the family had been going to the beach for years, they reassured one another that there was no other way to get where they were going.

The guest studied the map for a while in order to understand where they had come from and where they were going. Then he asked for a pen. The mother handed him a red magic marker.

With the red pen in hand, the boy began to trace, first one way and then another. When he was finished, he showed the doubting parents many different ways to travel to the beach. "You need to decide the advantages and disadvantages of each route," he advised. "One route has a wider road and probably would take the least amount of time. This road is in sight of the ocean," he remarked, pointing to one red line. "It would have interesting scenery. The red mark on this side," he stated, "is for a road that goes through a national park with wild animals. You need to decide whether you want to get to the beach quickly or whether you prefer to take more time and see sights along the way."

The family was intrigued and amazed. Year after year they had traveled the same road, without considering that there were other ways to go. They had also never considered that the journey might become a part of the vacation rather than a means to get to it. The idea that traveling to their destination could be educational and entertaining was new to them.

They picked a new route to the beach, stopping several times to enjoy sights along the way. At the end of the two weeks, they decided to return home a different way than they had come.

"That was the best vacation we ever had at the beach," the kids told their parents one day as they thought about their summer of swimming and fun. "I guess it's never too late to learn," the mother said thoughtfully, "that there are many ways to get where you are going and many things to learn along the way."

©1995
Nancy Davis, Ph.D.

The Dog Who Had Fleas

Problem(s) Addressed:

Assertiveness; fear of confronting a friend when their behavior creates anger

Appropriate for:

Ages 6 to adult

Message:

A true friendship involves being honest about feelings. Although speaking up to a friend sometimes causes problems in a friendship, being silent always does.

Symbols and Metaphors:

Owner demanding obedience: the manner in which not speaking up was learned

Fleas: any problem that bothers or angers one friend about another; the price of being a rebel

Tad: represents the freedom of a rebel or someone assertive; this type of person is usually difficult for a more passive person to confront

Getting in the pond: there is a solution to problems

No itch to scratch: once an anger is discussed and the problem worked out, the pain of the problem usually disappears

Note:

Many people have problems in being assertive. Rather than voice their complaints, they build up their anger until they begin to hate the person who once was their friend. These people often don't speak up because they are afraid of losing the friendship and in the end lose it because they did not speak up.

The Dog Who Had Fleas

Once upon a time there lived two dogs. Although both were Golden Retrievers, they lived very different lives. One lived with a dog trainer who demanded immediate obedience. This dog's name was Ben. Ben sat when his owner said "sit." Ben jumped when his owner said "jump" and he stayed when his owner said "stay." Sometimes Ben did not want to stay or jump or sit because he had a thorn in his paw or he was chewing on a bone. But Ben did not let his owner know this. Only by watching Ben very closely would one notice the small signals that he didn't like what he was doing.

Tad, the other Golden Retriever, lived a life that was free and exciting. He was not kept behind the confines of a fence because he had jumped the fence so often that his owner had given up trying to keep Tad confined. Tad ran through the woods and waded in streams. He chased squirrels and rolled in the mud. Along the way Tad also got fleas.

One day Tad noticed Ben behind the fence. Since they were both Golden Retrievers, Tad felt an immediate bond between them. Tad immediately jumped the fence into Ben's yard so they could play and wrestle. After a day of romping, Tad jumped back across the fence, heading home for the night.

Tad returned to play with Ben often, and they enjoyed playing tug-of-war and running up and down the fence. Ben generally let Tad take the lead in deciding what they would do, because he believed that Tad had far more experience with life. When Tad barked at something, Ben would seem afraid. "You can't bark, my owner won't like it," Ben said. Tad thought this was odd and perhaps even funny and sometimes barked anyway. "Dogs were made to bark," he told Ben. "How can you be a watchdog if you don't bark?"

Ben enjoyed the visits from Tad and they soon became good friends. One day after Tad had gone home, Ben began to itch. He realized that his friend had given him a flea, but when Tad came around again, Ben said nothing. He didn't want to bother Tad. "Besides," Ben told himself, "Tad didn't give me a flea on purpose and it isn't his fault he has fleas."

The more Ben and Tad played together, however, the more fleas Ben got. It wasn't long before Ben was scratching and biting himself all the time when Tad was gone. "Quit biting yourself," his owner demanded. But when a flea bit Ben, he couldn't help it—he scratched and he chewed.

Tad continued to visit Ben and Ben continued to keep silent about the fleas. He liked to play with Tad, but the more fleas he got from Tad, the less he looked for him as he went out in the yard each day. Soon Ben stayed further and further away from Tad as they ran and he didn't want to wrestle anymore. "What's gotten into you?" Tad asked. Ben always said nothing.

After a while, Ben had so many fleas that he stayed in the house to avoid Tad. Tad would jump the fence and look for him, but Ben would hide behind the curtain in the house pretending no one was home. He really missed the runs and the wrestling matches, but the fleas bit him so much that he could not ignore them.

One day when Ben was in the yard, Tad unexpectedly jumped the fence. Ben began to back away. "What is wrong?" Tad demanded.
"Nothing," responded Ben.
"I know there is something wrong and it's time you tell me what it is," Tad declared. Ben was trying to get in the house without saying a thing, but Tad blocked his way. All at once, it seemed that all the fleas on his back bit Ben at once. He yelped and started scratching and biting. "I know something is wrong, tell me what it is," Tad demanded again. The pain of the flea bites suddenly dissolved the need to remain silent that years of training had instilled in Ben.

"You have given me fleas and they are keeping me awake day and night," he yelled at his friend. "Almost every time you visit, I get more fleas. I've tried staying a distance away from you, but your fleas jump long distances to get to me. Being around you is making me miserable."
"Why didn't you tell me this when they first started bothering you?" Tad asked.
"I guess the years of my owner making me sit, jump and lay still have made me scared to say anything," Ben replied thoughtfully.

"Fleas don't bother me very much, but if they bother you, we'll get rid of them. Jump the fence with me and we'll go down to the pond. Once we get under the water, the fleas can't breathe and they'll drown and fall off."

Ben was almost as afraid to jump the fence as he was to tell Tad about the fleas, but when the fleas decided to use his skin for lunch again, Ben was convinced. Both dogs sailed over the fence and ran quickly to the pond. Tad showed Ben how to rub his head in mud so the fleas would stay on his body. Then both dogs walked into the pond, keeping their bodies under the water until they were sure all the fleas had floated away. To get rid of the mud, Ben and Tad dove and swam under the water.

When the two dogs emerged from the water, they shook and began to play and wrestle. Then they ran back to Ben's home and Ben jumped the fence back into his yard. Tad left after asking Ben to think about what he had learned from the fleas. That night, Ben lay peacefully inside the house with no itch to scratch. He was glad that he and Tad had gotten rid of the fleas. He thought about how miserable he had been just the day before and how good he felt now. He was just curling up to go to sleep and thinking about the fleas when he realized what he had learned: real friends never let fear get in the way of being honest about anger.

The Baseball Player

Problem(s) Addressed:

Pessimism; the ability to understand that people have different strengths and weaknesses

Appropriate for:

Ages 6 and up

Message:

Just because you fail in one thing does not mean you will fail in another; you can find and develop your strengths

Symbols and Metaphors:

Baseball and soccer: any skills, jobs, sports, subjects that might be attempted in life

Elements of the Story That Can be Changed:

Sex of main character; sport in which they fail and/or succeed

Note:

It is important for children to learn that all skills take work, to find strengths and develop them, to understand failure makes one human and should not be interpreted to mean that all of life will be a failure. Children can be taught to be optimistic (Seligman, 1995) and to believe in their ability to achieve in many things but not to be unrealistic.

The Baseball Player

Once upon a time there was a boy named Lewis who wanted to be a baseball player. His older brothers played baseball and from the time he was a baby, his family had watched Little League games. Lewis wanted to play baseball just like his brothers. Every spring Lewis watched as the players batted and hit the ball, threw runners out and pitched the ball. He noticed how they laughed as they played, became friends and had fun. Lewis really wanted to be a part of that.

When Lewis grew old enough to play baseball, his parents signed him up to be on a team. But lo and behold, Lewis wasn't very good at baseball. When he tried to hit the ball, he always missed. When he tried to catch the ball, it went right by him. He even had trouble throwing the ball to his teammates. He practiced and practiced with his brothers, but Lewis seemed to have a body that was not designed to play baseball. Because he was not improving, Lewis did not move up to a more skilled team the following year, as the other boys and girls his age had done. The kids on his team were much younger that he was. After a while, Lewis became discouraged and quit the team.

"I never wanted to play baseball anyway, it's such a stupid game," Lewis told himself. But, of course, he was lying.

When Lewis tried to watch his brothers play baseball, it made him feel very sad. Often while they were playing, Lewis would go to a field alone and ride his bike around and around in circles. He kept telling himself that it didn't matter that he couldn't play baseball, but in his heart, Lewis knew that it did.

One day when Lewis was riding his bike in the field, he noticed that a boy was walking toward him dressed in shorts and socks pulled to his knees. "How would you like to play soccer?" the boy asked. "Our best player just moved away."

Lewis didn't want to be hurt again, so he tried to take the safe approach by saying, "No, I don't know how to play soccer."

"We have a great team and a good coach. We'll teach you how to play," the soccer player told him. "Please play; we need you."

Lewis had been so bad at playing baseball that he was afraid he would mess up again. He told the soccer player about his baseball experience. The soccer player helped Lewis to understand that many people are good in one sport and not in another. The soccer player kept talking until Lewis decided he would try.

The team and coach taught Lewis about kicking, running and team work. Lewis practiced and practiced. He found that he was far better at using his legs for kicking than he had been at using his arms for throwing and batting. To Lewis' amazement, he learned to play soccer very well. It wasn't long before he was playing every game instead of "warming the bench" as he had in baseball. Lewis was happy and proud of himself. He began to feel like a part of the team. He was having fun and learning. With each game Lewis played, he liked soccer more and more.

After that, Lewis found that he could watch his brothers play baseball without feeling stupid and worthless. Lewis had learned an important lesson from playing baseball and soccer: many roads can lead to the same destination so if you find yourself on a road that is closed, it is important to look for a road that is open.

The Broken Car

Problem(s) Addressed:

Poor problem-solving skills; children who encounter many difficult situations in their life and need skills for dealing with them

Appropriate for:

Any age

Message:

You can learn how to repair or solve problems in your life and know when you might need to ask for help in solving them; learning to solve problems can increase self-esteem

Symbols and Metaphors:

Car breaking down: any problem that occurs in life
Neighbor: anyone who can teach you what you need to learn. This is very different from doing it for you
The tool kit: the skills necessary to handle problem situations

Elements of the Story That Can be Changed:

Working on cars is typically a male theme, but the character can be changed to female with messages about taking on new roles and challenges in an area where males typically dominate. The story then has a secondary message of empowerment to women.

Note:

I have observed that the source of many problems for people of all ages is their lack of problem-solving skills. Many have never had problem-solving skills modeled for them by parents or caretakers. When these people have a problem, they may try one or two solutions. If these do not work, they give up, deciding that there is no solution. It is important that therapists and teachers teach that it may be the 12th or 15th or even the 126th solution that solves a problem and the most important aspect of dealing with problems is the belief that they can be solved.

The Broken Car

Once upon a time there was a boy named Cory who was sixteen years old. When Cory was twelve, he began to save his money for a car. On the day he was old enough to drive, Cory took all the money he had saved and bought a shiny red used car. This car had a big problem, however, because it was always breaking down. Cory would be on his way to school in the morning and his car would stall at a stoplight. On another day, Cory would be taking his friends for a ride and smoke would begin to rise from under the hood. Sometimes when Cory drove his car after dark, the headlights would go out.

Cory spent all the money he made from his after-school job on car repairs. Sometimes the car would sit in front of his house for a long time until Cory could save enough money to have it fixed. Then after he spent every cent he earned to have the car repaired, Cory had no money to pay for gas. There were many days when Cory had to walk because his car was either broken or out of gas.

One day Cory was mowing his grass, wishing he had a car that never needed to be repaired. He noticed that a neighbor across the street was working on his old car. Cory walked over and watched the man work on his car for a while. The neighbor told Cory that he had taught himself to repair cars by reading car repair manuals and by working on a problem until he found a way to fix it. "I'm a pretty good mechanic," he told Cory. "I love repairing old cars."

Suddenly, Cory had an idea! "If I can figure out how to fix my own car," he told himself, "I can save a lot of money. The repairs will cost far less and then I will have money to buy gas for the car."

"Would you teach me how to repair cars?" Cory asked the neighbor. "Then when my car breaks down I will be able to fix it myself. I am tired of paying other people to repair my car."

227

"I don't have a son that I can teach to repair cars and I would love to teach you all I know," said the neighbor. "There are many repairs you will be able to do yourself. But sometimes the car will need major repairs and you will need the help of others," the neighbor told Cory. "Being able to understand what the car needs and whether you can fix it makes owning a car much more of a pleasure."

So day after day Cory spent time with the neighbor working on the neighbor's cars and learning how to repair them. One day the neighbor said to Cory, "Bring your car over to my house and we will work on it."

Cory spent all of his free time learning from his neighbor how to repair his red car. First they pulled the engine out of the car and took it to a shop to be rebuilt. The neighbor explained that this repair of the engine required special equipment and would be too difficult for them to do. When the engine was fixed, they tuned it and added new spark plugs. They fixed the muffler and the water pump. Cory bought a new tape player and the neighbor showed him how to install it in the dashboard. Then they repaired all the gauges on the dashboard and put new carpet on the floors. The neighborhood mechanic and his new assistant made sure that the headlights and taillights worked so everyone could see Cory was coming and know when he was stopping. They hammered out the dents and repainted the whole outside of the car so that it was a shiny, cherry apple red. Then together they waxed Cory's car until the red paint was so shiny that people walking down the street stopped to ask, "Whose car is that?"

At first the neighbor would tell them, "This is Cory's car and he spent many hours working on it." After a while, when admirers would ask, "Whose car is that?" Cory would reply proudly, "It's mine and I fixed it up with my neighbor's help. Now I know how to fix it myself."

The neighbor was so proud of Cory for learning to repair cars that he bought him a big chest and filled it with many of the tools Cory would need to repair cars on his own. Cory and the neighbor continued to share a special friendship even when there were no cars that needed repairs.

After that, Cory loved driving his friends to school and for food and to parties. One evening, when Cory and his friends were on the way to a football game, the car broke down. This time, however, Cory wasn't upset. He jumped out of his car and pulled his tool chest out of the trunk. While his friends watched in admiration, Cory fixed the car in no time at all. Soon they were driving off to the football game, arriving just ten minutes after the game started.

Everyone in school began to talk about Cory's skill as a mechanic and how he had found a way to learn so much about repairing his car. It wasn't long before his friends were asking him to teach them how to fix their cars. Cory was happy to help them; he liked repairing cars and teaching others what he knew. Cory was especially proud of himself for learning how to repair his own car so that he wouldn't be stuck when the car had problems. Cory had learned that there are many ways to solve problems and learning how to solve them makes life much easier.

©1995
Nancy Davis, Ph.D.

The Boy Who Never Forgot

Problem(s) Addressed:

Individuals who have an incredible memory for the bad and negative things that happen in their life, ignoring all of the positive and loving experiences of their past. Distortion of reality through putting a negative spin on everything.

Appropriate for:

Age 5 - adult **(This in not a story to be told to abused children in order to help them forget abuse memories. It is a story for children who are loved and nurtured, but distort this love into beliefs that they are hated and rejected).**

Message:

You can find the power to reverse the way you remember the past, so that positive experiences have much more power than negative ones.

Symbols and Metaphors:

Magic lady: any one who helps the child to change or the power of the unconscious to change itself

Baskets in the mind: memories

Balls with strings attached: the power of memories to influence thoughts, feelings and behavior

Waved the magic wand in front of his eyes: any change agent; this can also represent the eye movement of EMDR

Elements of the Story Which Can be Changed:

Sex of the main character; family constellation; the negative talk of the child; the types of negative things that the child emphasizes; the positive new experiences

231

Note:

This story was written for a 10 year old boy who constantly told his parents they did not love him and that they loved his siblings much more than they loved him. He remembered all the negative experiences of his past as well as all of the ways he believed he had been wronged. His parents were loving and well adjusted individuals, who seemed to be very appropriate parents. The boy was also very short. A personalized story tape was made for this boy. He was seen for three sessions after which the parents and the boy indicated that he was functioning in a very different and positive manner. It is not known if the directives to grow were effective.

The Boy Who Never Forgot

Once there was a boy named Trevor who seemed unhappy and angry much of the time. He believed that his family and his friends were mean to him and that no one loved him. Trevor put himself down because he made mistakes. In addition, Trevor had the kind of memory that never forgets any wrong, or any injustice or any mistake. Trevor would store all these painful memories of being wronged and imperfect in his mind. Trevor's memory looked like a basket filled with balls. The problem was that the basket filled with bad or negative things was always full and the basket with compliments and positive things was unusually empty.

"I must be a really terrible person," Trevor told himself. "No one loves me. Just look at my baskets. The basket filled with bad things is full and the basket for good things is nearly empty. That can only happen to someone who is a bad, terrible, horrible person."

Trevor got angry at all of his family and his friends and himself because he believed that no one loved him and he certainly didn't love himself. His anger was so strong that it interfered with his growth. Trevor stopped growing in height, he couldn't do his school work and he had problems in his family. School work also became a problem and so did playing sports.

One day Trevor had a particularly loud temper tantrum. His mom and dad became really concerned about Trevor because he wrote them a letter saying he was sure that they didn't love him even though they kept telling him they did. His parents tried telling Trevor that they loved him very much, but Trevor would not believe them.

Trevor's anger and unhappiness grew and grew. No one could convince Trevor that he was not seeing the world as it really was.

Trevor became more and more unhappy, until one day his class had a lesson on problem solving. Trevor listened and realized that he needed to learn to use these new problem solving skills he had been taught on himself.

"I'm tired of feeling this way," Trevor told himself. "I'm tired of being angry. I'm tired of being sad, I'm tired of being depressed and I'm tired of not growing and hating myself. I'm going to do something about this."

Trevor had heard about a magic lady who helped with problems so he went to see her. "I have these baskets in my mind." Trevor explained to the magic lady. "The basket which is always full contains memories of all the bad and negative things that have happened in my life. The basket which should hold the good and positive things from my past is almost empty. Because of these baskets. all I think about every day is the bad things that have happened, and the embarrassing things and the unhappy things. I am always thinking of unhappy memories. I remember that someone beat me up a long time ago and I remember all the negative things my parents said to me and I remember all the mistakes I made in class on tests, I remember all my mistakes at sports. All I think about is the bad things that have happened and thinking this way is making me miserable."

The magic lady talked to Trevor for a while and then she asked him, "What about the good things and the positive things that have happened in your life? Do you remember those?"

"I've had many good things happen in my life," Trevor explained. "I know they're somewhere in my memory, but I don't think about the good things very often."

"Hmmm, Hmmm," mumbled the magic lady, considering what Trevor had just told her. "I think you've got a lot of string attached to all these balls in the basket where you have stored your negative memories. Somehow these strings have become hooked onto your heart and your mind and your feelings. When you think about some negative part of your past, these strings tug at you and make you feel really bad about yourself. I think it's time that we changed what's happening. I'm going to disconnect all of those strings."

So the magic lady waved her wand back and forth in front of Trevor. He moved his eyes back and forth as he watched the magic wand. Trevor began to feel the strings that connected all the negative memories and hurtful thoughts to his heart and mind and feelings and then he felt them disconnect. The more she waved the wand, the more free Trevor felt. He felt all of the hooks in his heart and mind and feelings disconnect from the upsetting thoughts and memories that he kept stockpiled in this big basket.

"Wow, I can really feel a difference," Trevor told her. "I think it's time we get rid of the balls that represent all the negative things that I think about all the time. Do you think I can do that?"

"Absolutely," the magic lady told him. So Trevor imagined the basket being pulled out of his mind; the memories looked like tennis balls.

"It is time to throw all of these negative memories away, except the ones you really need to help you like yourself," the magic lady directed.

Trevor had never thought of throwing the balls away because the strings had interfered with his problem solving abilities. So Trevor began to pick up one ball at a time and throw them far away. As he threw away each ball, Trevor felt lighter and happier. "Wow," Trevor remarked. "This is really amazing."

Trevor continued to throw away balls until there were only a few left in the bottom of the basket. These were memories that Trevor needed to help him to learn and grow.

"Now I want you to look at this basket with really good and positive memories from your past," directed the magic lady. "Notice there is very little in it."

"Very few good things ever happen to me," Trevor said to the magic lady.

"I don't think that's true," she told him. "I believe you forget the good things so I'm going to give you a special power to remember them." At this, the magic lady waved her wand and memories started popping in Trevor's mind. Memories of all the times he had achieved something in sports, all the good grades and praise he had received in school, all the love and nice things that his parents had given him. He began to remember the compliments he had gotten from many different people and all the achievements and positive things he had done. He began to compliment himself, and to Trevor's surprise, the more he thought of all the positive things from his past, the more the basket was filled with balls. Soon this basket was nearly full.

"The balls in the basket with positive memories are the ones that need strings to attach to your heart", the magic lady explained. "By concentrating on the positive parts of your past, you will feel better about yourself and you will accomplish much more in life." So she helped Trevor create strings to his mind and his heart and his feelings to all of his positive memories. The magic lady understood that these strings would help Trevor to feel better about himself, like himself and let go of his anger.

"I think we've solved your problem," she said to Trevor. "Or really, you've solved your own problem."

"Thank you, thank you!" Trevor said, hugging her good-by.

In the days that followed, Trevor began to notice changes in himself. For one thing, he began to grow... it was absolutely magic how fast Trevor was growing. Then Trevor realized that he no longer became angry at himself when he made mistakes. Trevor learned to look at the world and his life in an optimistic way, believing that things would work out and that he could find ways to have friends and to do well in school. When Trevor's parents were nice to him, he stored that memory away, letting go of the negative things that happened to him. It wasn't long before Trevor was happier, he liked himself and he found it easy to go to school, to be in his family and to do sports.

Because Trevor had learned his lesson well, he made sure that the basket full of positive memories was always full and the basket of negative memories was almost empty. Trevor had learned that life is full of choices and choosing to like himself was the one thing that Trevor never forgot.

©1992
Nancy Davis, Ph.D.

The Car that Wanted to Race

Problem(s) Addressed:

Rigid thinking; the belief that there is only one way to be happy

Appropriate for:

Ages 4 - 11

Message:

There are many ways to feel appreciated and valued; love is one of the most important ways to find rewards in life

Symbols and Metaphors:

Racing car: any unrealistic dream of fame that a child creates in the belief that he will like himself if he achieves it

Elements of the Story Which Can be Changed:

Sex of the car; sex of the buyer; what the car dreams of being in the beginning of the story.

Note:

Many children and adolescents decide that they must have fame and awards to be happy. Usually these are children who do not have the skills to obtain these goals but have decided that they will be loved if they are "stars". This story helps these children to discover another point of view.

The Car that Wanted to Race

Once upon a time there was a little car who sat in a car lot waiting for someone to buy him. He very much wanted to be a racing car. In fact, what he wanted to be was a Ferrari that went 200 miles an hour around a racing track. He dreamed of being a candy apple red Ferrari. He wanted to win races, to get awards and to hear cheers as the crowds applauded his success.

One day a race car driver came to look the little car over. He had heard that the car wanted to race. After looking at the front and back of the car, opening the hood and sitting in the driver's seat, the driver began to speak to the car. "I'm really sorry, but you don't have the shape necessary to be a race car. You've got an engine that isn't powerful enough to be a race car and I'm afraid if you tried to be a race car, you would crash and really hurt yourself and the driver." The little car was very disappointed as he watched the race car driver leave taking his dream with him.

"If I can't be a race car, I guess I'm worthless," the little car sputtered to himself.
He was so unhappy that he blew smoke out of his tailpipe, he honked his horn and he made grinding noises with his brakes. The little car had been unhappy for several days when a man came to the car lot and announced to a salesman, "I need a very special car. I need a car to help me take food to people who are sick or old and can't get their own food. I work for Meals-on-Wheels². I must have a very sturdy car and it can't go too fast because if it goes too fast, the food might spill. I need a car that isn't flashy so no one will steal it. And I must have a car that I can really depend on because it must always be ready to take food to those who need it."

The salesman showed the man several cars, then it was the little car's turn to be checked out. He looked at the front of the little car and the back of the little car. He opened the hood to look at the engine, then he sat in the driver's seat, just as the race car driver had done.

---

1. A charity organization which takes meals to shut-ins.

239

"I think this is just the car I need," he announced to the salesman. He looked inside the car and in the trunk to make sure he'd have enough room to carry meals to people who couldn't go out or cook food for themselves. "I'll take this little car," he said as he laughed with joy, because he was happy that he had discovered the perfect car for his job.

The little car wasn't quite sure he wanted to be sold to a man who delivered food; he still dreamed of being a race car and that was a long way from going 200 miles an hour and winning trophies. The car, decided, however, that he had nothing to lose by giving it a try. So he performed well as the man drove him off the sales lot. The car was driven to a building where all the food for Meals-on-Wheels was cooked and packed for delivery. Several people loaded his trunk and seats with food.

Soon the little car arrived at the first house on his delivery route. As the man who had bought him got food from his trunk, an old lady came out of the house; she was so happy to get her food. She patted the little car and the car responded by making his engine purr. He was happy to discover that he had made someone's day better by delivering food.

Soon the man and the car stopped at another house where an old man came to the door to accept the food. The little car discovered that there was an old lady inside who was so sick that she couldn't get out of bed. Before the car could drive away to his next stop, the old man came out of the front door holding flowers which he placed on the hood of the car.

The rest of the day was just as rewarding. At each delivery site, someone called to the car or thanked the car or rubbed his hood. This made the car very happy. He began to realize that he was serving a purpose and he was helping people to feel better.

When all of the food was delivered, the little car began to think about what he had learned. He began to realize that delivering meals to those who couldn't get food without him was much more rewarding that being a race car. When he worked for Meals-On-Wheels, the little car didn't have to wait until he won a race to get a reward; he knew that he'd get rewards every day. Thinking about his new job made the little car very happy.

So the little car continued to deliver food for Meals-on-Wheels. One day, a red race car drove down the street in front of him with a huge trophy in the back seat. The car was happy for the race car, but he was also happy for himself. He realized that love and appreciation can be a far greater award that any trophies made of metal.

©1996
Nancy Davis

CHAPTER FOUR

Stories to Aid in Disclosure of Traumatic Experiences and/or Abuse

Victims of sexual or physical abuse often refuse to talk about their trauma or can not remember what happened to them. Sometimes fear and/or threats of harm are the basis for their silence. On other occasions, it is Post Traumatic Stress Disorder (PTSD) that has resulted in partial or total amnesia regarding the traumatic experience(s) (van der Kolk, 1994). Research with individuals experiencing PTSD has demonstrated that trying to put the experience into words often creates flashbacks; most victims will do almost anything to avoid these flashbacks. Employing sophisticated brain-imaging techniques with individuals experiencing induced flashbacks, Dr. von der Kolk (1995) discovered that flashbacks caused significantly increased activity in the right hemisphere of the brain, where intense emotion and visual images are processed. During a flashback, the left side of the brain, particularly the area that transforms subjective experiences into speech "shuts down." (Rauch and van der Kolk, 1994). Children may not disclose a traumatic experience, therefore, the memory is only in the visual and feeling part of the brain and has not yet been translated into language. The questioning of children by professionals may cause the child to have frightening flashbacks with no ability to talk about their experience.

The stories in this chapter are structured with imagery, symbolism and metaphor ... the language of the right brain (Erickson, Rossi & Rossi, 1976; Mills & Crowley, 1986; Rosen, 1982). In children under twelve years of age, it is recommended that disclosure stories be taped along with other stories that empower and heal. The caretakers of the child should ensure that the child listens to the stories as he/she goes to bed for the night. It does not matter if the child falls asleep as the stories play or seems not to pay attention, since the unconscious is always aware and listening (Siegel, 1986). It has been my experience that if the stories agitate the child, it may be because the child is in conflict about disclosing or the experience has not yet been translated into language. Research indicates that trauma may bypass the conscious or verbal memory and

243

located only in the feelings and perceptual memory (van der Kolk, 1994). If the child reacts negatively to the stories, have the caretaker play the stories after the child is in a deep sleep. Listening to the stories has not been found to cause a child who has not been traumatized or abused to make up stories; probably because the stories emphasize the importance of telling the truth. After disclosing a trauma, a child will often ask to hear the story tape as they go to sleep. There are many more disclosure stories in Therapeutic Stories to Heal Abused Children.

Children often have trauma symptoms from events other than sexual or physical abuse. A child may have symptoms of trauma which alarms their caretakers, who then assume the worse, i.e., sexual abuse. Disclosure stories help the child describe what has traumatized them. If a child discloses a traumatic event, (such as being victimized by a school bully) and adults intervene to correct the situation, the child's symptoms should disappear. The disappearance of trauma symptoms is an important way to evaluate if a child's trauma has been disclosed and dealt with appropriately.

In my experience as a therapist, I have found that adults can suddenly remember childhood abuse or trauma, even into their forties and fifties. Partial or total amnesia regarding traumatic experiences has been noted by many researchers (Briere & Conte, 1993; Elliot, 1994; Goldfield, Mollica, Pesavento & Farone, 1988; Kinzie, 1993; Loftus, Polensky & Fullilove, 1994; Madakasira & O'Brian, 1987; van der Kolk & Kadish, 1987). Many of my adult patients have validated these types of memories by talking to family members who experienced the same trauma or were present when the trauma occurred. Other family members may recall the experience, but have never discussed their memories. For example, one patient in her thirties, came to therapy because she began to remember that her brother, who was eleven years older, had raped her as a child. When she discussed this memory with her sisters, they replied, "Oh, he did that to all of us, we thought you remembered that and didn't want to talk about it."

I have had many patients who, as adults, began to have visual memories of childhood traumas; some of these long-forgotten incidents were of traumas other than sexual or physical abuse. This has been supported by other clinicians (Saxe, 1996). A patient from Korea indicated that in her twenties she obtained a copy of her birth certificate. The parents listed on that form were different from those whose name she carried. When she asked for an explanation, her parents replied, "Your family members were all killed by a bomb when you were eight. We took you in; don't you remember?"

Symptoms of PTSD may include inability to remember all or parts of the traumatic experience in the conscious memory. PTSD may occur when the mind dissociates a memory from conscious awareness, but records the memory as body sensations, perceptions and emotions (van der Kolk, 1994).

The discovery that some memories of childhood trauma are accurate, does not signify that all recovered memories of past trauma are accurate, or that abuse that is remembered as an adult actually took place for the following reasons: 1) trauma can cause amnesia and yet deposit a variety of emotions and body sensations that remember the trauma; 2) individuals who become amnesic or dissociative for one traumatic experience will continue to do this for other traumas in their lives, resulting in a visual memory which is very fragmented; 3) these memories will nevertheless be unconscious and will imprint styles of helplessness, victimization and betrayal.

These individuals are very vulnerable to suggestion and to constructed explanations that give meaning to their trauma-based emotions. These explanations may have little relationship to the trauma that caused their amnesia (van der Kolk and Fisler, 1995).

Some adults may remember abuse that did not occur because:

1)   He/she may have a number of symptoms and conclude through reading and/or attending groups or therapy that his/her symptoms must have been caused by abuse. The person's unconscious co-operates by creating memories, particularly if they have friends who tell them that they were abused or if they read books which claim that such symptoms had to result from sexual abuse;

2)   The memories may be symbolic of other types of abuse. For example, an adult woman may have a memory of being raped by the devil. She may have been raped in childhood, dissociated the memory and is now remembering the trauma in a metaphoric or symbolic form.

3)   Therapists who have been taught that they can recognize abuse histories in their patients even before the patient remembers may, through hypnosis or other powerful suggestions, create images in the patient to please the therapist;

4)   A patient, often with a borderline or histrionic diagnosis, may unconsciously decide that in order to be the center of his/her therapist's attention it is necessary to be the most brutally abused patient the therapist treats. Since these type of patients often lie, and even believe their own lies, they are capable of presenting realistic stories. However, if the facts of such cases are explored, the stories will contain have major flaws that clash with reality. It should be noted, that many researchers believe that borderline personalities are created by trauma or child abuse. In other words, this type of patient supports the previous assertion of van der Kolk that the intense feelings associated with previous trauma cause victims to create a reason for these feelings that may have little to do with the trauma that was originally experienced.

Because abuse and trauma can be dissociated for years before memories surface and because adults can unconsciously create inaccurate or false abuse memories, it is important that a therapist be extremely cautious about interpreting symptoms to a patient by telling them, "Your symptoms mean you were abused as a child." It is also vital that the therapist not suggest, especially under hypnosis, that a patient has been abused, the patient will remember past abuse, or is a multiple personality. Hypnosis is a powerful tool for healing, but it also must be used with caution. Patients can take suggestions made under hypnosis as commands and comply with them as a way of pleasing the therapist (Erickson, Rossi & Rossi, 1976).

On the other hand, abuse memories should not be discounted or denied. Understand that, as a therapist, you may not know if the abuse happened or if the events recalled about a particular abuse are accurate. It is helpful to see if family members or friends can support the new memories. In some families, siblings may not recall the abuse until they are older. Others do not forget, but have not talked about their abuse. These siblings can often corroborate the memories. Non-offending parents, relatives and friends can often fill in holes of the memory as well. When a patient states that he/she has no memory of his/her childhood, be extremely suspicious that the lack of memory is related to a childhood with long-term traumatic events, since these cause a lack of autobiographical memories (Cole & Putnam; 1992). This viewpoint is supported by research showing that people who have normal, nontraumatic experiences do not fragment these experiences or dissociate from them. These types of memories are automatically integrated into conscious memory (van der Kolk & Fisler, 1995).

In other words, there is no magic formula to decide if a memory is or is not accurate. There are professionals who believe that all memories of childhood abuse are accurate and those who believe no memories of childhood abuse are accurate. The truth seems to lie somewhere between these two positions.

I used to believe that one had to remember and disclose details of abuse before healing was possible. However, I have now observed that some patients who had amnesia for some or part of their trauma and/or refused to disclose the details of their abuse because of the trauma or embarrassment involved, have nonetheless been able to decrease their symptoms dramatically — so this assumption has been revised. Do not use disclosure stories as battering rams to the unconscious, believing that an individual has been abused and you must force them to remember and/or disclose. These stories are based on the belief that has created all of the therapeutic stories in both of my books: the unconscious is wise. Almost all people have a core or essence which is healing and wise and will find what is needed to heal. Let these stores aide in this healing. However, if no memories surface or if disclosure does not come, you must find other ways to heal your client.

The Spider Webs

Problem(s) Addressed:

Children who live with an abusive person, but deny that they are being abused as a way of protecting themselves from their feelings. Foster children who have been removed from a parent because of brutal sexual or physical abuse, but continue to deny the impact of this abuse on their functioning.

Appropriate for:

Ages 5-16; this story can also be effective with battered spouses

Message:

You can find a way to "let go" of the distortions in your functioning that keep you from protecting yourself

Symbols:

Spider webs: distortions of any sense or of thinking and belief systems
The monster: any abuser--can be parent, sibling, caretaker, relative
Vacuuming out the spider webs: any technique that clears out the distortions
See the scenes in her mind and put the scenes into words: the challenge to move the trauma from the right brain into the left brain and put the trauma into a narrative

Elements of the Story Which Can be Changed:

Sex of the child; the monster can be given a sex instead of 'it'; the types of things the monster does to the child; if the listener is an adult, then change the story to more closely match their life.

Note:

Research indicates that trauma interferes with declarative memory (the ability to consciously recall experience) but does not interfere with implicit memory, i.e., the memory which holds the feelings and body sensations related to the trauma (van der Kolk, 1994). "Memories of the trauma tend to, at least initially, be experienced primarily as fragments of the sensory components of the event: as visual images, olfactory, auditory, or kinesthetic sensations, or intense waves of feelings" (van der Kolk and Fisler; 1995). "Failure to organize the memory into a narrative leads to the intrusion of elements of the trauma into consciousness as terrifying perceptions, obsessional preoccupations, and as somatic reexperiences such as anxiety reactions" (Janet, 1909; van der Kolk & van der Hart, 1991).

"Children have fewer mental capacities to construct a coherent narrative out of traumatic event" (van der Kolk and Fisher, 1995). This means that even when they remember the trauma and can put this trauma into words, the skill to translate their experience is far below that of an adult. Furthermore, research by Crittenden (1996) in attachment and memory indicates that children "can mentally protect themselves by omitting some information from awareness, by distorting information, or by falsifying information so as to mislead others about their feelings or intentions. The most dangerous condition is that of parents who are dangerous or who fail to protect children. Maltreated children often use mental transformations of information to increase their safety and reduce awareness of vulnerability."

This story is written to help a child or adult translate information about danger clearly so that they can be protected.

The Spider Webs

Once upon a time there was a little girl named Amy who lived in a big house. In this house there were many spider webs, which hung everywhere — from the doors and windows, under the stairs and above the beds. The spider webs wound throughout this house because one of the members of the house was a monster. This monster was especially mean and hurtful and was not at all concerned about the pain he caused the other members of the house, especially Amy.

Amy lived in this house because she had nowhere else to go, or so she believed. Being around the monster caused her great pain and much fear. Each day that she lived around the monster, Amy's pain became greater and her fear turned to panic. Soon Amy's pain and fear increased and became almost more than she could bear, so Amy tried many things to make herself feel better. Because the monster remained in her house, nothing she attempted worked until she tried the spider webs.

The spider webs weren't her first choice; she tried them in desperation when she had no success with other techniques. Amy wrapped the spider webs around her eyes; then she stuffed the spider webs in her ears. She wrapped the spider webs around her heart, and she wrapped the spider webs around her mind. The spider webs lessened her pain and fear in a very unusual way. They changed her eyes so she looked but did not see. They changed her ears so they listened but did not hear and her mind so it thought but did not understand. The spider webs allowed her to answer, "No!" when people asked her, "Doesn't living with a monster scare you?" The spider webs allowed Amy to answer, "Why would I be afraid, it's a very nice monster?"

Amy's friends would say, "I heard the monster growling and hitting you," and Amy would reply, "Oh, no, the monster never hit me. I don't remember that."
Her cousin would say, "I heard you crying yourself to sleep," and Amy would reply, "You must be mistaken. I don't remember crying myself to sleep."

One day, some of her friends visited Amy on a day when the monster was in a very grouchy mood. The monster tore up her schoolbooks and it tore up her homework. The monster said very mean and cruel things and hurt her in other ways too. Amy's friends were amazed and afraid. "Aren't you angry at this monster?" one friend asked softly. "How dare the monster treat you in this way," another friend stated loudly.

Because the spider webs were wound oh so tightly around her feelings, Amy replied politely, "Oh, no, it's a very nice monster. It wasn't so bad."

When Amy went to school the next day, her teacher noticed that her homework was destroyed and her book bag was torn up. There were also signs on Amy that the monster had been attacking her again. This teacher was very concerned and sat down beside Amy and asked, "What is happening to you? Tell me about the monster. What is it like to live with a monster?"
Amy smiled sweetly and replied, "I love the monster and it never hurts me in any way."

Now those who loved Amy became more and more distressed and afraid for her. Even though she continued to maintain that the monster was nice, the signs that the monster wasn't nice were very clear to those who didn't have spider webs in their eyes and mind. Those who loved Amy settled on a plan. They quietly entered her house and hid a video camera. They made sure the camera recorded the way the monster treated Amy. Her friends then retrieved the tape and took it to Amy's school. Then the teacher, the counselor and Amy's girl friends sat her in a room with a big screen and began to play the tape they had made of the monster. Amy watched the tape which showed the monster being very mean and cruel to her. Then the teacher asked her, "How is that monster acting?"

The people in the room were not surprised at all when Amy continued to maintain, "It's acting fine. It's a nice monster." At that the teacher announced, "It is time that we vacuumed all those spider webs from your mind and your eyes and your ears. If the spider webs hadn't been allowed to hang in your house, you never would have gotten entangled in them."

At the thought of losing the protection of the spider webs, Amy began to cry. "Don't take my spider webs; they keep away my pain."

The teacher knew better. "These spider webs are keeping you in danger," she declared. "We have to destroy them so you can find a way to get rid of your pain rather than hide from it." At that, the teacher began vacuuming the spider webs out of Amy's eyes. Then the teacher vacuumed the spider webs out of her ears, out of her heart, out of her mind and out of her feelings. It was hard at first, the spider webs really didn't want to let go. The spider webs had become entangled in so many ways in all parts of her. But the teacher was determined, and she kept vacuuming and vacuuming and one by one, the spider webs *Let Go and Set Her Free.*

The teacher then rewound the video of the monster and played it again, talking to the Amy as she watched. "You see, this monster is very cruel to you and you don't deserve to have anyone treat you like that. No child deserves to be treated in this way. See and understand now that your eyes do not have spider webs. Listen to the monster's words with ears that can hear, and use your mind to think about how you can get away from the monster; then you won't have to hide from your feelings."

As Amy watched the tape with new eyes and a different understanding, feelings that had been buried within her for a very long time began to come up in a strong and powerful way. She felt anger, a feeling of power, and an understanding that she did not deserve to be treated this way by anyone, especially someone who lives in her home. The more Amy watched, the more her anger grew until she found words to talk about all of the things that had happened as she lived with the monster. Amy began to see all of the scenes in her mind that had caused her such pain and she put these scenes into words. Amy had not talked about her pain for such a long time, that she talked and she talked and she told and she told. And as she told, she noticed that her pain began to lessen. Then, because Amy was free of all the spider webs, she was able to help those around her find ways to make sure the monster never hurt her again.

One night after the monster was gone and she felt very safe, Amy sat on her bed and thought about what she had learned. She had learned about monsters and telling. She had learned that friends and teachers can help you even when you don't know you need to be helped. And most of all she had learned that spider webs do not get rid of pain, they just tie it up in a big knot.

©1995
Nancy Davis, Ph.D.

253

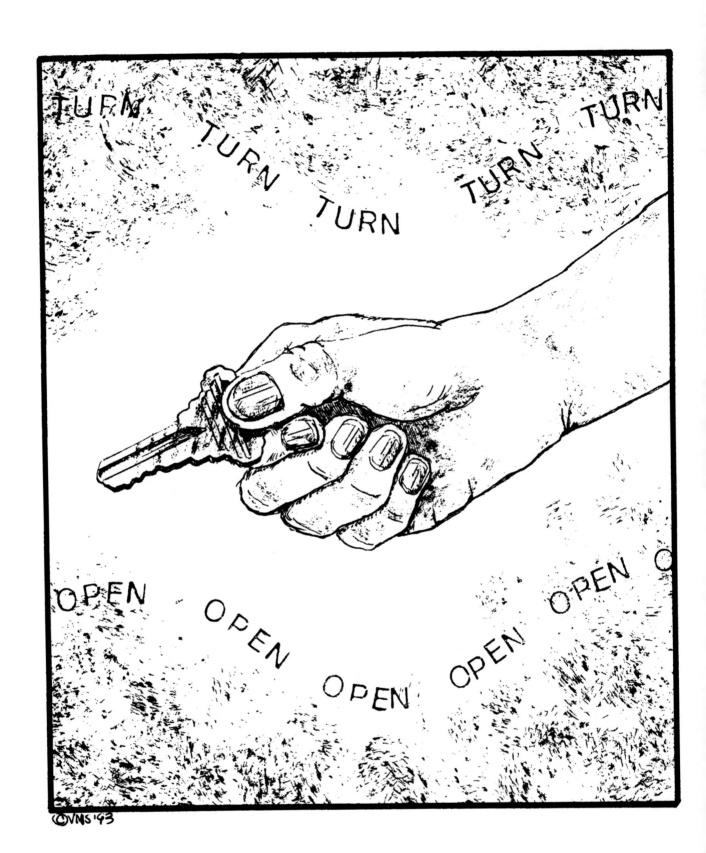

The Girl and the Basement

Problem(s) Addressed:

Unremembered trauma.

Appropriate for:

Can be used for very young children; adults also like this story

Message:

You can find the key to remembering what is important about your past, putting this memory into words and use this information to heal. If you are a child, you can describe your trauma to an adult who can protect you and help you heal.

Symbols and Metaphors:

Basement: the place where the trauma occurred; the place where memories reside in the mind.

Locking the doors: forgetting traumatic events of the past

Key: what is needed to remember

Elements of the Story That Can be Changed:

Sex of the child; symptoms; what happens when the memory is retrieved.

Note:

This story was designed for a five-year-old who had obsessive-compulsive symptoms suggestive of sexual abuse. She had been left with a babysitter from age six months to three and one half. Another parent, whose child also was left with the same sitter, had alleged that her child was sexually abused there. Although the child for whom his story was designed was never able to put the trauma into words, she did experience flashbacks to the fear arising from the experience. This is consistent with research which indicates that although a child may not have a narrative memory for a trauma until age three, the memory which holds feelings and bodily sensations begins to operate shortly after birth (van der Kolk, 1994). The hippocampus, a part of the brain which enables experiences to be translated into language and conscious awareness, is not fully developed until the third or forth year of life; this is thought to be the basis for the amnesia that humans normally have regarding the first years of their lives. (Schacter & Moscovitch, 1984).

Although this child could not consciously remember any trauma, her obsessive symptoms were reduced through therapeutic stories, EMDR, behavior therapy and brief medication.

The Girl and the Basement

Once upon a time there lived a very special girl named Angie who loved to laugh and play. Angie was happy almost all the time until the day she started to go into the basement. Now, the basement was a very dark and scary place. Something happened to Angie while she was in the basement that caused her happiness to disappear. She started to cry a lot and she had trouble sleeping. Perhaps she saw things that little girls are not ready to see. And for some reason, when Angie was in the basement, she came to believe that things that happened in the basement were secret. So each day when Angie left the basement she didn't tell about it.

After Angie began to visit the basement, she began to act much older. She seemed to lose her joy and began to be afraid and angry.

One day, Angie left the basement for the very last time. As Angie walked up the stairs, there were many doors to go through. So, as she moved through each door, Angie closed the door and locked it. She closed and locked one door after another until they were all locked. Angie locked all the doors because she was very sad and scared about the basement and she did not know how to put those feelings into words.

Even though Angie had locked the doors, something strange happened. Angie continued to feel sad and angry, but she couldn't remember why. Angie wanted to remember what had happened, but the doors to the basement were locked. Angie believed she did not have the keys to open them again.

One night when Angie was sleeping, she dreamed about the key and opening the doors. Her dream let her see how to find the key. When Angie awoke in the morning, she remembered her dream. She found the key that she needed and opened all the doors to the basement so she could explain why she was so sad and scared and angry. She found words to tell everyone who needed to know what happened in the basement.

After that, whenever Angie felt sad or scared or angry she used her keys to help her explain her feelings and she made sure she always kept these keys as a part of her life.

©1995; Nancy Davis, Ph.D.

The Monster in My House

Problem(s) Addressed:

A parent who denies the existence of an abuser in the home.

Appropriate for:

Any child or parent who needs awareness that abuse is wrong and needs to be disclosed; any parent who looks but does not see.

Message:

Talk about your abuse or your fear until someone listens, believes you and helps you

Symbols and Metaphors:

Monster: any abuser (this can be a parent, sibling, relative, etc.)
The monster gets bigger: when abuse is denied or kept secret, the fear increases and the abuser seems more and more powerful
Takes the monster out of the house: this can represent physical removal of the monster, or the changing of the monster's behavior through intervention

Elements of the Story That Can be Changed:

Sex of the child or parent

Note:

A parent who does not notice that his/her child is being abused may have closed down their own perceptual process, often because of previous trauma (van der Kolk and Fisler, 1995; Crittenden, 1996). This parent may be in a chronic Post Traumatic Stress Disorder, causing thoughts and memory to be so fragmented that he/she cannot protect their own child. It is important for the professional to assess whether this is the case and aid this type of parent in getting help for his/her symptoms so that the child can be protected.

The Monster in My House

Once upon a time there was a girl named Lorin who lived in a house with her family. One day as Lorin was getting out of bed, she saw a monster at the end of her bed. It was a small monster, but it looked mean and scary. When the monster went, "Grr, grr," Lorin ran to her mom crying, "There's a monster in my room!"

"Don't be silly," her mother replied, "there's no such thing as monsters; monsters only exist in story books."

The monster continued to sit on Lorin's bed as she got dressed for school. Lorin was so scared that she got dressed quickly, and buttoned her sweater wrong and put her pants on backwards. Then she ran downstairs to eat breakfast. The monster followed her and got on the breakfast table. Lorin knew that no one in the house was allowed to sit up on the table, not even the cat, so she yelled to her mother again, "Mom, there's a monster on the table."

"Don't be silly," her mom replied again, "Quit pretending; there's no monster on the table."

The monster smiled and seemed to grow bigger with the words of Lorin's mom. When Lorin was trying to eat her cereal, the monster grabbed the bowl from her and ate it. This caused the monster to grow even bigger.

"Quit eating my breakfast!" Lorin yelled.

Her mother looked around, and asked Lorin, "Who are you talking to?"

"I'm talking to the monster," Lorin replied.

Hearing Lorin talk about the monster again made her mother very angry. Pointing her finger at Lorin, she yelled, "I don't want you to ever say anything about a monster again. There's no such thing as monsters. What's wrong with you, talking about monsters?"

As she was running to catch the school bus, Lorin looked back at the monster and noticed that it was smiling again. It wasn't a nice smile; it was the kind of smile a brother smiles when he tells on you and gets you in trouble.

261

That afternoon when school was over, Lorin walked in the front door hoping the monster would be gone. But to her dismay, there it was, sitting in her favorite chair playing with her toys. The monster was even bigger than it had been in the morning. She started to tell her mother about the monster again, but then she remembered that her mother didn't want to know.

That night when Lorin went to bed, the monster had her so scared that she had problems sleeping. She had nightmares about the monster all night and wet the bed because the monster was so scary.

When Lorin woke up the next day, the monster was even bigger. She didn't say anything to her mom even though she wanted to, because it was clear her mom didn't want to hear anything else about the monster. She tried to see things as her mother did, mumbling to herself, "Maybe I'm just imagining this. Maybe there really isn't a monster."

But Lorin kept seeing the monster, and it kept stealing her food. Lorin was afraid all the time. She started to have problems doing her schoolwork. She had difficulty with her spelling and she didn't pay attention in class. The teacher, who was usually so nice, even got mad at her, asking, "What has been wrong with you lately?" Lorin was afraid to tell the teacher that she was unable to think about anything but the monster — she thought the teacher would blame her for having a monster in her house.

So the problem with the monster continued, and each day the monster grew bigger and bigger. It scared Lorin more and more. She found it very strange that no matter how big this monster became, her mom acted like she couldn't see it.

One day Lorin invited a friend over to her house to play. The friend entered the house, saw the monster and began to scream, "AHHHH! Look at that monster! What's that monster doing in here?"
"Can you see that monster?" Lorin asked hopefully.
"Well, of course I can see the monster," her friend answered, "anybody can see the monster. We've got to find a way to get it out of here. It's scary."

Lorin immediately felt a lot better because now she realized that other people could see the monster; it wasn't just in her imagination. Lorin realized the monster scared other people, too.

A police car happened to be driving by Lorin's house, so she and her friend quickly ran out yelling to get the police officer's attention. "You have to help me with this monster in my house," Lorin begged the police officer. The police officer followed the girls into the house and saw the monster. "You're right. This is a very big, mean monster. It certainly doesn't belong in your house."

At that, the police officer began to talk to Lorin about the monster. The more Lorin talked to the police officer, the smaller the monster became. It wasn't long before the monster was very small. "Monster, you're going to have to come with me," the police officer ordered. The officer took the monster out of the house so Lorin wouldn't be bothered by it anymore. When the monster was gone, Lorin told her friend how happy she felt to find there were people who could help her with monsters.

That night Lorin found it easier to sleep. The next day when she went to school, she was able to do all her schoolwork just like she had before the monster ever appeared. She thought about what she had learned about monsters and wrote a story about monsters for an English assignment. It was an interesting story and the teacher asked Lorin to read it to her class. As Lorin told her story to the class, she made sure that everyone in her class understood that if you have a monster in your house, you must keep telling people about it until someone believes you and takes it away.

©1995
Nancy Davis, Ph.D.

The Indian and the Dragon

Problem(s) Addressed:

Abuse that occurs to a boy outside of the family

Appropriate for:

Males age 5 - 14

Message:

Putting your traumatic experience into words and finding someone to help with your symptoms, will heal your pain.

Symbols:

Dragon: an abuser

Burned: abused

Lungs burned: sexual abuse; trauma not visible to an observer

Medicine woman: any healer

Going out in the woods alone: being abused outside of the home

Elements of the Story Which Can be Changed:

This story is more appropriate for males, but can be adapted for females or read as is, trusting that the unconscious of the child will understand and personalize the meaning of the story.

Note:

If statistics based on disclosures are correct, boys are abused by people outside of the family far more often than are girls. (Lanning, 1986). Reports of abuse of boys over nine years old made to child abuse hotlines are small in comparison to those regarding females of similar ages (Putnam, 1996). Boys appear to be more embarrassed to report abuse, perhaps because male on male abuse may appear homosexual and female on male abuse is often condoned or minimalized by our society (Personal communication, Lanning, 1991). Perhaps because males in our society emphasize status in conversation (Tannen, 1991), reporting victimization is more difficult because it implies a lack of status.

This story was created for a ten-year-old boy who had been abused by a 15-year-old male. This male would assault the boy in the woods near their homes. The mother of the boy did not know the abuser. This client was in severe PTSD when he entered therapy. A combination of therapeutic stories, EMDR and audio tapes with direct messages to change behavior were used to help him function. He would not (or could not) describe his sexual abuse, but the symptoms of trauma were dramatically reduced with the techniques mentioned above.

The Indian and the Dragon

Once upon a time, many years ago, an Indian tribe made their home in the wilderness. This tribe was a very large one, with many tepees surrounded by deep woods and tall, majestic mountains. As is true in most cultures, this tribe had many customs and ceremonies. One of these customs centered around boys in the tribe becoming men. When the tribe believed a boy was ready to be treated as a man, the elders would grant permission for him to demonstrate his courage and skill by surviving alone in the woods. Upon his successful return, the boy was honored at a ceremony which symbolized he was now a man in the eyes of the tribe and could be called a Brave.

Early in the life of a male child, his parents began to prepare him for his journey into manhood. Each boy was taught all the skills he would need to become a man. He learned to find food in the forest, to build fires by hitting rocks together, to keep warm by making shelters from storms, to climb trees and to track animals.

Within this tribe there was a boy named Bear whose time had come to journey alone into the wilderness. To ready himself for the trip, Bear gathered all his tools, clothing and other needed items. Bear was excited to reach where he could use all he had learned. He was also a little afraid, but did not let his mother and father know of his fear when he bade them goodby.

Bear walked into the wilderness, and continued walking and walking until he was far enough away to feel really alone. Things went well for a while. He was feeling very good about his skills and his success. Bear was able to find enough food, he was able to keep warm and he was able to build his own tepee against the side of a mountain. He explored the rivers and mountains around him, learning much as he traveled. His teachers had drawn maps for him of the wilderness surrounding his tribe, and he recognized much of what he saw.

One day, Bear discovered a valley. As he explored the unknown valley, he met a dragon. Not only had the valley not been described to him, but never, in any Indian lore, had anyone talked about dragons. Bear was curious, but even though he was friendly to the dragon, it began to breathe fire. At first, the fire only scared him. On days that followed, however, when Bear began to encounter the dragon in unexpected places, the fire began to burn him.

Bear became terrified. He thought about returning to his tribe without spending the required number of days alone, but he was afraid that the Braves would laugh at him and he would be disgraced. That seemed even worse than being burned by a dragon. Bear hid in his tepee as much as possible, venturing out only to eat, to hunt, and to find other supplies in the forest.

Bear was always afraid when he went into the forest, because he never knew where or when the dragon would appear. His fear was so great that, even when he was safe in his tepee, he trembled and couldn't stop thinking of the dragon. On the days when Bear encountered the dragon, the fire would burn him so much that even when he was safe in his tepee, the burns would ache and cause him much pain.

Although the days seemed to go by slowly, at last it was time to return to his village. Bear was very relieved and returned as quickly as possible to his tribe and to his family. Everyone in the village was overjoyed at Bear's return and asked about his journey. Bear talked about hunting and building a tepee. The men of the village readied the ceremony to recognize that Bear was now a man.

Bear's family noticed that, although Bear claimed everything had gone as expected during his journey, he seemed to be in pain and sad much of the time. After much coaxing from his family, Bear told them about the dragon. Bear described how ugly the dragon had looked as it breathed fire. He also described how mean the dragon was.

The tribe was very surprised. The wise men of the tribe hadn't known that dragons lived near their village. They asked Bear to tell them more about his encounters with the dragon. Telling the tribe about the dragon reduced some of the fear Bear brought back with him from the wilderness. But talking did not help the pain deep within his chest. During his encounters with the dragon, Bear had breathed in the fire. Because of this, Bear was badly burned in places not visible to the tribe. Bear believed that if he let others know of his burns, the ceremony making him a man would be canceled. So Bear kept silent about his burns hoping the burns would heal by themselves. But rather than healing, the burns became more painful. Bear became sadder and more upset. He had trouble learning the things that he needed to know for the ceremony.

Bear's mother asked him about the dragon. Bear's father asked him about the dragon. Even the medicine man and the medicine woman asked him about the dragon. Bear continued to tell them he had seen the dragon, but had kept far enough away from the dragon's fire so he had not been burned. Bear grew more and more afraid that telling about his burns would cause the tribe to laugh at him, he would be banned from becoming a Brave and the tribe would send him away from the village in disgrace. So Bear kept silent about his burns even though he was in pain with every breath.

Bear spent more and more time alone, trying to hide the pain from all he knew. One day, as he was sitting alone in the forest, the medicine woman walked slowly toward him, smiling a little as she said "hello".

Bear's pain was very clear to the medicine woman. She began to talk to him, telling stories about the tribe so he could see that she was someone he could trust. As she talked softly to Bear, he became more aware of the pain of his burns. Bear decided that he was tired of hurting and that it was time to heal. So Bear found words to talk to the medicine woman about the dragon. In a very quiet voice the Indian boy began to describe how he hurt and how he had gotten burned by the dragon. The medicine woman listened quietly; she didn't react the way he had feared she would. The medicine woman did not get angry. She didn't yell at him and she didn't say anything about him leaving the forest or the tribe. She explained that the whole tribe did not have to know about the burns, because healing Bear's wounds was important and could be accomplished without everyone in the tribe finding out about the burns.

The medicine woman and Bear talked and talked that day. She showed him a powerful medicine and he allowed her to heal his wounds and his burns. Soon Bear noticed that when he took a breath, he felt a sense of calmness. He noticed that he no longer felt the pain of the burns and this brought a sense of relief.

When Bear returned to the village, he let his parents know that the medicine woman was able to heal the burns from the dragon. As his pain got smaller and smaller, Bear found that he didn't think about the dragon, and the world began to look happier and more inviting.

The ceremony was held, and Bear was recognized by the tribe as a man. After the ceremony, Bear continued to learn about himself and about being a man. He noticed that he felt better and better about himself. When the time came for other boys from the tribe to journey into the woods so they could become men, Bear was comfortable in explaining to them how to stay away from dragons. He also let each boy know that if he happened to get burned by a dragon, there was medicine that could heal their pain and permanently rid them of their burns.

©1995
Nancy Davis, Ph.D.

269

The Boy Without a Mouth

Problem(s) Addressed:

The inability to put a traumatic experience into words; making therapeutic stories more potent.

Appropriate for:

Ages 5 - 8

Message:

You can find the words to describe your traumatic experience

Symbols:

Lost his mouth: inability to put a traumatic experience into words and the silence that resulted from the numbing and withdrawal caused by Post Traumatic Stress Disorder

The Magic Lady: any therapist

Elements of the Story Which Can be Changed:

The sex of the main character; the elements of the trauma; the sex and name of the therapist.

Note:

This story was written for a six-year-old boy. While baby-sitting, an adult male relative had entered the bathroom when Mack was taking a bath and sexually assaulted him. Mack was very traumatized by the experience and could not find words to describe the experience. This story and others helped Mack to eliminate the symptoms of trauma.

The Boy Without a Mouth

Once upon a time, there was a boy named Mack. Mack loved to play. He liked to roll on the floor and wrestle. Mack yelled at football and basketball games and talked about all kinds of things until a very dark night when someone came in the bathroom and stole Mack's mouth. It was absolutely amazing because Mack didn't know anybody could steal his mouth. But when his mom came home that night, she noticed that Mack had eyes, eyebrows and a nose, but he didn't have a mouth. "What's wrong with you, Mack?" asked his mom. "Where is your mouth?" But Mack couldn't tell her because he didn't have a mouth to talk. "Why do you look so scared?" asked his mom, "explain to me what happened." But Mack didn't have a mouth, so he couldn't tell her.

Mack's mom asked all of her friends if they knew what happened to Mack's mouth, but nobody knew. Mack became quieter and quieter. He couldn't yell at basketball games and he couldn't say, "Hey, I want to see that TV program." And worst of all, he couldn't eat breakfast or lollipops — Mack had a really big problem.

Friends and relatives and teachers tried to get Mack to talk even though he didn't have a mouth, but Mack couldn't do it. Then, Mack's mom took him to a magic lady that someone had told her about. She told the magic lady that someone had stolen Mack's mouth. "He's really got a mouth," said the magic lady, "he just thinks it's not there." The magic lady explained to Mack's mom that when the man went into the bathroom with Mack, her son had gotten so many feelings about what had happened that he was having trouble finding words to describe it. "Because he thinks his mouth isn't there," she said, "it appears that way to everyone else, too."

"Oh, no," exclaimed his mom, "can you help Mack?"
"Of course," replied the magic lady. "I can help Mack."

Well, the magic lady sat down with Mack and began telling him stories. She told him stories about tornados, stories about bandages, stories about dragons and stories about monsters. The more she told him stories, the more Mack's mouth came back. It was an amazing thing to see. After she talked about many other things, Mack's mouth was completely back.

When Mack's mom came in and asked him why he had lost his mouth, Mack told her all about the man who came into the bathroom. Then Mack told the magic lady all about the man too. "Will you tell somebody else about this man?" asked the magic lady.

"Sure, I've found my mouth back and no one is ever stealing it again," replied Mack.

From that time on, it was impossible to keep Mack from saying whatever was on his mind. When Mack grew up, he became a newscaster on TV because he wanted to be able to explain what was happening in the world to many people who needed to know. One day, Mack told his listeners that when he was young, that he had lost his mouth. Everyone found this hard to believe because it was clear that Mack now had the words to say everything he needed to say.

©1995
Nancy Davis, Ph.D.

The Girl Without a Memory

Problem(s) Addressed:

Dissociation and inability to access memory due to traumatic experiences.

Appropriate for:

Ages 9 - adult

Message:

You can find the way to integrate the dissociated parts of your memory, to process these memories and to become friends with yourself.

Symbols and Metaphors:

Saw many faces looking back at her from the mirror: dissociation, multiple personalities
Began to spin: anything that can integrate the fragmented memories and make them available to process

Elements of the Story Which Can be Changed:

Sex of the main character, individualizing elements of the story that mirror the person to whom the story is being told.

Note:

This story was written for a twelve-year-old girl who had memories which were either dissociated or she had multiple personalities. Her twenty-year-old sister had testified against their father in a criminal trial and the father was found guilty of physical and sexual abuse and sentenced to jail. This older sister had multiple personalities which fused as she was being seen for therapy. This fusion occurred in church after hearing a directive that all of her parts would become friends with each other and learn to co-operate. She reported that she experienced herself spinning as she fused. In addition, after fusing, this patient indicated that she had difficulty in experiencing feelings, pain, etc. because she had never been aware of the manner in which feelings were connected to experiences. The experience of moving from a victim status by testifying against her father seemed to give her the freedom to fuse her disassociated parts.

Disassociation is often a part of traumatic experiences. "Dissociation refers to a compartmentalization of experience: elements of the experience are not integrated into a unitary whole, but are stored in memory as isolated fragments consisting of sensory perceptions or affective states." (Nemiah, 1995; van der Kolk & van der Hart, 1989, 1991; van der Kolk & Fisler, 1995). It is significant that those who have learned to cope with trauma by dissociating are at risk to do so in response to even minor stresses (van der Kolk & Fisler, 1995). Because dissociation is a major barrier to the use of logic in decision making, it is important that therapists find ways to help those they work with to function in an integrated manner.

The Girl Without a Memory

Once upon a time there was a girl named Carol who couldn't remember from one period to the next what had happened in school. When she went home after school Carol forgot that she had homework. When a friend who had been sick asked Carol what had happened in English that day, Carol said, "I can't even remember being in English."

Sometimes Carol would be talking with her friends and they would ask, "Carol, remember last year when we were at the beach?," Carol said "no" because she couldn't remember being at the beach. Sometimes Carol's teachers would punish her for breaking some school rule. Carol would protest, "But I didn't do that, I did not break that rule." Carol's classmates disagreed and told her, "Oh, yes you did break that rule; I saw you do it."

One day, Carol said to herself, "I must be getting Alzheimer's disease; I can't remember anything. I must have lost my memory." Then, as Carol tried to think about her past, she didn't know if she had ever had a memory because all she remembered was that she forgot.

Life without a memory was very difficult for Carol. She not only had problems at school, but she had trouble keeping friends, as well. Carol was always getting in trouble with teachers because she didn't do her homework or she forgot an assignment or they would say, "Carol," and she couldn't remember the question that was asked. Carol was constantly in trouble with her friends because she forgot to go to parties, and she forgot to call them and she forgot to do a favor that she had promised to do.

For a while having no memory seemed normal to Carol. Then, as Carol grew older and wiser, one day she announced to herself, "I am tired of not having a memory; I am going to find my memory." So Carol looked all over the house, but her memory wasn't there. Then she looked outside the house but her memory wasn't there, either. Carol looked in books and trunks, she looked in closets and in the trunk of her car, but Carol couldn't find her memory anywhere. Carol did not give up. The Carol who looked for her memory was different from the old Carol. She had decided that she did not want to grow up unable to remember much of what had happened in her life.

One day, Carol saw a television program on the power of dreams. So, that night, when Carol went to bed she said to herself, "I need to find my memory. I need a dream to help me find my memory."

That night, as Carol slept she started to dream. In this dream Carol got out of bed and looked at herself in the mirror. As she looked at herself, she realized that she could see many Carols looking back at her. At that, the images from the mirror began to speak to her and said, "Carol, you have not lost your memories, they are all inside you. Your memories are not connected together. You have split up your memory so that you have many different minds in the same body."

"Well, I'm tired of having different parts of me and I'm tired of not remembering. I want to be in control of myself. So I want all the different parts of me to merge together and be friends and cooperate. I want all of the different parts to become one and to quit hurting me. I want my memory back." All of a sudden, Carol started to feel like she was spinning and she could see the image in the mirror spinning. In this dream she saw her mind spinning and felt her body spinning and spinning and spinning. Carol was not sure how long the spinning lasted, but as the spin settled down, she looked at herself in the mirror again and there was only one Carol looking back at her. There were no longer many Carols; there was only one. The image from the mirror told her, "We're becoming friends and we're cooperating and we remember." As the dream ended, Carol continued to sleep.

Each night, when she slept, Carol continued to have the same dream until one morning she awoke with the understanding that she was different. When she brushed her teeth, Carol remembered that she had homework that needed to be finished. So Carol did her homework before she went to school. As Carol attended school that day, she remembered everything that she was supposed to do. She remembered every class, she paid attention and Carol was able to remember most of what she heard. When, a friend asked, "Carol, do you remember?" Carol was happy to respond, "Yes, I remember."

Then, parts of her past that used to be blank and hidden from her, suddenly became words and pictures in her memory.

When Carol recovered her memory she had difficulty with the feelings that these memories brought with them. Carol started thinking things she never thought before; she began to realize that she was different from the old Carol. After a while, however, she found that the new Carol stopped being strange to her. She got used to the feelings, she got used to the memories, she was comfortable with the new way of thinking and she liked the way she smiled. She liked the new Carol and she realized she had created her.

From that time on, whenever Carol saw anything that was spinning, she smiled. Carol remembered how the spinning had brought back her memory, had given her the ability to use her intelligence and helped her to realize just how smart she was. From that time on, Carol did well in school. She got very good grades. Carol liked herself more and more each day as she found a way to put her memories in a place where she could retrieve them if she wanted to, but they stayed in the past, where they belonged.

©1995 Nancy Davis, Ph.D.

CHAPTER FIVE

Stories for Children Who Must Testify in Court Proceedings

Because our system of justice usually requires that in criminal proceedings the accuser must face the accused, each year hundreds of children are required to testify and face an abuser. Although only 3-4% of children who report abuse testify in criminal trials (Saunders, Kilpatrick, Resnick, Hanson & Lipovsky, 1992) many are required to testify in preliminary hearings, grand juries or other types of proceedings (Goodman et al., 1992) These proceedings often are as traumatic as the abuse itself.

If you are responsible for preparing a child witness, there are many ways that you can turn the experience into one which helps the child feel competent and personally powerful, rather than re-victimized.

1) Become familiar with court procedures so that you do not give information to the victim or the victim's family that causes needless problems. For example, there are some proceedings which do not require the presence of the witness or in which the defense asks for delays that are routinely granted. In court sessions where the testimony of the child is required, there is a window of time when the child must be available at the courthouse. On occasions when the child does not have to be there, do not require them to be. Children are developmentally unable to sit quietly and wait patiently. What seems like an hour to an adult, will be more like a day or even a week to a child, particularly when they are stressed.

2) Learn how children remember and how they give testimony. It is important not to expect more of a child than they are capable of giving. The Suggestibility of Children's Recollections edited by John Doris and Jeopardy in the Courtroom by Ceci & Buck and "Effects of Cognitive Interviewing and Practice on Children's Recall Performance" by Saywitz, Geiselman and Bornstein are particularly helpful.

3) If the child is terrified, perhaps the judge will allow changes in the way testimony is taken. Sitting on the floor with the prosecutor in front of the jury is one way. In one child abuse trial in which a child was required to testify to sexual and physical abuse by his mother and her boyfriend, the judge ordered that the accused abuser and her attorney move to the back of the courtroom. He then seated the child victim at the prosecutor's table with a deputy on either side so the child felt safe and could not view their mother's reaction to the testimony. (State of Maryland v. Karen Bethea, CT89-0677B, Prince George's Co. Maryland Circuit Court). It is especially important for attorneys to understand how to question children to elicit the most information. Many cases are lost because adults did not understand how to help the child articulate his or her knowledge or memories.

4) Many child victims have symptoms of Post Traumatic Stress Disorder from their traumatic experience. Attorneys may inadvertently or purposefully increase these symptoms. At times the symptom increase is deliberate as a way of keeping the victim silent by delaying the trial again and again or attacking the child through questions. On other occasions, a lack of understanding of child development is the basis for the child's increase in symptoms. Asking anyone to recall a traumatic experience can increase symptoms, especially if PTSD is involved. Children who are experiencing Post Traumatic Stress Disorder, often have fragmented memories. Partial or total amnesia for traumatic events is common in individuals of all ages with memory varying in detail with time (van der Kolk and Fisler, 1995). Helping the child witness to reduce or eliminate symptoms of PTSD will usually result in memory recall which is less fragmented (Foa, Molnar & Cashman, 1995).

The most effective way that I have found to decrease the symptoms in children is through a combination of therapeutic stories and Eyemovement Desensitization and Reprogramming (EMDR). In my experience, many children relate more details of their abuse in a much more connected manner when these types of treatment are used. As an example, a 14 year old female who had recently alleged sexual abuse by a male friend of the mother (not a boyfriend) was referred for treatment. The victim had provided only one or two details of her abuse to the police. Both the victim and her mother, who felt guilty that she had not known about the abuse, were diagnosed with PTSD. After two sessions of EMDR and therapeutic stories, the victim gave a 50-minute detailed account of brutal abuse that had spanned a five-year time period. These allegations were tape recorded Grand Jury testimony was used to explain why the victim was able to give more details of her abuse after being in brief therapy. They accepted the explanation and the abuser was indicted.

5) Use techniques which are visual and action oriented. If the abuser is not a parent or someone that the child will continue to have to deal with in his/her life, have the child draw the abuser, then stomp on him/her. As they stomp on them, have them repeat statements such as, "I am not afraid to testify against you. I am going to tell the truth about everything you did to me.

I am very mad at you for hurting me. I am not afraid of you." If the child is too afraid to draw the abuser, ask them how to draw him/her and you draw the figure. If the child is too afraid to stomp on the picture, you stomp on it first, saying whatever it is that needs to be said. Then tear the picture up into little pieces and flush it down the toilet. Make sure all pieces are gone. As you are flushing the toilet, have the child repeat a statement like: "You are out of here" or "I'm not afraid of you any more". Tell the caretakers or parents that the child can use this technique as much as necessary at home to reduce their fear. Make sure that you explain to the child and their caretakers that this technique is releasing the power that the abuser has in the child's mind and does not mean that they can attack the abuser physically. Because children are so afraid of the power of an abuser and, in my experience, are afraid to even stomp a picture of the person, this technique has not resulted in any aggressive behavior beyond finding the strength to testify against a terrifying adult.

You can also have the child draw the abuser on an erasable board and then erase them, repeating the same type of statements mentioned above. Erasing and flushing are metaphors which speak to the right side of the brain. These visual messages help the child to process the memory of the abuser and let go of their fear.

6) Make a tape of therapeutic stories that the child can listen to as they go to sleep in the days before the trial. "Rags\Taffy and the Invisible Magic Band-Aid" or "The Heavy Rocks" from Therapeutic Stories to Heal Abused Children are particularly good for such a tape. Play the tape as they wait to testify. Let children take some kind of stuffed animal or blanket to help them feel safe into the witness box, if they are young or developmentally delayed.

You can also use the story "The Boy Who Got Rid of His Nightmares" with individualized changes, as follows, to help with a child's fear. Have the parents buy a watch for their child with a superhero on it. Tell a variation of this story using the child's name. Have the superhero appear and get rid of their fear. The superhero then tells the child that they can get rid of their own fear by touching the watch. Following this, provide situations in the story where the child is afraid and by touching their watch, their fear goes away. Then give them the directive that they can find a way to handle any fear that comes up in their life. You can add examples of court testimony with the child touching their watch when they are afraid and experiencing their fear going away.

7) When the trial is over, no matter what the verdict, if the accused abuser is someone that the child will not have to see again, have them again draw the abuser. Take the picture outside and burn it. Then let them stomp on the ashes and have them blow away in the wind. Say, "You are out of my life, [fill in name of abuser], out of my dreams, my thinking, etc"; and have them repeat this statement, including anything that the child wishes to add.

When a victim faces an abuser in court and describes what happen, they cease to be a victim. They have taken on the abuser on equal terms and they have told the truth. At times, if the child is prepared correctly, testifying can be as valuable as months of therapy in creating a feeling of being powerful and in control.

The Teddy Bear and the Truth

Problem(s) Addressed:

Child witnesses who must be able to tell the difference between the truth and a lie in order to testify.

Appropriate for:

Young child witnesses, 4-6 years of age

Message:

You can learn to understand the difference between a lie and the truth

Symbols and Metaphors:

Real: telling the truth

Elements of the Story That Can be Changed:

Sex of the Teddy Bear

Note:

This story was written for a five year old who had to testify about being sexually abused by a babysitter. She was very protected when growing up and her family environment had provided very limited stimulation; even at age five she had never held a crayon. When initially interviewed, she could not explain the difference between the truth and a lie. With this story and additional work, she was able to distinguish these two concepts and was qualified as a witness.

The Teddy Bear and the Truth

Once upon a time there was a fuzzy little teddy bear who wanted so much to be a real bear. She dreamed of living with other bears in the forest and being alive. She dreamed and wished, "please let me be a real bear. I need so much to be a real bear." But no one heard her, so she sat on a shelf in a room day after day.

One day the bear was once again wishing to be real when a magic fairy appeared. "I heard you making a wish," the fairy said as she flew back and forth in front of the teddy bear.

"I want to be real," the teddy bear said hopefully. "I want to be a real bear and live in the forest."

"I can help you become a real bear," the magic fairy promised the teddy. "But you have to learn something before this can happen."

"What?" asked the teddy curiously.

"To be a real bear, you have to learn the difference between the truth and a lie because if you don't know the difference maybe your wish is a lie and I would be wrong in granting it."

"I don't know the difference between a lie and the truth, but I can learn," the teddy told the magic fairy. "What is the difference?"

"The truth is when something really happened. The truth is when you are saying what is right. The truth is when you are saying what really happened to you," the magic fairy explained. "A lie means that you are making something up. A lie means that what you are saying did not happen. A lie is when you say that something is real but you are making it up."

"I can learn that," the teddy responded. "I am really smart and I can learn. I will learn the difference between a lie and the truth because it is very important to know."

"I will help you learn by asking you questions," the magic fairy replied. "If I say, `I am a magic fairy' would I be telling the truth or telling a lie?"

"I don't know," the teddy said with a frown on her face.

"I am telling the truth because I am a magic fairy" she said. "Think about what is the truth and what is a lie and I'll come back in the morning to help you again."

The teddy thought and thought about the difference between the truth and a lie before she went to sleep. Then the teddy had dreams which helped her answer questions about the difference between the truth and a lie. She was very determined to learn the difference between the truth and a lie because she needed to know that in order to become a real bear.

The next day when the magic fairy returned, she understood! "I know what a lie is," the teddy said proudly to the magic fairy. "A lie is when you say that something happened when it didn't. A lie is when you say something that is not true. A lie is when you make up a story."

"That's very good," the magic fairy said impressed with how much the teddy had learned. "Now tell me what the truth is."
"When you tell the truth that means it really, really happened. When you tell the truth that means what you say is real. When you tell the truth that means what you are saying is true."

"I'm going to give you a test to see if you really understand the difference between the truth and a lie," the magic fairy said. "If I say you're a teddy bear, is that true or is that a lie?"
"That's true because that's really what I am," answered the teddy bear.

"You're right," the magic fairy told her. "If I tell you that you are green is that true or is that a lie?"
"That's a lie because I am brown," the teddy replied, getting more sure of herself.
"If I say that it is night time, is that the truth or a lie?" she asked.
"That's a lie," the teddy said. "I can see the sun shining through the window."

"Another test", said the magic fairy. "If I told you that I was a big, mean tiger and I was going to eat you for my dinner, is that true or that a lie?"
"That's a lie," said the teddy bear, "because you're a nice fairy and you wouldn't hurt me."

"You are doing great," the magic fairy announced. "I'm going to ask you one final question. If I told you that teddy bears could fly, is that the truth, or is that a lie?"
"Oh, that's a lie," said the teddy bear, "teddy bears can't fly."
"That's right," the magic fairy told her

Then the magic fairy asked another question, "If I ask you if you want to change into a real bear, is that true or is that a lie?"
"Oh, that's so true," cried the teddy.

"You have passed the test," exclaimed the magic fairy. Then she touched the teddy bear with her magic wand and the teddy bear changed into a real bear. She was very happy to be real. The real bear was glad that she had learned the difference between the truth and a lie because she did not want to tell lies; she wanted to tell what really happened and what didn't happen. And now she could tell the difference every time.

The Girl Who Lost Her Voice

Problem(s) Addressed:

Young children who must testify in court and become so afraid that they cannot talk about what happened to them.

Appropriate for:

Children ages 4-7

Message:

Tell the truth. Talking will get rid of your fear and allow adults to protect you; your voice is your power and your friend.

Symbols and Metaphors:

Lost voice: can't speak because of fear

Elements of the Story That Can be Changed:

Sex of child in story; sex of the victim-witness coordinator or prosecutor (referred to hereafter as the court officer); it is recommended that the name and title of the court officer be inserted in the story in places where the brackets [ ] appear.

Note:

This story was designed for a child who had to testify against an abuser who had been her mother's friend. The child was terrified of the offender and was allowed to testify by closed circuit camera for a jury, after a pre-trial hearing established that her fear of the offender was so great, she would be unable to tell the truth if she had to face him directly.

It is common for anyone who has been traumatized to have partial amnesia for the traumatic event (van der Kolk & Fisler, 1995) and for the memory to sometimes alternate between becoming clearer and fading. Talking about traumatic events typically causes an increase in symptoms. Put this story on a tape with other stories which are comforting and healing.

The Girl Who Lost Her Voice

Once upon a time there was a little girl named Mandy. Mandy liked to play and laugh. She liked to watch movies and tell about all the things that happened to her.

But one day, and for many days, Mandy had some big problems. When these things happened, her voice seemed to disappear. It wasn't that Mandy said, "Voice, go away!" Mandy lost her voice because she began to feel so sad and so scared inside and so upset.

When Mandy lost her voice, she stopped eating and stopped laughing. She also stopped telling everyone around her what had happened to her during the day. Those around her asked Mandy repeatedly, "What's wrong with you, Mandy? What's wrong?" But Mandy had lost her voice, so she couldn't explain what was wrong.

One day Mandy's feelings got so powerful that she found her voice and told her family what was wrong. Her family was happy that she told them the truth and promised her that they would never let those bad things happen to her again. "We're going to protect you, Mandy," they assured her. Later, they told Mandy that she would have to tell what happened to many people, especially a person who worked at the court named, **[court officer's name]**.

When Mandy's family took her to the court person, the lady/man asked Mandy questions. When she heard these questions, all the feelings that had taken Mandy's voice away before came back and she lost her voice again. The court person asked, "What happened, Mandy?" But Mandy didn't answer. She was afraid, and her voice was gone.

Then Mandy went to visit a special doctor. The doctor said, "Hello, Mandy." But Mandy didn't say anything. "How old are you, Mandy?" the doctor asked. Mandy remained silent. Trying to get Mandy to talk, the doctor turned on her tape recorder and showed Mandy a microphone. "Let's talk on a tape," the doctor said. "What's your name?" But Mandy had lost her voice, and she said nothing.

When Mandy continued to be silent, the doctor went to the closet and returned with a mirror. The doctor held the mirror in front of Mandy so that Mandy could look at her face. "Mandy, I want you to look at this, the doctor told her, pointing to Mandy's mouth in the mirror. You have a mouth, and it is a very pretty mouth, especially when you smile. But a mouth is for more than smiling, and even for more than eating! It is also for talking. "The more you talk about things that happened to you, the better you will feel because your voice is your friend. Your voice is the part of you that can tell adults what they need to know to protect you."

Mandy continued to sit in silence for a minute, then she said quietly, "My name is Mandy."

"I'm so glad you found your voice," the doctor said to her. "Do you know what telling the truth means?"

Mandy thought about this question. "Yes," she told the doctor. "When I tell what really happened, that is the truth. When I pretend or make something up, that is not the truth."

"That's right," the doctor told her. "When you make something up that did not happen, that is a lie."

"I know that," Mandy said with growing confidence that her voice was here to stay.

"Tell me what happened to you, Mandy," the doctor said. "Make sure that you tell me the truth and that what you tell me really happened."

Mandy's voice had found a way to work and be her friend. She told the doctor everything that had happened to her and why she was so afraid. Mandy began to understand and believe that her voice was her friend.

The next day when Mandy went to visit with [court officer's name], she found her voice and answered her/his questions. Mandy made sure that everything she told was the truth and that everything she said had really happened.

When she went home after the visit with [court officer's name]. She discovered that telling everything that was bothering her, helped her scary dreams to disappear. Each day Mandy talked more and more about many things in her life and she smiled all day with the voice that had become her friend.

©1995
Nancy Davis, Ph.D.

CHAPTER SIX

Stories to Reduce and Eliminate Nightmares

Nightmares are common in young children. Nightmares and night terrors are also common in children and adults who have experienced trauma (Cuddy & Belicki, 1990). Nightmares with violent abuse-related themes are often found in those experiencing sexual abuse-related PTSD (Briere & Runtz, 1993). Night terrors occur in a different stage of sleep than nightmares and are believed to be flashbacks that occur during sleep. The dreamer often awakes in fear, with no memory of the content of the dream except for the feelings that remain. Parents need to be educated that night terrors are often a sign that their child has experienced some type of trauma. It is important to remember, however, that many experiences which traumatize a child have nothing to do with child abuse or the kinds of experiences that often traumatize adults. For example, a child may have night terrors if a classmate at school is bullying him/her. Parents can be feel confident that they have found and dealt with the source of a trauma if the symptoms displayed by their child dissipate.

To help a child deal with nightmares, read one or more of the stories in this chapter on audio tape for a child. Personalize the story by adding the child's name as the main character; tell the story in the gender of the child. Add the name of the child's favorite super hero. Add additional stories to the tape that deal specifically with the other problem(s) of the child. By listening to a personalized tape at bed time, the nightmares of the child should be significantly reduced or eliminated in a very short period of time.

The Girl Who Learned to Control Her Dreams

Problem(s) Addressed:

Nightmares, especially those in which the dream is of being hurt by someone familiar.

Appropriate for:

Ages 10 and below

Message:

You can find the power to change your dreams from frightening to pleasant

Symbols and Metaphors:

Sleeping Beauty: the part of the unconscious that is wise and helpful

Elements of the Story Which Can be Changed:

This story is often most successful when the name of the child is added as the main character. Other elements which may be changed to personalize it: the age and sex of the child; the themes of the nightmares; the people with whom the child gets in bed with when he/she is scared.

Note:

Research has supported that dreams can be changed by conscious intervention. Often by going through the dream and changing the ending, a repetitive dream will change. Other therapists have taught their clients to go into the dream and challenge the scary figure. Since children are developmentally different from adults, this story gives them a message that they can change their dreams demonstrating that it can be done through the ending.

Make a tape of this story, along with other therapeutic stories, so the child can listen to them as they go to sleep.

The Girl Who Learned to Control Her Dreams

Once upon a time there was a girl named Heather who had scary dreams every night. Often her dreams were of sharks and monsters and people hurting other people. When Heather had these dreams, she would get so scared that she would jump out of her own bed. Then she would run to the bed of someone in the family who helped her to feel safe. Because no one in her family wanted Heather to sleep with them every night, she always had to return to her own bed the next night. Each night, when Heather tried to go to sleep, she was afraid and didn't feel safe.

One night Heather was lying in her bed really scared when the princess from "Sleeping Beauty" appeared to talk to her. This princess knew a lot about sleep because she had slept a very long time without having any nightmares at all. The princess told Heather, "I can help you with your nightmares. The next time you see a monster, I want you to stick him with a pin and you'll find out he is just an old balloon monster and he'll just pop and disappear."

Heather wasn't so sure. "I don't know whether that's going to happen or not. I don't know if I believe you," she said.

The princess responded, "Let's just try it. I'll be with you, beside your bed and in your dreams. I'll help you to make all the monsters go away."

So Heather went to sleep and it wasn't long before she started to dream. As she was dreaming, a big monster appeared. The princess came into Heather's dream, holding out a pin. "Here's a pin," she said. "Stick that old monster and make him go away."

Heather was a little scared, but the princess held her hand and helped her stick that monster and "POP", he disappeared. "See," said the princess, "you have the power to get rid of monsters in your dreams."

"That's great," said Heather. "But I have dreams about other things that scare me." So

299

the princess told Heather, "I will stay with you and will help you to get rid of all the things in your dreams that scare you."

So Heather went back to sleep. Soon she was dreaming about somebody that she loved trying to hurt her. When the princess appeared, Heather exclaimed "I don't want to stick them with pins, I'm scared." The princess agreed. "You and I will stand up and talk to this person and tell them to quit trying to hurt you. We will tell them that people that love you aren't supposed to hurt you. We'll talk so firmly and loudly that they won't hurt you in your dream."

So the princess and Heather stood right in front of the person that was supposed to love Heather but was going to hurt her. They both demanded, "You cut that out. You're not supposed to hurt somebody you love. Now you cut that out." Then the person just faded away; it was so amazing. The rest of the dream was a happy dream because Heather dreamed that she and her friends went to the movies and they had such a good time.

The next morning when Heather woke up she was in her own bed. Not only was Heather surprised, so was her family. Heather announced to them, "I'm getting bigger and smarter and more powerful and I can figure how to take care of my own dreams."

The next night, Heather wasn't even afraid to go to sleep. Her mother couldn't believe it. When the monsters and sharks came in her dreams, Heather called the princess to help her. Heather stuck them with a pin and, "Puff," they disappeared. When people that were supposed to love her were trying to hurt her in her dreams, Heather found a way to make them disappear.

Soon Heather was having more nice dreams and better dreams and she started looking forward to going to sleep. She stopped having to get in bed with her mother because she was becoming so powerful that she was able to have nice dreams in her very own bed. After that, whenever Heather needed to, she would go to sleep and call the princess to help her. Then she and the princess would get rid of all the monsters or any other scary things in her dreams. And Heather learned something else from her dreams: she learned that she was smart and she was powerful. She also had discovered how to tell those around her what she wanted and needed and say things in her mind that helped her to feel good about herself.

©1995
Nancy Davis, Ph.D.

The Sisters Who Dreamed of Monsters

Problem(s) Addressed:

Nightmares

Appropriate for:

Ages 10 and under

Message:

You have the power to change your nightmares to happy dreams

Symbols and Metaphors:

The Superhero: the wisest part of the child that knows how to deal with problems

Elements of the Story Which Can be Changed:

Insert the name of the children into the story; the sex of the child; the themes of the nightmares; add the child's favorite super hero.

Note:

Even children who sleep together have nightmares. But teaching them to handle their bad dreams will give them confidence that they can handle other problems.

The Sisters Who Dreamed of Monsters

Once upon a time there were two sisters named April and Crystal. They were very smart little girls and they were very good at coloring and making cards and playing and being very happy. When they had bad dreams, however, they were not happy at all. April and Crystal had dreams about monsters and they had dreams about getting hurt. When this happened, they would wake up very afraid. Then they couldn't sleep because they were afraid that the nightmare would start again. Often their dreams were so scary that they didn't even want to go to sleep at all. Sometimes the sisters believed their dreams would come true.

One night as April and Crystal were going to sleep, [¹   ] entered their room and said, "I understand you have both been having nightmares."
The sisters replied, "Yes, [   ], yes [   ] will you stay here all night so the nightmares won't scare us?"

[   ] said, "I can do something even better. I can teach you things to do so you won't have nightmares anymore. I can teach you to get rid of your own nightmares."
Well Crystal and April weren't too sure about that. They asked, "Are you sure, [   ]?"

[   ] replied, "I wouldn't be [   ] if I couldn't do things that no one else can do, would I?"
The sisters replied, "Well, we guess not."

[   ] said, "Go to sleep and when you have a nightmare, wake up and tell me."

Well April and Crystal both went to sleep and it wasn't long before they were both dreaming and they had a dream about a monster. They both yelled, "[   ], help us, help us, help us."

---

¹ Insert the name of any super hero they choose.

303

[   ] said calmly, "I don't need to help you." He/she gave them both a pin telling the sisters, "Stick the old monster with this pin and you will find out that he is not real at all. He is just like a balloon." So Crystal stuck the monster and he disappeared just like a balloon. And April stuck the monster and he disappeared and was gone. It was so wonderful because the monster was gone from their dreams.

[   ] announced, "I'm going to show you some other ways to handle your nightmares. When you see a monster, you can just point your finger at it and say, 'Go away' and make it disappear. Or you can take your mind and you can shrink it until it is little and tiny and then you can step on it. You can change all those monsters in your dreams so they are not scary at all. I know you can do it, I'm going to stay here all night while you go back to sleep and prove to yourselves that you know how to get rid of your own nightmares."

"What about ghosts and witches?" asked April.

"What about mean animals and mean and scary people?" asked Crystal.

"No problem," replied [   ], "I can teach you how to get rid of anything scary in your dreams."

Crystal and April were very happy about that because they wanted to get rid of their scary nightmares. So they went back to sleep. Soon Crystal started dreaming about a mad bomber. She yelled, "Get away, Mad Bomber!" Remembering what [   ] had taught her, she used her mind to shrink the mad bomber until he was tiny and then she kicked him like a ball and he bounced away. Then Crystal's dream became a happy one. She was at a restaurant eating lots of pizza and playing all the video games.

April started having a dream about a mean witch that was coming into her bedroom. So April imagined that she squirted her with a water gun and she just melted and disappeared. April exclaimed, "This is really great," and her dream turned into believing that she was at the movies having a good time.

April and Crystal were both so happy that they could figure out how to handle monsters and witches and scary things in their dreams. They exclaimed, "Thank you, thank you, [   ]. Thank you so much."

Then [   ] said, "Keep doing the things I taught you every time you have a bad dream and you are going to find out that in no time at all your dreams will be good ones."

Crystal and April said, "Thank you, thank you, thank you."

Well every night when the sisters went to sleep they remembered what [   ] had taught them. If any monsters or other scary things tried to go into their dreams, they figured out ways to get rid of them. It wasn't long before both of them were having very happy dreams and smiling in their sleep. Of course, both April and Crystal were very proud of themselves because they had learned to control their dreams and make monsters disappear. So when their teacher asked them to write a story, each girl wrote about getting rid of nightmares so that they could teach the class everything they had learned.

The Boy Who Got Rid of His Nightmares

Problem(s) Addressed:

Nightmares, night terrors

Appropriate for:

Ages 10 and under

Message:

You can get rid of your nightmares, feel safe and sleep in peace.

Symbols and Metaphors:

Super hero: wisdom of the unconscious

Shined a light on them and they disappeared: knowledge helps to get rid of old fears

Laser Stick: used instead of a gun, because of the mounting violence in our society with guns

Elements of the Story Which Can be Changed:

Put the child's name into the story; also insert the name of their favorite super hero at the brackets [ ]; sex of the child; themes of nightmares; behavior caused by nightmares or inability to sleep; specific examples of improvement in life functioning that are appropriate to the child hearing the story. For example, "He had dreams to help him do well in school or that helped her understand how to make friends or to like herself."

Note:

This story was the favorite of a boy in PTSD who was stealing, lying, hoarding food, and keeping his brother awake because he couldn't sleep. The other stories which were created for him and taped were "The House and the Hurricane", "The Hunger that Wouldn't Go Away", "The Dark Sunglasses", "The Hole in the Heart" and "The Boy Who Became a Fireman." His foster mother played these stories for him nightly. Initially, he said the witch in this story scared him,

307

but after listening to the story again and again, it became his favorite. He is now sleeping through the night, rarely lying and is very happy. He has been adopted by the foster family. He steals food about every three months, at which point he returns for one therapy session and his stories are played again for a week for two as he goes to sleep. His speech and vocabulary are greatly improved and his grades have soared.

The Boy Who Got Rid of His Nightmares

Once upon a time there was a boy named Rick who was having really scary nightmares. Sometimes his nightmares were so bad he couldn't sleep at all. At other times he would have nightmares about a wicked, old, mean, ugly-looking witch and he would wake up and have to get in bed with his brother. Well, his brother didn't like that very much because it woke him up. People would say to Rick, "Why can't you just go to sleep?" Rick didn't know. He didn't want to stay up, he just couldn't help himself.

One night when Rick was dreaming he saw that old witch. Suddenly [^{2}] entered his room and said, "Rick, I'm going to show you how to get rid of that old, wicked witch in your dreams so you don't ever have to dream about her again." He/she gave Rick a great big pin. Then he/she handed Rick a stick with a special kind of laser beam and said, "You can use whichever one of these two things you want to use. You can put the laser beam on the witch and she will just melt or you can stick her with a pin and she will just pop like a balloon."

Rick said, "I'm a little bit scared to do either of those things, can you help me?"
"Okay, let's do it," [   ] agreed. "Point over there with that laser beam."

Rick pointed over there and, "Whoosh," the witch disappeared. "Hey, this is pretty neat, I like this," Rick told [   ]. "Are you going to stay with me every night and help me get rid of witches and bad monsters in my dreams?"
[   ] said, "I don't have to stay with you every night. I'm going to leave you the laser stick and the pin and you can do it yourself."

Well, Rick wasn't quite sure that [   ] really knew what he/she was talking about but Rick decided this was better than having nightmares. The next night when Rick went to sleep,

---

^{2} Insert the name of the child's favorite super hero.

he had a dream about an ugly, green, slimy monster. He grabbed that laser stick and pointed a beam of light at the monster and "ZAP!" that ugly monster disappeared.

Rick said happily, "This is great. I love this. I can control my dreams. This is wonderful." Then Rick started dreaming about going to the Convention Center and watching a basketball game instead. That was a really nice dream.

The next night, Rick had another bad dream. The dream began with Rick being chased by robbers. Then Rick pulled out that laser stick and he pointed it toward those old robbers, shining a beam of light directly on them. They turned into mice and they started running around going, "squeak, squeak, squeak." Rick laughed and said, "This is great, I love this, I am really smart."

Then he had a dream about a big monster. Rick was feeling very brave because he had been so successful getting rid of his nightmares, so he grabbed the pin and stuck the monster. It popped like a balloon and went into the air, blowing far, far away. "I have so many ways of getting rid of nightmares," Rick told himself, "that I am never going to be afraid of going to sleep again."

Well, after that night, Rick had fewer nightmares and he knew that if a nightmare did appear, he could easily get rid of it. He could use his laser beam or pin. Rick knew how to make any monster disappear. He stopped getting into bed with his brother and Rick began to have more and more good dreams...dreams about being happy and playing and going to Disney World. He had dreams to help him do well in school and feel safe. Every day he felt better and better about himself. He improved so much he could talk better, think better and be happier and happier.

After that, whenever someone in class said they had a scary nightmare, Rick smiled to himself because he knew how to get rid of nightmares and he knew that made him very smart.

©1995
Nancy Davis, Ph.D.

310

CHAPTER SEVEN

Stories for Children Who Have Not Followed
a Normal Developmental Path

Although many times a child's development delays may be due to genetic factors or the result of physical trauma, other types of trauma can also cause such delays. Chronic Post Traumatic Stress Disorder (PTSD) in children can make them appear retarded, particularly if it began at a very young age and was of a long-term nature. Because these children are often withdrawn and tend to shut out the world, the longer they remain in this stage, the more likely it is that retarded functioning will become permanent. Conversely, children can have significant increases in IQ scores after effective treatment. It is important, therefore, to determine which of the symptoms are permanent and which can be eliminated by treatment.

Children are often misdiagnosed as being hyperactive or attention deficient when they are actually in PTSD. The symptoms often appear much the same, as they both demonstrate irritability, problems concentrating, poor boundaries and social difficulties. Children in PTSD differ from hyperactive children in that they may have problems sleeping, have rage reactions, and they may "mess their pants" when something triggers a fear reaction. Look for a history of trauma in children who look hyperactive. Children in PTSD will get worse when placed on Ritilan as it is a stimulant and their brains are already over-stimulated. They do best on an anti-depressant medication which slows down the part of the brain which is over-stimulated in PTSD, coupled with therapy techniques which deal with the right side of the brain (van der Kolk, 1996). Refer them to a doctor for evaluation to determine if medication is appropriate.

Handicapped individuals have a variety of problems that respond to the use of therapeutic stories. However, it has been my experience that if an individual functions in the moderate range of intellectual functioning, these stories are not very effective.

Glen and the Teddy Bears

Problem(s) Addressed:

Uncontrollable rage reaction in a retarded adult; acceptance of handicap

Appropriate For:

Children or adults who are retarded or handicapped

Message:

There are solutions to problems; you can "fix" uncontrollable rage reactions and change your behavior so that everyone is happy; you can like yourself so that being handicapped is not a source of low self esteem.

Symbols and Metaphors:

Teddy Bear Fairy: wisdom of the unconscious

Stuffing out of bears: symbol of the handicapping condition

Replacing the stuffing & sewing: even with handicaps, if an individual can function at their optimal level, everyone around will be happier

Elements of the Story Which Can Be Changed:

The sex of the main character; family member who goes to store.

Note:

This story was created for a 32 year old male who was retarded. When he wanted something or became unhappy, he would throw temper tantrums and strike his mother. This story and others were created to help him get his behavior under control.

Glen and the Teddy Bears

Once upon a time there was a boy named Glen who had lots and lots of teddy bears. There were teddy bears that were big and there were teddy bears that were small. Some were fuzzy and some were rough. Glen had played with the teddy bears so much that the stuffing was missing from many of them. This meant that Glen's teddy bears had lumps and holes.

Glen loved his teddy bears, but he was very unhappy that many of them were full of holes. "I am so tired of having teddy bears that aren't like the ones in the toy stores," Glen said to himself one day. Then he would get angry and stomp his teddy bears. He would say nasty words to them and kick them. When this happened, more and more stuffing fell from the teddy bears and they looked even worse than they had before.

So things were stormy for Glen and the teddy bears. The more the stuffing came out of the teddy bears, the more angry Glen became. Then Glen would treat his teddy bears in a very abusive way and they would lose even more stuffing.

Glen became more and more unhappy, but he had no idea what to do. One night, while he slept, a teddy bear fairy came to him in a dream. "You can fix those teddy bears if you want to," the teddy bear fairy announced.
"How?" Glen asked.
"Go to the fabric store and buy some stuffing. You can stuff the teddy bears and sew them back up. Then you won't have to be angry at your teddy bears for being full of holes. If you fix the teddy bears they will be soft and fluffy. Then you can be happy and the teddy bears can be happy."

Glen wasn't sure that repairing the teddy bears would make him happy. "If I sew them up the teddy bears won't look the same as they did when they were new," Glen said to the teddy bear fairy in his dream.

"What the teddy bears look like on the outside will not matter," the teddy bear fairy told Glen. "You will love them and love can make anything beautiful. You have so many teddy bears that you will have one to sleep with, one to talk to and one to sit with you when you watch TV." Then the teddy bear fairy faded away and Glen slipped into a sound sleep.

When Glen woke up the next morning, he sat at the breakfast table remembering his dream. "I have an idea," Glen told his mom. "Let's go to the fabric store and get some stuffing."

"What did you say?" Glen's mom asked. So Glen repeated his request to her again. After breakfast, Glen and his mother drove to the fabric store. They found a huge bag of stuffing at the store that seemed just right for teddy bears.

When Glen returned home, he restuffed each and every teddy bear. Then Glen asked his mom to teach him how to sew. Using a needle and thread, Glen then sewed up all the teddy bears so that the stuffing would not fall out. When Glen was finished, he sat down with his teddy bears, admiring his repairs. He was happy and the teddy bears were happy, too.

Even after the repairs, each of the teddy bears had a little lump here and a little lump there, but all of the teddy bears looked better than they had before they were repaired. Glen used one of the teddy bears to sleep with and one of the teddy bears to keep him company while he ate. A fuzzy brown teddy bear was selected to sit with Glen when he watched TV, and Glen used others to talk to or to play with.

The visit with the teddy bear fairy seemed to help Glen find a way to treat his teddy bears with love and respect. No longer did Glen get angry and throw and hit. Repairing his teddy bears had taught Glen an important lesson: There are solutions to problems and you can find ways to solve your own problems.

Then Glen smiled to himself because he liked the new way he was acting and he loved having the teddy bears which he had repaired all by himself.

©1995
Nancy Davis, Ph.D.

The Radio That Was All Mixed Up

Problem(s) Addressed:

Mixed up thinking, schizophrenic thinking or thought disorders. Children who can't stay focused when they begin to speak or tell a story.

Appropriate for:

Elementary school children

Message:

You can find a way to focus and override any interfering thoughts which are trying to mix you up.

Symbols:

Radio playing on two different stations: confused thinking or conversation
Radio tower: interfering thoughts because of psychotic or disassociated thought processes or racing thoughts
Special Antenna: the wisdom of the unconscious to figure out a way to keep inappropriate thoughts from interfering with normal thought processes

Elements of the Story Which Can be Changed:

Sex of the main character

Note:

This story was created for a seven year old who had difficulty staying focused on one subject during conversation. Her inability to focus caused her many social problems, since the other children regarded her as strange. She was made a tape of stories that included this one. After listening to it repeatedly, her teacher reported improvement in her functioning.

318

The Radio That Was All Mixed Up

Once upon a time there was a girl named Melanie who owned a radio. Melanie play music on the radio, and she danced and sang along with her favorite songs. Melanie wanted to hear music when she woke up, she wanted to hear music when she came home from school and she really loved to hear music when she did her homework.

One day Melanie noticed that her radio had a problem -- it wouldn't stay on a station. She would put the dial on her favorite station and begin to dance. Before long, sometimes almost without her noticing, the radio would slip off the station and mix up music from different songs, as if two or three stations were trying to play music all at the same time.

Melanie asked her dad to help her, "Would you put this radio on a station and make it stay?" Her dad would adjust the knob and turn the controls to a station. He would then hand the radio back to Melanie. Soon the radio had slipped off the station and was mixing up two different ideas. Melanie then asked her mom for help. Her mom would change the dials and even put tape on the knob so it wouldn't move. But when Melanie turned on the radio and began to dance, she was soon listening to a Rap song blended with a Rock song and the news. Melanie began to get angry because she wanted her radio to stay on one station at a time and play only one song at a time. She pounded on the radio, but that just seemed to make the problem worse. She tried being nice to the radio and telling it how special it was, but the radio continued to slip off the station.

One day Melanie went into her back yard to think about her radio and why it was getting so mixed up. As she was sitting in the yard, she looked up and noticed a that there was a big radio tower just down the street. It had been there for years, but Melanie had never noticed it. "I wonder if that tower is sending out signals that interfere with my radio?", she said to herself.

Melanie had a friend that lived across town, so the next time that she spent the night there, Melanie took her radio with her. Just as she had suspected, the radio worked fine when there was no other interfering signal from the radio tower. "Well," Melanie said to her friend. "I have found the problem, but I haven't found the solution...but I know I will."

319

So Melanie thought and thought. "Perhaps there is a way to get my radio to ignore the signals from the radio tower," she said to herself. So Melanie went to a store that specialized in radios and recording devices. After listening to her problem, the clerk pulled a small box out of a drawer. "I have a special antenna that makes the signal from the station you are listening to so strong that your radio will totally ignore the signals from the nearby tower which are trying to interfere." the clerk told her. "In that way, the radio can stay on a station and you will only hear one thing at a time."

Melanie immediately bought the special antenna and rushed home with her radio. The clerk was right - - the antenna was able to help the radio stay on a station by ignoring the signals from the radio tower that was trying to mix it up. Melanie was very happy that she had found a way to solve the problem with her radio. From that time on, Melanie made sure that the special antenna was always in place so that her radio always stayed on just one station at a time.

©1996
Nancy Davis, Ph.D.

The Little Girl Who Couldn't Tell If
She Was Asleep or Awake

Problem(s) Addressed:
Inability to distinguish between fantasy and reality; lies

Appropriate for:
Elementary school children

Message:
You can find a way to separate reality from fantasy

Symbols and Metaphors:
Dreams from what really happened: reality from fantasy

Elements of the Story Which Can be Changed:
Sex of the main character; specific behaviors of the main character reflecting the inability to distinguish between reality and fantasy

Note:
Many children have problems in distinguishing reality from fantasy. These children may be psychotic, may have distorted perceptions because of abuse or some other trauma in their lives, or may come from a home where they have modeled such behavior. Combine this story with others that are appropriate for a particular child. Do not interpret this story as you tell it.

The Little Girl Who Couldn't Tell If
She Was Asleep or Awake

Once upon a time there was a girl named Amy who had big problems; she dreamed all night long and when she woke up in the morning she couldn't tell whether she was still dreaming or whether she was awake. Amy also had problems figuring out whether she was really doing things or whether she was just dreaming about doing them. It was so strange. Sometimes, in her dreams, Amy hit kids in the neighborhood. Then she couldn't remember if she had really hit someone or if she just dreamed it. Sometimes she dreamed that she had a banana split with chocolate ice cream and whipped cream and cherries and nuts and candy all over it. But when Amy later thought about eating the ice cream, she couldn't figure out if she had simply dreamed about it, or if she really had eaten her favorite treat.

Amy's inability to tell the difference between her dreams and what really happened got her into big trouble. Sometimes Amy would tell the teacher that things she dreamed about really happened. "Did you know a great big monster came and pulled my hair and took all of my pretty bows that I put in my hair?", Amy asked her teacher.

"That didn't happen", the teacher told Amy.
"Yes it did," Amy responded, because she really believed that her dreams were real and that her dreams had really happened.

Then, at other times, Amy would dream she did her homework when she didn't. She would dream that she studied for a test when she didn't. Then she would take a test and she wouldn't do well on it. It was really weird!

Well, Amy kept getting in trouble. She got in trouble at home and she got in trouble with the teacher. Amy also got in trouble with her friends because she was always telling her friends things that never really happened. "Did you know that I went to Hollywood last week and I'm going to be a movie star?" Amy asked her friends.

"You did not go to Hollywood, you were here with us all week," her friends said in disgust, "You were at school with us!"

Amy was confused because she had dreamed that she had gone to Hollywood and she could have sworn that it was true.

One day, after all the kids at school were so angry with her that Amy felt like she didn't have a friend in the world, she sat down on the steps outside of her house. "Not knowing whether I am dreaming or awake is getting me in big trouble.", Amy said to herself. "I am going to have to figure out some way to stop this." So Amy thought, and she thought, and she thought.

"I think I will try something tonight", Amy said. "I'll tell myself, 'Self, when I wake up in the morning, you be sure to tell me what I dreamed during the night so I can know the difference between what is dreams and what really happened.' " Then Amy laughed at herself because she realized that what she was doing was pretty strange, but she really wanted to change.

That night Amy dreamed about monsters, and going to Hollywood and dancing. She dreamed about candy, and she dreamed about people kicking her. When she woke up, Amy laid on her pillow for a minute and voice in her mind told her, "These are the things you were dreaming."

When Amy got to school that day, she didn't tell the teacher about things that she had dreamed as if they had really happened. Amy told the teacher only the truth.

After that, every night when she went to bed, Amy made sure she talked to herself, "Tomorrow, when I wake up, I must make sure I understand the things that I dreamed about and the things I really did." she would say. When she woke up, she would always hear a voice telling her what she had dreamed and what was real.

After a while, Amy didn't have to remind herself to let her know the difference between dreams and reality, because her mind did it automatically. Then, life was so much easier for Amy because she didn't mix up her dreams and what really happened. Amy became happier and happier each day and she was able to make more and more friends. Amy even did better in school. It wasn't long before those around her no longer remembered that Amy had been the girl who didn't know the difference between what was real and what was a dream.

CHAPTER EIGHT

Stories to Deal With Death, Loss and Illness

Grief is an adaptive response experienced by a person as he or she works through the meaning of their loss. The most common and the most severe grieving is normally associated with the loss of a loved one. However, people sometimes undergo a grieving process when they lose or are deprived of a part of their own personal or professional life. This is particularly true of a person whose image and self-worth is closely bound to that aspect of his/her life. For example, a medical doctor or attorney who loses the ability to practice because of health or even alleged misconduct may experience a grieving process in attempting to redefine his/her life without that career. The same may be true of a gifted athlete whose career is cut short as a result of injury or illness. The task of the griever is to re-define themselves without the loved one who has died or without that special part of their life which has been lost.

Grief is a normal process that each survivor must go through in their own way. There are recognized stages to grief:

Stage One: Shock, Numbness and/or Turmoil;
Stage Two: Yearning and Searching;
Stage Three: Disorientation and Disorganization
Stage Four: Resolution and Reorganization
                          (Parkes, 1975).

When grief is being processed normally, the griever will progress through these stages, although many grievers indicate they may bounce back and forth among these stages, sometimes even in a manner of minutes. At other times, they may remain in the same stage for days.

Despite the tendency to sometimes move back and forth or occasionally to stay in the same stage, normally the griever reports feeling better than they did a few weeks before, i.e., "I'm having a few good days"; "I still feel horrible, but I can sometimes think of the good times we had"; I'm having more good days than bad" (Marcey, 1995).

Grief which does not process has been referred to as "morbid grief reactions" (p. 67 Lindemann, 1979) or complicated bereavement (Demi & Miles, 1987), but appears to be a combination of PTSD and grief symptoms. Post Traumatic Stress Disorder causes an individual to stay frozen in repetitive flashbacks which interfere with the normal and healthy progression through the stages. In other words, grief normally moves through these stages with a gradual lessening of the pain; PTSD does not allow the grief to progress, resulting in the griever being stuck in one stage with little or no decrease in the symptoms.

The loss of a loved one, especially if the person who dies is young and the loss is sudden, is often experienced as a traumatic event. Dr. Marcey (1995) studied loved ones who had lost someone to homicide, drunk drivers, sudden death or accidental death. She discovered that over 50% of survivors who viewed the death of a loved one as preventable continued to have symptoms of Post Traumatic Stress Disorder five to seven years after their loss.

It is important for therapists to learn to recognize the symptoms of Post Traumatic Stress Disorder in grievers and the techniques to help them quickly eliminate the flashbacks so that the grief symptoms can be worked through and resolved. As PTSD symptoms are eliminated, many survivors discover that they have moved through many of the stages of grief without conscious awareness.

The stories in this chapter deal with specific problems related to loss. Therapeutic Stories to Heal Abused Children contains additional stories which deal more directly with the pain of lossing a loved one..

Going Through the Door

Problem(s) Addressed:

A child with a terminal illness

Appropriate for:

Children and adolescents who are terminally ill, many terminally ill adults also find this story comforting

Message:

You can find a way to come to peace with dying and leave gently and with love

Symbols and Metaphors:

Door: death

Elements of the Story That Can be Changed:

The stages of a particular child's grief reactions can be rearranged in this story. When appropriate, the child's religious beliefs may also be incorporated into the message.

Note:

This story was written at the request of a therapist who works in a hospice. It took may months to create. Thinking about a child dying is difficult for most adults in the helping professions, even in the abstract.

The emotional reactions of the child to dying are often different from an adult because a child is fearful of leaving his/her parents and is concerned about who will take care of him/her.

328

Going Through the Door

Once upon a time a boy was born and his parents named him Mark. Shortly after his birth, Mark joined his family in a very special room. In this room, there were toys and good things to eat. There was a place to sleep and activities and learning to fill almost every need. The room was a very happy one. When he was very young, someone, perhaps his parents, let Mark know, "You will live in this room a very long time and then, when you become an adult, you will gladly move to another room."

One day, Mark noticed a door at the end of the room. "Why is that door in my room? I never use it." he asked those around him. "That's a door we all have to go through, but you won't have to go through it for a very long time," one of his parents replied. "You don't have to think about it right now, it's a door you can think about when you are very old." So Mark didn't think about the door. He played and he laughed. He had fun and he learned. Mark found much joy in being in the room that was his home.

One day, an old and wise woman visited Mark. She asked him if she could sit down for a serious talk. "Do you remember asking about the door that's at the end of this room?" she inquired.

"Yes, I remember," Mark replied, while playing with a toy, "but I don't have to think about that door yet, because I won't have to go through that door for a very long time."

"Well, Mark, I have to tell you that things have changed," the wise woman revealed with a look of concern. "You will be going through that door very soon." Mark looked at the wise woman in disbelief for a moment. Then Mark began to scream.

"No, I don't want to go through that door. I want to stay right here in my room. I'm not going anywhere. No one can force me to go through that door!"

After the woman left, Mark tried not to think about the door, continuing to play as if no one had ever talked to him about doors. Several days later, the wise woman appeared again, sitting down next to Mark. She gently said, "You are going to have to go through that door very soon."

"No way," Mark replied firmly, turning his back on the wise woman. After a minute of silence, Mark declared. "I will be very good. I will eat all my vegetables and do all my homework. I will do all my chores without complaining. I'll never say mean words again...but I'm not going through that door."

A few more days passed, and the wise woman returned at bedtime for another discussion. Sitting on the side of his bed, the wise woman held Mark's hand gently while she spoke. "Very soon, it will be time for you to go through that door. It's a journey we all have to make. You are going before the others in this room. Because you are such a curious person and you like new experiences, perhaps you will find a way to turn this into an adventure."

Mark glared at the woman with angry eyes. "Why do I have to go through the door? I'm not going," he screamed. "No one can make me go, I don't like adventures." At this, Mark jumped out of bed and kicked the wall. He kicked his toys and he even kicked himself. His face turned red and then he began to scream.

On a day that followed, the wise woman approached Mark again, putting her arm around his shoulder to comfort him. "Let's talk about the door," she said quietly. When the door was mentioned during this visit, Mark became very sad.
"I don't want to go," Mark whispered as a tear ran down his cheek. "Thinking about the door makes my heart hurt." So the wise woman held him as he cried and cried.

In a few more days the wise woman returned again. But this time, before she could speak, Mark announced, "I know I have to go through the door, but I'm afraid." So, the wise woman and Mark talked for a very long time about journeys and about new experiences. They talked about changes and transitions. They talked about parents and friends. They talked about how Mark could take love with him and move through the door in peace.

When he was alone again, Mark remembered the meeting with the wise woman and allowed the meaning of the words to settle into his heart until his understanding was complete. When the day came to move through the door, Mark was ready. He found a way to understand and accept that this was the day of new beginnings, of journeys and of change.

Mark walked through the door with love in his heart, allowing it to close gently behind him as he passed through. He carried with him a bag filled with memories, love and the wisdom he had gained while living in the room and learning to go through the door.

©1994
Nancy Davis, Ph.D.

The Trees on the Mountain

Problem(s) Addressed:

In reacting to the death of a spouse, a grieving parent naturally withdraws into themself. When this happens, their children have lost not only the parent who had died, but the grieving parent as well. During this time, the grieving parent does not have the energy to guide or discipline his or her children. Because of the withdrawal of the parent, these children experience grief for the lost parent and confusion and concern at the behavior of the remaining one. When the grieving parent begins to emerge from his/her withdrawal and grief, he/she may find that the children are out of control from the lack of discipline and the anxiety of raising themselves. The children may also have symptoms of Post Traumatic Stress Disorder, particularly if the death of the parent was sudden or violent.

Appropriate for:

This story is for a woman who has lost a husband to violent death. It can be altered so that it is appropriate for men and for losses due to illness, as well.

Message:

Reach out to friends and relatives for help in rearing your children until you can heal and take on the full responsibility yourself. Ask others to help you in guiding and disciplining your children and in helping them deal with their grief and anxiety.

Symbols and Metaphors:

Trees: family members

Cutting down the tree: any violent death

Dropping leaves, withering flowers: the withdrawal that is a part of the normal grief process where the world is re-organized without the person who has died

Putting supports beside the trees: giving needed support that would not be necessary if the loss had not occurred. This help is temporary, although temporary may be a period of months or years

Environmentalists: the wisdom of the unconscious
Pulling the other trees over for protection: having friends and neighbors help with the children until the parent is ready to resume their role
Dropping flowers on the stump: the ability to look back and smile at the positive memories of the lost one without getting flashbacks or overcome with grief

Elements of the Story Which Can be Changed:
This story can be changed to reflect other types of death:

1) For the death of a male from a long-term illness: One spring day, the large tree began to have a grey growth all over his leaves. Soon the leaves began to wither, then fall. Then the life which made the tree so tall and strong slipped away. (death of male from long term illness)

2) For the violent or sudden death of woman: One summer day, as is common in the mountains, a storm began to form. Then, almost without warning, a bolt of lightning struck the smaller tree, breaking the truck so violently that it split and fell to the ground. (Of course, the tree can also be cut down by the loggers.)

If the story is for the death of a female, some of the symbolism in the story will need to be changed, such as the flowering of the remaining tree. The flowering tree could be cut down or die and the remaining tree could become an oak.

Note:
It has been my experience, as noted above, that the violent loss of a parent is devastating to children for several reasons: sudden loss means that the loss is unanticipated and, therefore, must be processed totally after the loss (rather than being processed gradually as is typical in long-term critical illnesses.) Children do not fully appreciate and experience the permanence of death until about eight years of age and may process their grief long after the loss. (Marcey, 1996) The remaining parent and children may be experiencing Post Traumatic Stress Disorder from the loss. Many people create their own flashbacks by hearing stories of how the person died and re-creating the scene in their minds. This scene becomes the flashback and is a hallmark of PTSD. In my experience, Therapeutic Stories for younger children and Eyemovement Desensitization and Reprogramming are effective way to reduce or eliminate these flashbacks so that grieving can progress normally.

The Trees on the Mountain

Once upon a time, somewhere on the side of a tall mountain, there grew many trees. There were tall and sturdy trees that had been there for many years. There were young and small trees that grew beneath the branches of the older ones, protected from the wind and storms by the trunks and leaves which provided shelter. Each spring the larger and older trees would flower or produce seeds in some way. Those seeds that fell to the ground would soon began to grow. So, not only did the mountain have trees of many varieties, there were also trees of many sizes in different stages of maturity.

In a small cluster, stood the tallest and sturdiest tree on the mountain. A tree with a trunk so strong and a bark so thick, it seemed strong enough to withstand the most violent of storms. Next to this tree grew a smaller version of the large tree, filled with blossoms that would soon turn to seeds. This tree had lived and grown alongside the larger tree for many years, and they were close companions.

One summer day, when everything seemed right with the world, a group of men came to the mountainside with one goal in mind...to cut down a tree. They wanted the tree for a contest that was being held in a nearby river. In this contest, the last man to remain upright on a log rolling in the river would win a large amount of money as a prize. Spotting the large tree, and without a moment of reflection or regret, the loggers cranked up their chain saws and quickly cut it down.

In what seemed like an instant, these men brought in a large truck with loading equipment, picked up the trunk of the tree and were gone. The tree was taken away so quickly that it seemed as if one minute he had been standing full of life and the next minute the only thing left to show the tree had lived was a ragged stump.

The flowering tree was so stunned from the loss of her close companion, that at first she couldn't respond at all. Overwhelmed with guilt because she had no way to stop the loggers from cutting down such a majestic tree, and traumatized by her inability to control the events in her world, the flowers of the tree withered and dropped to the ground. Soon many of her leaves also dried up and blew away because she was unable to take in the rain or let in the sun that was needed to keep her leaves green and alive.

Soon the younger trees began to wither and shake. They were responding not only to the loss of the huge and majestic tree, but also to the loss of the flowering tree as they had known her in the past. It was clear from viewing the stump that the larger tree was gone. The flowering tree had changed so much in reaction to the loss that she seemed also to be gone, even though her trunk was still standing and a few green leaves remained on her branches. With the loss of the larger tree, and the withering of the tree that had been flowering, the smaller and younger trees were no longer protected from harsh winds and the burning summer sun. Because they were not yet strong enough to protect themselves from the elements or grow without support in the forest, the leaves of the younger trees also began to drop. Sometimes the wind blew them so violently, that their branches beat against the trunk of the larger tree or knocked them against each other.

One day a group of environmentalists were hiking through the forest and sat down for lunch beside the large stump. Because these were people who understood and cared about life in the forest, they talked about the trees around them as they ate. Soon they noticed that the tree beside the stump seemed almost devoid of leaves, although it seemed to be alive. As they moved to observe this tree, these people noticed the smaller trees which also seemed to be struggling to grow.

As they studied the trees and looked at the stump, they understood what was happening. Realizing that it might take some time for the larger tree to recover, the environmentalists constructed a brace to support her trunk so that she could continue to stand. Then they used ropes and supports to bend nearby trees so that the younger trees could be protected from the elements. They watered the smaller trees, and constructed a brace for them as well.

"The flowering tree will recover", the environmentalists told the young trees. "She will learn from this loss and perhaps will grow in new directions. You may find that her flowers and her leaves will be slightly different as she recovers, to signify that loss has made her stronger. But she will allow the trees around her to help protect you until she is strong enough to protect you all by herself.

As the environmentalist left the forest, the younger trees responded to the new supports by standing taller and sturdier against the wind. Soon their leaves had returned and they grew taller, as they were intended to grow. The larger tree allowed the neighboring trees to give support as long as necessary until she was strong enough to provide it. Somehow in realizing that the smaller trees needed her to recover, she was able to speed up her healing and even grow a stronger trunk.

When the environmentalists next returned to the forest, they smiled at seeing the trees which had grown in new directions. Soon they were using the stump as a picnic table as they laughed and ate their lunch. Flowers soon fell from the tall tree which had found a way to bloom again. "The flowers are decorating our picnic table", one of the environmentalists said to another. Then as they looked up at the tree she seemed to smile.

The House Filled With Light

Problem(s) Addressed:

Grief being prolonged by traumas experienced on the job; rejection of children because of the grief and trauma

Appropriate for:

Adults who have lost a spouse and who have had other traumatic experiences

Message:

You can find a way to let go of all the trauma that you absorbed from your life experiences, to process your grief and to let your children be a part of your life and healing

Symbols and Metaphors:

House filled with light: a wife who loves and is loved

Pockets of darkness: trauma related to job or life experiences

The light went out: the wife died of illness

The dark pockets began to gain strength: by losing his wife, the unresolved trauma from the past began to grow and interfere with his functioning

Built walls around him: isolated himself

The walls closed off his vision: the man was unaware of the impact of other traumas on his functioning and the resolution of his grief

The other sources of light: his children

The waterfall: the power of the unconscious to let go of traumatic memories

Found a way to let the other sources of light heal his wounded heart: let his children's love help him to heal from the loss of his wife

Elements of the Story Which Can be Changed

This story can be changed so that it addresses the death of a male

Note:

Professionals who deal with trauma as a regular part of their jobs (e.g., law enforcement officers, fire and rescue workers, emergency room personnel and even therapists), often find that the love of significant people in their lives softens the impact of that exposure. If this love is suddenly lost, the combination of the grief of the loss and the trauma they experience on the job often becomes overwhelming. This story was created to address such situations.

The House Filled With Light

Once upon a time there lived a man with many gifts. The greatest of his gifts was a house filled with light that nourished and inspired him. In the beginning the light opened up his resources, helped him to believe in himself, and kept him going when the road was rough and stormy. As months and years passed, the house that was filled with light empowered him, and taught him to let in light from other sources.

When he moved in new directions and traveled far from the house, often he would return filled with pockets of darkness in his heart, in his mind and in his body. Perhaps he had pockets of darkness from a younger age; nevertheless, he picked up more and more of them as he moved through the roads that made up his life. He was protected from this darkness by the light from the house; this light was so powerful that it kept the pockets of darkness contained, perhaps to the point that the man even forgot they were there.

Then, over a period of time, the light from the house began to fade, finally going out on one dark and lonely day. The loss of the light created craters of pain and sorrow in the man's heart, in his mind, in his body and in his soul. Wounds that were deep and wide and seemingly endless. Wounds that had a voice all their own and could not be ignored.

As the man journeyed out in the world separated from the light in the house, the dark pockets within began to gain strength. They expanded and fused together, filling him with clouds of darkness that not only invaded his mind and his body, but helped to kept the wounds in his heart raw and festering. The darkness extended beyond his skin, building walls around him that kept out light from other sources that might have helped him to heal.

At first, those around the man left him alone, allowing time for his wounds to begin to mend. Then, as they tried to approach him, the walls continued to be a barrier pushing away much of what would have been healing and empowering. Although the walls were invisible, their power was experienced in a way that made those around him reluctant to intrude.

Although the man felt the darkness and the wounds, he had problems making sense of what had happened to him. The walls seemed to close off his vision, making him unaware of the source of the darkness and how it separated him from sources which could have helped. The darkness made all that he had learned while the light of the house had been bright seem useless and wasted.

One day as he searched for answers, the man happened upon a waterfall which fell into a warm and bubbling spring. He was drawn to the water, somehow sensing the healing power that it offered. First he stood beneath the waterfall, then he immersed himself in the spring. As the clean and clear water washed away the darkness from within, the walls around him began to fall and his eyes opened to a new reality. He remained in the water, allowing it to continue to wash away the darkness and further open up his eyes.

Leaving the healing waters, the man returned to the house that had given him such comfort. Although it was now dark, he noticed that the light from this house had not disappeared; it had left behind many other lights, slightly different in form.

With new eyes, the man found a way to allow the other sources of light to heal his wounded heart. When imprisoned by the dark walls, he had believed that he had been left with nothing, but the man now understood that this was not true. This understanding helped him to make the slightly different forms of light as a part of his life.

As he went on through the days and nights of his life, the man found a way to honor the house that had been filled with light by using all that he had learned when the light gave him strength and empowerment. As this happened, the man became aware that he had allowed himself to become a source of light, while learning to use any small pockets of darkness that had remained to teach and inspire him.

© 1996
Nancy Davis, Ph.D.

The Big Fear

Problem(s) Addressed:

Fear of death that causes obsessive compulsive behavior

Appropriate for:

Ages 6 - 13

Message:

You can find a way to shrink your fear and make it disappear

Symbols and Metaphors:

Being invisible: dying

Ball of fear: any intensive feeling of fear that creates inappropriate or obsessive behavior as an effort to reduce the feeling.

Throwing the ball away: using the wisdom of the unconscious to eliminate their fear

Elements of the Story That Can be Changed:

The sex of the child, the obsessive behaviors that the fear creates, what the child is afraid of (if this is changed, it should be in symbolic form so hearing the words in the story does not create more fear), the response when the child gets rid of the fear.

Note:

This story was created for a seven year old who developed a phobia about dying. His grandmother had died two-and-one-half years prior to his symptoms, and he had observed his mother cry about this loss on many occasions. The boy had also watched the nightly news where the announcers talked about a child dying from eating a hamburger made from contaminated meat in a fast-food restaurant. He became afraid of meat (especially raw hamburger), germs, touching things and even swallowing his own saliva (because he thought it might contain germs). In addition, he started washing his hands numerous times each day.

Research at the National Institute of Health has recently discovered a relationship between the strep germ and obsessive-compulsive disorders and Tourette's syndrome. Research suggests that in some children, strep can attack a part of the brain which controls obsessive-compulsive behavior. (Swedo, et. al., 1997). Children with this disorder may be eligible for research at NIH; contact: Dr. Garvey, 301-496-5323..

The child for whom this story was created had repeated bouts of strep throat which could not be treated with penicillin, because he was allergic to it. There is some research which suggests that penicillin or a penicillin derivative is necessary to kill the strep germ and keep it from attacking the brain. Treatment with therapeutic stories and EMDR decreased his symptoms, but his symptoms rebounded after a strep infection. Once this research was discovered, the parents had his tonsils removed and his strep infections stopped.

These techiques can be used in combination with medical treatment and diagnosis. Make a collection of empowering stories, such as "The Boy Who Had to Catch a Dragon," "The Hero," etc., and use "The Boy and the Tornado" from Therapeutic Stories to Heal Abused Children, adding the symptoms that the child is exhibiting. For example, for a child who is washing hands obsessively, "the tornado made him wash his hands many times a day and. . ." Have the parents play the tape nightly, letting it play several times a night, if possible. EMDR can also be used while having the child imagine the symptoms or while talking about the frightening event.

The Big Fear

Once upon a time there was a boy named Wes who loved to play, especially with his brothers. Wes enjoyed playing video games and jumping on his trampoline.

One day, Wes started to think about being invisible. He knew that other people became invisible, especially when they grew old. When Wes watched the news, the announcers sometimes told stories about children who became invisible. Wes began to think that he might become invisible, and he did not want to leave his mom and dad. As Wes thought more and more about being invisible, a big ball of fear started to grow in him. He tried not to think about it, but when he went to school, watched TV or heard his parents talking, Wes was reminded about being invisible. His fear grew and grew. Sometimes when he was asleep, Wes had nightmares about being invisible and he woke up even more afraid. The more Wes thought about being invisible, the bigger and stronger the ball of fear became. The ball of fear seemed to have a scary voice that talked to Wes.

Wes didn't like feeling afraid, so he tried to make the fear go away. Sometimes he washed his hands to make the fear go away, but the fear just got bigger. Sometimes, when the fear was talking very loudly, he didn't swallow, but the fear kept growing. Then Wes tried not to touch anything with his hands, hoping that this would make the fear go away, but it just kept getting bigger. He tried to stop eating to make his fear go away, but his stomach growled so loud that this didn't work either. It wasn't long before the ball of fear was so big, so strong and so loud that Wes was thinking about being invisible day and night.

Wes tried playing with his brothers and his friends to make his mind forget about the ball of fear; sometimes this worked and sometimes it didn't. Wes even had trouble doing his school work because the ball of fear had grown long sharp points that started to stick him.

One day Wes was watching a football game with his parents. The ball of fear with the sharp points kept talking to him, just like the announcer on television. Wes watched as the quarterback threw the football again and again. He noticed the ball going further and further in the air away from the quarterback who had thrown the ball. Then he watched as one of the football players kicked a field goal. The football went up into the crowd where one of the fans grabbed the ball and ran out of the stands before any one could take it away from him.

After the football game was over, Wes's parents changed the channel to watch a baseball game. Wes watched as the first batter hit a home run into the stands. A fan grabbed the ball and showed it to everyone sitting near to him.

Suddenly Wes had an idea. Because Wes was very smart and wanted to get rid of the ball of fear with the sharp points that kept scaring him, he had figured out a solution to his problem.

"I'm going to take a nap," Wes told his parents. They were surprised; usually Wes had to be ordered to go to bed. His parents told Wes that they would keep his brothers from bothering him. Wes shut his bedroom door and laid down on his bed. He closed his eyes and imagined what this big ball of fear with the sharp points might look like. Wes was determined to get rid of the ball of fear. He kept his imagination going for as long at it took him to picture the ball of fear in his body. When he could see the ball, Wes imagined that it got smaller and smaller and moved into his hand.

Then Wes started speaking to the ball, "I'm tired of you talking to me all the time and scaring me. I'm tired of being stuck with your sharp points. I'm tired of thinking about you day and night. I am getting rid of you for good." Then Wes saw himself break all the sharp points off the ball, throw them to the ground and step on them. After that, Wes threw the ball of fear so far away from him and with such force that when it landed on the ground, the ball broke into a million pieces and disappeared. "I'm smarter than any ball of fear," Wes said triumphantly. "And I have just proved that by throwing that ball so far away from me that it disappeared"

Then Wes got off of his bed and went back into the room where his parents were watching television. "I'm hungry," Wes told them. "Can we have hamburgers for dinner tonight?"

Wes's parents weren't sure what had happened to him; he had refused to eat hamburgers for so long they had stopped serving them. "Sure," they said, "Do you want anything else for dinner?"
"I want french fries, chocolate cake and ice cream," Wes told them. "And I want to help fix the hamburgers. I've decided that I am old enough to learn how to cook."

After going to the grocery store, Wes and his parents made hamburgers for dinner. Wes only washed his hands twice, once before preparing the food and then after patting the meat into patties. He was so hungry that he ate two hamburgers with lots of french fries. "I am so glad to be rid of that stupid ball, " Wes said to himself.

After that, when Wes thought about being invisible, it was like any other thought in his head. He would think about it, then he would think about other things. He only washed his hands when they were dirty, and swallowing was so automatic that Wes forgot he was doing it. Wes also continued to be interested in cooking and became so good at it he soon was fixing meals for his brothers all by himself.

Wes also became a good athlete in all sports that used balls. He had learned that he was smarter than any ball, and he had figured out how to control the ball so it did not control him.

©1995
Nancy Davis, Ph.D.

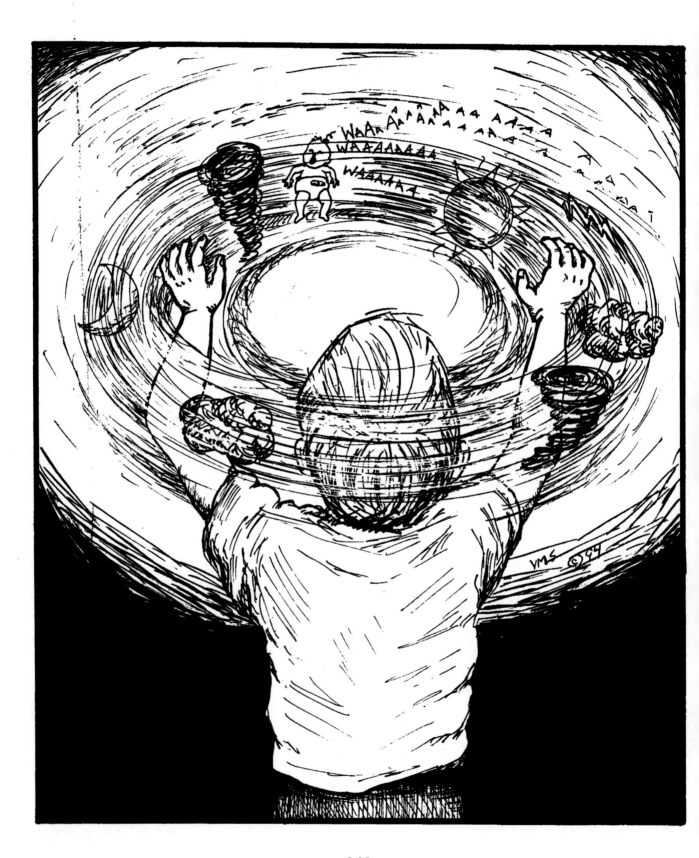

348

The Boy Who Believed

Problem(s) Addressed:
A child who believes that he is responsible for the illness of his sister and mother

Appropriate for:
Ages 5 - 9

Message:
You are not responsible for the sickness or pain of your family or of the world

Symbols and Metaphors:
Tornados, sun rising: anything that is outside of a child's control
Wished he could disappear: a child's conceptualization of wanting to be dead

Elements of the Story Which Can be Changed:
Sex of the child; the details of what the child believes; the family make-up; this story can also be adapted for a child who believes that they are responsible for other events which are clearly not within their control, such as a divorce, the death of a family member, etc.

Note:
This story was created for a five year old who felt responsible for the serious illness of his mother and sister. When the mother was pregnant with his sister, she had contracted a flu-like illness. It was later discovered that the illness was a virus that attacked the heart of both his sister and mother. His sister was born with the left side of her body very swollen because of the way that the virus interfered with normal growth in utero. The mother also had to be hospitalized shortly after the sister was born and her condition was listed as critical. His sister was also subsequently hospitalized on several occasions.

When the mother and daughter were better, the boy was brought for therapy. His guilt seemed to stem from overhearing his mother comment that she only recalled being sick once during her pregnancy, when she caught the flu from him. (The mother was not, in any way, trying to blame the illness on her son). The boy took responsibility for their illness, even though it was explained to him that it was not his fault. This story was effective in resolving this problem.

The Boy Who Believed

Once upon a time there was a boy named Bruce who believed that he was the one that made the sun come up in the morning. Bruce also thought he was the one that made the sun go down in the evening; Bruce even believed that he caused tornados. When the weather was bad or tornados destroyed things, Bruce felt very sad.

Bruce was most sad, however, because he believed that he had made his mommy and his baby sister sick. He said to himself, "I am such a bad kid cause I made them sick and only . somebody really bad would do something that awful. I'm a terrible person. I probably should run away from home and never come back because I know nobody wants to see me because of what I did." Because Bruce believed he was bad and had made his mommy and sister so sick, he was sad and his heart got sad, too.

"I'm so powerful and all I ever do is bad things," Bruce whispered to himself and he wished that he could disappear.

Bruce's baby sister, Christine, was in the hospital. Bruce loved his sister very much and he wanted to visit her. Bruce also felt guilty because he believed that he had made his sister sick and it was his fault that Christine had to be hospitalized.

When Bruce entered the hospital, he met a very special doctor named Dr. Cockrum, "Why are you here?", the doctor asked Bruce.

"I'm here to see my baby sister, " Bruce told her, "I'm a very bad person because I made her sick. It's my fault Christine is in the hospital."
Dr. Cockrum was a very wise doctor. "Bruce, do you really believe that you made your baby sister sick?"

"Yeah," said Bruce hanging his head. "I made my mom sick, too. I am very powerful, but it seems that all I do is bad things."

"If you are so powerful that you made your sister sick, then you should be able to make her well too. So, make her well," Dr. Cockrum told Bruce.

"Well, I can't do that," Bruce answered.

"You didn't make your sister and mother sick because if you were so powerful that you could make someone sick, then you would be powerful enough to make them well," the doctor told him.

"I never thought about that," Bruce said, wrinkling up his face.

"I heard that you believe that you can make the sun rise?", Dr. Cockrum asked.

"Yeah," Bruce said.

"See the sun out there?", the doctor asked. "Make the sun go the other way."

Bruce said, "I can't do that."

"If you really controlled the sun, Bruce, then you could make it go in any direction that you wanted to," the doctor told him.

"I never thought about that either," Bruce replied.

"Make a tornado in the sky right now," Dr. Cockrum requested.

"I can't really do that either," Bruce told her, beginning to feel uneasy.

"Bruce, you're not the person that makes bad things happen," Dr. Cockrum told him as she hugged him. "Bad things just sometimes happen sometimes and they are not your fault at all. In fact they are often no one's fault. You're a very special boy and I can tell you really love your mommy and your sister. You didn't make your baby sister sick or your mom sick."

"I guess you're right. I never thought about it like that," Bruce told her and began skipping off to his baby sister's hospital room. Bruce held her in his arms and said, "I'm your big brother and I love you." However, it wasn't long before baby Christine began to cry. "Wah, wah, wah."

Bruce immediately became upset. "I made her cry, I made her cry," Bruce moaned. "I bet she's going to throw up too, and that will be my fault, too."

A nurse heard Bruce talking and took Christine from his arms. "You didn't make your sister cry. All babies cry because they can't talk," the nurse told him. Then the nurse took Bruce to the nursery where there were many babies. There must have been a hundred babies, and most of them were crying.

"Bruce, did you make all of these babies cry?", the nurse asked.

"I don't know," Bruce answered, squinting his eyes like he was thinking very hard.

"If you made all these babies cry, then you can make them stop crying," the nurse told Bruce. Bruce couldn't make all the babies stop crying.

"If you really could make all these babies cry, then you would be able to make them stop," the nurse told Bruce. "Since you can't make them stop, you're not responsible for their crying, are you?"

"I never thought about it that way," Bruce told her.

"Babies cry because they don't know how to talk," the nurse said. "The only way a baby can get people to pay attention when they need food or their diaper changed or to be held is to cry. Don't you cry sometimes when you want some attention?"

"Yeah, but I don't have to do it very much," Bruce responded.

"That's cause you have a voice and you can tell people what you want. The only time you have to cry is when no one seems to understand what's going on inside you or you don't have words to explain how much you hurt. Then you can cry and those around you will understand that you need attention."

Bruce said, "Yeah, I guess that's right."

After talking to Dr. Cockrum and the nurse, Bruce began to think about things in a very different way. He realized that he hadn't made his mommy sick or his sister sick. Bruce figured out that he didn't make the sun rise or all babies cry. So Bruce stopped wanting to run away from home or thinking he was bad. Soon Bruce was happy most of the time.

As Bruce grew up he was a wise and caring person. Sometimes Bruce would think about how he had believed that he was in control of the world, and he would smile. Then Bruce realized that he could make his baby sister smile and that was a memory that made him very happy.

© 1993
Nancy Davis, Ph.D.

CHAPTER NINE

Stories to Help With Problems Relating to Parents, Siblings, Adoption, Foster Care and Divorce

Since most children grow up in some type of family, and families range from healthy and appropriate to unhealthy and dysfunctional, it is natural that many emotional problems are related to the family and how it functions. The stories in this chapter deal with a variety of problems -- abusive parents, dealing with a verbally abusive parent during visitation, enmeshed families, adoption, divorce and foster care problems. Some of the stories in this chapter are appropriate for children; others are more appropriate for adults.

The Girl With the Broken Heart

Problem(s) Addressed:

Parents who change dramatically because of problems such as alcoholism, drug abuse, accidents, job loss, etc. and a child who responds to this change by becoming numb and shutting down. This could be, if trauma is involved, the numbing stage of Post Traumatic Stress Disorder.

Appropriate for:

Ages 6 - 16

Message:

You can find appropriate ways to heal your pain, by talking to others and by coming to peace with your father's behavior; withdrawal and silence will not heal your pain

Symbols and Metaphors:

Evil spell: anything which causes a parent to change dramatically and act inappropriately; in this case it was alcoholism
Switches: the controls for emotions, thoughts and behaviors
Wise Teacher: the wisdom of the unconscious

Elements of the Story Which Can be Changed:

Sex of the main character; sex of the parent; behaviors of the parents; consequences of turning off the switches

Note:

This story was created for a 13 year old whose father, over a brief period, went from a loving and supportive parent to a violent and dysfunctional alcoholic. Although he had been drinking for some time, the alcohol had previously not been a major problem. He had previously been a very caring and successful parent and businessman.

Her mother had to separate from the father when he refused to change and his behavior threatened the safety of their children. The daughter totally "shut down" or closed off her feelings and response to the behavior of her father.

The Girl With the Broken Heart

Once upon a time there was a princess named Kim who lived in a kingdom with her parents, the king and queen. They were a very happy family, filling their lives with many activities until, one day, an evil spell came over the king and he began to change. When the king changed, the family changed as well. The laughter was gone, the fun was gone and love seemed to have moved out of the castle. The evil spell made the king act in very mean and destructive ways. He yelled at the princess and the queen. He threw things. He tore things up and he neglected all the duties that were required of a king. Although his loyal subjects talked to him and begged him to find a way to rid himself of this evil spell, the spell seemed to have a tight hold on him. The king seemed unable to find the key to help himself.

As the behavior of the king became worse, Princess Kim, who loved her father deeply, noticed that her heart was aching and her heart was breaking. She didn't like the feelings nor the thoughts connected with the broken heart. She didn't like the way the sadness in her heart made her body feel. So something deep within Princess Kim decided to find the switches that controlled her thinking and her feelings and the way her body reacted and to turn them off. It wasn't that she sat down and said to herself, "I'm going to turn off these switches." It was just that she couldn't stand the feeling of the broken heart and everything connected to it, so her mind found a way it thought would help her.

Turning off the switches did not mend her broken heart. In fact, as the evil spell got a tighter and tighter hold on the king, her heart broke more and more. Because all the switches in the body of the princess had turned off, her pain had nowhere to go. It was like an infection deep within her that she was trying to ignore, even as it got bigger and bigger. Turning off the switches hurt Princess Kim in ways she did not understand, ways even more painful than the feelings associated with a broken heart.

One night, as the Princess Kim lay sleeping, a wise teacher came to her in her dreams and spoke about all the switches that the princess had turned off. This teacher talked to her about her broken heart and other ways to handle her pain. She gently helped the princess to understand the many different ways to help herself, to heal herself and to be a friend to herself.

The next morning when Princess Kim awoke, she understood that she had learned much from her dreams during the night. She found herself acting in new and different ways, ways that allowed the pain from her heart to be released. She allowed her friends, her family and other adults to help her with this pain. As she did these things, Princess Kim came to a new understanding of how to deal with the evil spell, and the way it caused the king to behave. It wasn't long before the broken heart of the princess was mended. Her heart healed in such a way that only a tiny scar remained to remind her of her conflict with the king. She learned much from her experience which she used to deal with the king as well as with other problem people she encountered.

As Princess Kim went through life, she had many friends, found herself able to use her many talents, and never again closed her mind and her feelings to things she needed to see and understand.

©1995
Nancy Davis, Ph.D.

The Girl With the Broken Heart (Second Version)

Problem(s) Addressed:

Parents who change dramatically because of problems such as alcoholism, drug abuse, accidents, job loss, etc. and a child who responds to this change by blaming him/herself for the behavior and problems of the parent.

Appropriate for:

Any child who takes responsibility for a problem they do not own

Message:

You cannot solve a problem that is not yours to solve. You are not responsible for the dysfunction of your parents. You can find a way to get rid of your pain and deal with this parent realistically.

Symbols and Metaphors:

Evil spell: anything which causes a parent to change dramatically

Switches: the controls for emotions, thoughts and behaviors

Wise Teacher: the wisdom of the unconscious

The Key: the solution to a personal problem that must be discovered by the person owning the problem

Elements of the Story Which Can be Changed:

Sex of the main character; sex of the parent; behaviors of the parents; what the child tells him/herself when they take responsibility for the behavior of their parent's. This story could be adapted for a child whose parent has died or has a serious or terminal illness, if the child takes responsibility for the death or the parent's illness.

Note:

This story was designed for a child whose father had lost his job and became violent and abusive to both she and her mother. Children commonly blame themselves for the behavior of parents since they are self-centered and need to maintain the illusion of the parent as all-knowing and loving. Many adults continue to believe that they were responsible, as children, for events that were outside of their control. Because it is impossible to solve problems that belong to someone else, the issue of responsibility is an important one.

The Girl With the Broken Heart (Second Version)

Once upon a time there was a princess named Kim who lived in a kingdom with the king and queen. They were a very happy family, filling their lives with many activities until the day when an evil spell came over the king and he began to change. When he changed, the family changed as well. The laughter was gone, the fun was gone and love seemed to have moved out of the castle. The evil spell made the king act in very mean and destructive ways. He yelled at the princess and the queen. He threw things. He tore things up and he neglected all the duties that were required of him. Although his loyal subjects talked to him and begged him to find a way to get rid of the evil spell, the spell seemed to have a tight hold on him. The king seemed unable to find the key to help himself.

As the behavior of the king became worse, Princess Kim, who loved her father deeply, noticed that her heart was aching and her heart was breaking. She didn't like those feelings that came from her heart. She didn't like the thoughts connected with the broken heart or the way it made her body feel. Princess Kim decided that somehow she must be responsible for the evil spell that came over her father because, she reasoned, he wouldn't give the spell to himself. Because Princess Kim felt responsible for the evil spell, she also felt responsible to find the answer to get rid of the evil spell. Princess Kim searched and searched and tried to find the key, but nothing she did seemed to help.

As the evil spell got a tighter and tighter hold on the king and he became more and more abusive, the heart of the princess broke more and more. So she searched even harder for a key to help him return to the way he used to be. Although Princess Kim tried many solutions, none worked. Because Princess Kim blamed herself for the behavior of the King, the pain in her heart got bigger and bigger and hurt her in ways she did not understand.

Each night Princess Kim went to sleep with tears in her eyes. She was sad because she believed that she had caused all the problems in her family. She was also sad because she couldn't figure out the key to solving the problems. One night, as she fell into a deep and troubled sleep, a wise teacher came to her in her dreams. This teacher spoke to Kim about the evil spell, about the king, and about the key. "Your father has locked himself in a prison of his own creation," she said, "you cannot find the key to open the doors of his prison. Your father must find the key to free himself." Then the teacher spoke to Princess Kim of many other things, of love and responsibility, of being a parent and being a child, of healing a heart and being a friend to herself.

The next morning, when the princess awoke, she understood that she had learned much during her dreams. It seemed as if a giant weight had been lifted off her shoulders. She found herself behaving in new and different ways. Princess Kim stopped searching for the key to solve her father's problems, although she still loved him and hoped he would discover the key for himself. As she did this, the pain in her heart seemed to lessen. Princess Kim also allowed her friends and family to help her with this pain. Soon she came to a new understanding of how to deal with the king. And it wasn't long before the broken heart of the princess was mended.

As she grew and traveled through life, Princess Kim met other people with evil spells. Because she had learned much by dealing with her father, she never again blamed herself for problems that she did not create. She had learned that it is important to focus only on problems that were hers to solve. When Princess Kim became an adult, she wrote books on problem solving and conflict management as her way of helping others to deal with the problems in their lives which could be solved.

©1995
Nancy Davis, Ph.D.

The Princess and The Warriors

Problem(s) Addressed:

A child who is afraid of the inappropriate anger of a parent. (This is not an appropriate story for a child who has a parent who is violent or whose anger is abusive)

Appropriate for:

Ages 6 - 12

Message:

Free floating anger, or anger that is not directed at you, will not hurt you. You have a right to tell your parent(s) how their anger is affecting you.

Symbols and Metaphors:

Castle surrounded by a fort: the home of the child
Warriors: the angry parent
Knocking on the walls: the verbal expression of anger

Elements of the Story Which Can be Changed:

The sex of the child; the behavior of the warriors; the sex of the warriors. Do not change the story so that the warriors do what the child tells them to do, because a therapeutic story should not promise behavior that is out of a child's control.

Note:

This story was written for a six year old whose father has become a loud and aggressive alcoholic. The mother separated from the father, but he would often come to their house and pound on the doors. He screamed and threw things, but was generally harmless. This girl had become so afraid of his outbursts that this fear was spilling over into all of her behavior. The cleaning of the room was added because the girl was very messy. This story not only helped

365

to alleviate her fear, so that she expressed her feelings to her father, but her mother reported that she began to clean her room, as well.

368

The Princess and the Warriors

Once upon a time a princess named Kerry lived in a castle surrounded by a fort. Most of the time the castle was very peaceful except when the warriors from another village tried to attack the walls. These warriors would run at the walls, they would hit the walls and they would shoot arrows at the walls. When this happened, the quiet castle would turn into a very angry and scary place to be. Princess Kerry would hide under her bed to escape the anger of the warriors. Sometimes when she tried to hide under her bed, there were so many of her toys and clothes there that she couldn't get under it. Then she tried to hide in her closet but her closet was so messy, she couldn't hide there either. Rather than cleaning up her room, she told herself, "My mom is making me more afraid because she should have cleaned up my mess so I would have a place to hide."

Since the warriors kept coming and knocking on the wall and scaring Princess Kerry, she found a blanket to crawl under, she covered her head up and cried herself to sleep.

The warriors attacked the walls of the castle more and more, so Kerry became increasingly afraid. She began hiding much of the time. One day she realized she had been in the closet all day and hadn't played with anyone. "I'm tired of being scared. I'm tired of hiding. I'm tired of getting into closets and getting under covers and trying to get under beds when there is so much stuff I can't get under them. I'm not running away anymore," she told herself firmly. So, the next time the warriors came to attack the castle, Kerry went to the window and she cried, "Stop it."

The warriors were so surprised to hear the princess yelling loudly that they did stop for a minute. Then they resumed hitting the castle walls and shooting their arrows. At that, Kerry began to realize that the warriors really were pretty harmless except for all the noise and all the threats they made. Although the warriors made lots of noise and shot their arrows, they never seemed to hit anything or to damage the castle. She realized that the warriors were just making noise to scare the members of the castle. So Kerry gave up being afraid. She watched the way they attacked the castle and shook her head, commenting to herself how silly they looked. As she stopped being afraid, she gave up trying to hide and she no longer put the covers over her head. Sometimes she'd get angry at the warriors and she'd yell at them, "Why are you acting so crazy and attacking my castle? Why don't you go home and find something else to do?" This made her feel better, but the warriors didn't listen to her very often.

Princess Kerry changed so much that she realized it was her responsibility to clean up her closet and under her bed. When she cleaned her room it surprised her mom, the queen, so much that she took Princess Kerry out to dinner as a reward.

As Princess Kerry grew, she carried with her all she had learned. She was no longer afraid of warriors who tried to intimidate her by making a lot of noise and threats. She had learned that there can be a big difference between noise and danger.

©1995
Nancy Davis, Ph.D.

The Parrot and the Eagle

Problem(s) Addressed:

Children who take on the belief systems of inappropriate or abusive parents, using these beliefs to devalue themselves

Appropriate for:

Ages 6 - 13 (Also appropriate for adults abused as children)

Message:

Find value in yourself and give up the mimicking of the abusive words of your parents

Symbols and Metaphors:

Parrot: child who mimics the words of their abusive parent(s)
Eagle: wisdom of the unconscious or any helping person who challenges unhealthy beliefs

Elements of the Story Which Can be Changed:

Sex of the parrot; the person who is copied; the words that are copied; sex of the eagle

Note:

This story was written for a 12 year old. His mother had been physically abusive and his parents were in the middle of a nasty separation. Both parents blamed this boy for many of the family problems. He had a very high IQ, and yet seemed stuck in mimicking the disturbed attitudes and beliefs of his parents. Therapy was focused on helping him to see the world, his parents and himself realistically.

The Parrot and the Eagle

Once upon a time there was a parrot that lived with a family with a mother, father and three boys. This parrot had learned how to repeat everything that the mother or the father would say. When the family had visitors the parrot would talk and the visitors would comment on how smart the parrot seemed to be. Although it appeared that the parrot was talking, he was only copying the words that he heard from the parents as they talked. If the parents commented on how good they were, the parrot would say the same thing. If these adults said, "The parrot is bad", the parrot would say, "The parrot is bad."

Often the parents called the parrot and each other nasty or mean names and would sometimes hit each other or the parrot while yelling. Then they laughed as they heard the parrot repeat mean words about himself, like "I am ugly," "I am stupid" or "I hate myself."

People outside the family came to see the parrot that talked. When they tried to get the parrot to repeat what they were saying, the parrot remained silent. He was a loyal parrot so he only repeated what the mother and father in the family would say. When the parrot repeated the words of the parents, he spoke very clearly and precisely. Visitors would say in amazement, "Wow, this parrot is very intelligent."

One day the parrot got out of the house. It wasn't that the parrot intended to fly away, but someone left a window open and the parrot instinctively flew through the opening. He could not remember ever having been outside and the sun shining from a bright blue sky was very appealing. So the parrot flew up and he flew down, enjoying the freedom of flying wherever he wanted to go. When he got tired, the parrot found a tree and landed on a limb. An eagle had also landed in the tree. Soon the parrot looked at the eagle and said, "I'm bad, I'm worthless, I'm no good."

At that, the eagle looked at the parrot thinking he was very strange; he had never heard a parrot talk in this way before. The parrot continued to talk saying, "I'm responsible for anything bad that happens in the family, I'm a terrible, evil bird."

The eagle listened as the parrot continued to talk. Because the eagle was wise, he began to understand what had happened to the parrot. So the eagle began to question the parrot. "I'm an eagle," he said, "do you know what kind of bird you are?"

"I'm an eagle," replied the parrot.
"No you are not an eagle," the big bird replied. "You are a parrot."
"You are a parrot," the parrot responded.

"You are a parrot," the eagle repeated. "That means that you repeat everything you hear. You are like a tape recorder that repeats everything without understanding. When you are a parrot, nothing that you say comes from inside you. You are just mimicking everything you have heard because that's what a parrot does."

The parrot got a very strange feeling as it listened to the words of the eagle. He had not realized he was repeating everything he heard. He had believed that he meant what he said. "I want you to look in your heart and discover what you really know, what you really feel and what you really want to say," the eagle said. "Think about these things for a while. Then I'll come back and I want to hear words that reflect what is in your heart, not words that you parrot from other people."

The parrot stayed perched on the limb and thought and thought. The words in his heart began to move into his head and into his voice. As his words became clearer and clearer, the words that he had mimicked seemed to be erased. Soon the eagle reappeared. "Let's hear what you really think."

"I'm a very special bird and I don't deserve to be in a house where people hurt me and make me say things that are not true and make me mimic words that hurt my heart," the parrot stated with determination. "I have realized that mimicking the mean words of others has made me hate myself and I'm ready to be free."

"I see you're not much like a parrot anymore," the eagle remarked.
"I'm still a parrot but I'm a different kind of parrot," he answered. "From now on, I'm going to parrot the words that are in my heart rather than what other people say to me."
"That's great," the eagle responded.

After their talk, the eagle and the parrot flew together. They were a strange pair but they became the best of friends. Parrots, by their nature, are good learners and the eagle continued to teach the parrot about power and freedom. People came from miles around to take pictures of the pair and to see that a parrot can copy in many ways, learn new things and depart from the hurtful ways of the past.   ©1995 Nancy Davis, Ph.D.

The Strings

Problem(s) Addressed:

Siblings who are fused inappropriately, too dependant on each other, or sibling relationships in which one older or more intelligent sibling feels responsible for the younger or developmentally delayed sibling at an inappropriate level.

Appropriate for:

Ages 6-13

Message:

You are not responsible for your sister's happiness and success; you are strong and can find ways to be happy and secure without being fused to your sister

Symbols and Metaphors:

Strings: fusion occurring between two people so that they have no sense of where one ends and the other begins

Elements of the Story That Can be Changed:

The name and sex of the child; family relationships; the move; what the dependant child says when the independent child wants to break away

Note:

This story was written for sisters, ages 7 and 9. Their foreign-born mother had physically abused them while their military father was out of the country. The mother lost custody of the children because of the abuse and the father moved the girls a great distance from her. The mother had fused with the children and with other relatives in the family. The older sister, who was very intelligent and much better adjusted than the younger one, took responsibility for her sister. The younger sister stuck to the older one like Velcro. She interfered with her friendships, she entered her classroom and interrupted it to hug her and she held on to her sister for her every need. This story helped the older sister feel powerful enough to detach from the younger sister in many ways, giving the more dependant child a chance to find her own personal power.

The Strings

Once upon a time there was a family where everyone was tied together with strings. The mom was tied to the daughter and the daughter was tied to her sister. The sister was tied to her aunt and the aunt was tied to the mom. Being tied together was a very big problem because when one member of the family did anything, the strings of the other family members were pulled. Because all the family members were tied together, each felt the need to do the same things and to be tied together in order to be happy.

Now it is unclear where or how this family became tied together. Perhaps it happened a little at a time, so no one noticed it was happening. After the strings were in place, however, it didn't matter how the family had learned to be connected in that way. Everyone just seemed to try to melt together as if they were one.

As things would have it, two of the family members named Molly and Sue had to move far away from the others. To leave, the strings that connected the two sisters to other family members had to be untied. Because of their belief that all family members needed to remain tied together to be happy, there was much crying and moaning by the other members as the strings were disconnected.

Molly and Sue kept the strings which connected them as they moved to the new place. It was as if they were Siamese twins; what one did the other one wanted to do. Eventually Molly grew tired of being tied to her sister, Sue. "I am untying all these strings," she announced one day.

Sue loudly protested, "No, no, you can't do that. If you untie the strings, I'll get sick, I'll die, I'll be unhappy. If you untie the strings, something terrible will happen and the earth might open up and swallow me."

"No, it won't," Molly replied, feeling very determined to disconnect, "When we untie the strings then we will both be able to do what we need to do in order to learn and be happy.

When we are free of these strings, we can each have friends and find different things to do."

Molly, who wanted to untie the strings, and Sue, who wanted to stay all tied up, had many conflicts. One day, feeling very determined, Molly used scissors to cut the strings so the two sisters were completely separated. Sue kept waiting for the earth to open up and swallow her. She kept waiting to get sick or for something terrible to happen because they weren't tied together anymore. But nothing happened. In fact, Sue noticed that her life actually got better when the strings were cut. She had many more friends who called the house and asked to speak just to her. Her teachers were happier with her and Sue discovered that she was even happier with herself.

Soon Sue realized that she did not have to have strings to be happy. One day Sue decided to fly a kite all by herself. She let the string out and the kite flew higher and higher. Then Sue smiled as she looked at the string which kept the kite from flying away—Sue understood that although strings help a kite to fly, they imprison people who are connected by them.

©1995
Nancy Davis, Ph.D.

The Endless War

Problem(s) Addressed:

Parents who develop such hatred for one another during separation and divorce that they cause serious emotional damage to their children. Also, parents for whom the hatred and punishing of each other has become more important than the emotional welfare of their children.

Appropriate for:

Parents involved in a violent, angry separation and/or divorce. This story may be one of many given to their children on audio tape; the unconscious of the parent will understand that the story is directed at them. Do not explain the story, since their conscious mind may resist the message and negate it's power.

Message:

The consequences of war in the home are far more significant than victory. Consider the cost to your children of your anger and behavior while going through a separation and divorce. No matter what concessions you receive from your spouse, if you destroy your children in the process, you lose.

Symbols and Metaphors:

Two countries at war: parents separating and/or divorcing
Peacemakers: anyone who tries to get the parents to be rational, to settle their differences and to end their war

Elements of the Story Which Can be Changed:

This story is for both sexes. The consequences of a bitter divorce could be more defined, but this story is generally understood by adults without personalization

Note:

This story was written in frustration after seeing many children used as pawns in the divorce process. For many of these parents, the war became the central focus of their lives and went on for years and years. Hearing this story helped to re-direct some of these parents toward compromise.

The Endless War

Once upon a time there was a very large country that was ruled by a communist dictator. After long years of problems in this country, the people who lived there became so angry at the behavior of the government that they overthrew it. The large country had originally been formed by conquering small ones, and the overthrow of the government allowed many small countries that had once been free and independent to become free and independent again. Most of the newly formed countries that had split seemed to find ways to govern themselves and to do things in a new way. But Tosnia was immediately in conflict because its residents were composed of two very different religious groups that had come to hate each other.

Each group believed that they were vastly superior people who were born rulers. Both groups also came to the conclusion that the country was too little to be shared; each wanted the country all to itself. The drastically different views of who would rule and inhabit Tosnia resulted in increased anger and escalating violence. Soon war broke out. As is typical of war, many residents died and the countryside was bombed, destroying everything in sight.

Peacemakers came from outside the country begging the residents to stop the fighting. They tried to convince each side, saying, "You need to settle this conflict; this country is big enough for both of you to share." But one side or the other would reject the peacemakers efforts, exclaiming, "Never! This country is ours and we are going to have it all to ourselves." So the war continued with more pain and more destruction.

Other peacemakers arrived in Tosnia and tried to settle the conflict. Then some of the peacemakers took sides, threatening to join the war on one side or the other to ensure that it quickly ended.

But hate had made the two warring factions blind and rigid. Each side declared, "This country is ours and we're going to eliminate our enemies. They no longer have a right to live in Tosnia."

383

So the bombing, the killing and the destruction continued.

Of course, there were innocent children living in this country. Children who could not avoid the hatred, the bombs and the attacks. Children whose only concerns were being safe and being loved. Children were crippled. Children were killed. Children became so fearful and upset they couldn't grow or learn properly..

As the bombing continued, with each side trying to occupy the entire country, buildings and national treasures were permanently destroyed. Factories, businesses and parks were damaged.

People in other parts of the world became increasingly concerned, resulting in visits from additional peacemakers. They sat each of the warring sides at a bargaining table. "Look at what this war is costing you," the peacemakers begged. "You're destroying everything in your country that is valuable." But the war seemed more important than the cost, for hate and rage had made them blind. "Nothing is more important than winning," each side declared. Eventually, the majority of the valuable buildings in Tosnia had been damaged by bombs, and most of the people and animals and been injured or killed—but they continued to fight.

One day, for no apparent reason that anyone could determine, the eyes of both sides were opened and they began to see in a new way. They looked at their country and recognized that most of what they loved had been destroyed. The trees were gone, the buildings were damaged, and all of the natural resources had disappeared. Many of their children were dead or handicapped. All of the children were severely traumatized by having to witness all the horror that war brings. Doctors informed them that the children had been traumatized in a way that would leave permanent scars and pain.

As the impact of the war sank deeper into their hearts, each side began to understand the price of war. The country as they had known it was gone; both sides had lost. This understanding opened their hearts to the value of negotiation and peace and as a result, they found ways to work together. As they came to understand the trauma that war had caused their children, they wished again and again that their eyes had been opened earlier.

So they built a museum in the center of the largest city with pictures of the destruction of their war to show that everyone loses in a war where fighting is more important than the cost.

©1995
Nancy Davis, Ph.D.

The Button Story

Problem(s) Addressed:

A parent who allows others to easily irritate and upset them. Often this person is a spouse.

Appropriate for:

Anyone who is easily upset by others

Message:

You are in control of your anger and the people or situations in your environment which upset you. You can change and reduce your reactivity

Symbols and Metaphors:

Buttons: the situations that result in an angry response or one of intense agitation
Tornados: moving around in high levels of anxiety, anger or agitation

Elements of the Story Which Can be Changed:

Sex of the main character; sex of the parent upset; individualize situations that cause the buttons to be pushed

Note:

This story was created for a 12 year old whose father became so hyper-agitated at almost anything that was said or done by his mother, from whom he was separated, that he could talk about nothing else. When he became upset, the whole family became upset. They would be stuck in talking about the last thing that the mother/wife had done and how awful it was. The wife, of course, delighted in upsetting him. This story was recorded on tape with instructions to the 12 year old to play it within earshot of the father.

The Button Story

Once upon a time there was a man who was covered from head to toe with buttons. Because these buttons were so visible, the people around this man could not resist constantly pushing them. When his buttons were pushed, this man turned into a swirling and very destructive tornado.

Because kids often reflect the behavior of their parents, the children of this man also became covered with buttons that were easily pushed. Then these children would become swirling tornados, just like their father. At times their home was torn apart by the swirling tornados created by pushing the buttons of this man and his children.

As time went on, the man's buttons became easier and easier to push and he swirled around more and more out of control. Many people around the man became concerned and tried to counsel him. "Why don't you stop letting everyone push your buttons?", they asked. "Stop and think before you become so upset." The man told these people that he couldn't help himself, but, of course, this was not true.

One of the man's children, a son named Matt, got tired of having tornados in his home. and decided to talk to his father. So Matt sat down with his father one night and said, "You've got to do something about your buttons. You've got to lock them in a way that they can't be pushed. You've got to put some glue around them or find some other solution so that this house isn't constantly filled with tornados. Living in this home filled with swirling tornados is making me depressed."

"I can't change", his father responded. "There's no way to keep my buttons from being pushed."

"Of course you can change," Matt responded with determination. "When I started to play Little League, I didn't know how to bat or to pitch or to catch a baseball. You can learn to get change all of your buttons that you're allowing everyone to push. You're as smart as I am, so

I'm sure that if I can figure out how to bat and pitch in my baseball games, you can learn how to keep your buttons from being pushed. You can discover the answer within yourself that you need to eliminate your buttons."

Matt's talk had an effect on his father, who began to think about the things Matt had said to him. Perhaps because his son had been the one to talk to him, the words Matt had said began to make sense. "I am going to find a way to keep everyone from pushing my buttons", he said to himself firmly. "I'm tired of becoming a tornado and being upset all the time."

Certain people around this man had been able to push his buttons more than others. So, in the beginning, he focused on changing the way he responded to one of these people. The next time this person tried to push his buttons, the buttons wouldn't push. Instead of becoming a tornado, he smiled. That made the button pusher really, really angry. When this happened, the button pusher tried even harder to push his buttons, but the man no longer allowed his buttons to be pushed. He just laughed and didn't pay any attention to the button pusher at all.

His son, Matt, was happy that his father had learned to behave in a new way. As the father stopped letting people push his buttons, the other members of the household learned to change their behavior, too. Everyone discovered how much easier it was to live in a house without tornados and buttons that were constantly being pushed.

In the days that followed, Matt's father became better and better at refusing to let anyone push his buttons. He was so successful at learning new behaviors that it wasn't long before the day arrived when no one could see his buttons at all....they had disappeared. The man had discovered that anyone can learn and change.

©1993
Nancy Davis, Ph.D.

388

The Adopted Christmas Angel

Problem(s) Addressed:

A child adopted by a loving, caring family has difficulty coming to peace with her own adoption

Appropriate for:

Ages 4 and up; this story must be told only to children adopted into healthy, loving homes

Message:

You are where life intended you to be; you have the power to understand and come to grips with your adoption. [note that Heather is empowered to choose her adoptive parents]

Symbols and Metaphors:

This story is fairly straightforward with little symbolism

Elements of the Story That Can be Changed:

Name and sex of child, along with appropriate characteristics; parent's names, religious symbols

Note:

This story was designed for a six year old friend of my son. Heather became upset about her adoption and began to talk to her teachers and family about it. When she was being punished, a frequent retort was, "My natural mother wouldn't punish me!" This story appeared to resolve the issue of adoption for her at this developmental level. Children who are adopted have different issues about being adopted at each developmental age.

Angel design by Jan Patten; Merry-Go-Round Stained Glass Center, (417) 882-7746.
Design is copyright protected and may not be used without the permission of the artist.

The Adopted Christmas Angel

Once upon a time, on Christmas Day, God looked down from Heaven and saw two people praying for a baby. Their names were Butch and Pat, and they very much wanted a little baby girl to love and to be a part of their family. God knew that Pat could not have a baby in her very own tummy, but He wanted very much to answer their Christmas prayer. So He looked around Heaven and found a beautiful little angel named Heather. Heather had brown hair and brown eyes and beautiful little white angel wings that fluttered in the breeze. She was the sweetest little angel that God knew. Calling Heather to Him, God said, "Heather, do you see those people down there on earth praying for a baby girl?"

"Yes," replied Heather.

"Do you remember how you once asked me if you could go down to earth and be someone's baby and be their little girl and be loved and be a part of a family?" God asked.

Heather replied, "Yes, I remember."

"Well," said God, "I have decided that as an answer to Butch and Pat's special Christmas prayer, I am going to send you down to earth to be their very own little girl. But because Pat cannot have a baby in her own tummy, I am going to have you grow in someone else's tummy. Then, when you are born, she will give you to Butch and Pat. Then everyone will know that they are your mommy and daddy who will raise you until you grow into an adult."

"Are you sure that Butch and Pat will raise me and love me and never leave me?" asked Heather.

"Of course," replied God. "I would only pick the most special people for my special Christmas angel. They will love you and make you a part of their family and they will never leave you. When you grow up to be an adult, you will move away from their house to have a family with your children, but Butch and Pat will always love you. I have picked them to be your parents because they are full of love and laughter and have many friends and they can teach you many wonderful things about life."

Then Heather asked, "Will they ever be mean to me? Will they ever be angry with me?"

God replied, "Well, of course they'll get angry at you. All parents get angry with their kids, because that's part of being a parent. All kids do things they're not supposed to do--that's part of being a kid. To teach their children to grow up to be the best adults they can be, parents sometimes punish their kids, too. This happens when the kids do things they're not supposed to do. Parents may send them to their rooms or take away privileges. It is the job of parents to teach their children to be responsible."

"I don't know if I'm going to like that!" said Heather.

"Well, that's part of being a kid," explained God. "It's all part of growing up and learning and becoming an adult who loves herself. Why don't you think about this for a while and let me know if you would like to go to earth and be their little girl."

"I don't have to think—I know. I've been waiting for a very long time to be placed in a family that loves me," Heather told God.

So God changed the angel Heather into something very tiny, and put her into a lady's tummy where she grew until it was time for her to be born. When she was born she was a very special baby. Then she was given to Pat and Butch to be their very own daughter, to be loved by them and raised by them until she was an adult. However, Pat and Butch never knew that Heather was an angel before she came to them. Heather kept that as her very own secret because she had joy in her heart that she and God had chosen Heather to be the answer to Butch and Pat's Christmas prayer.

©1986
Nancy Davis, Ph.D.

The Baggage Handler

Problem(s) Addressed:

"Parentified children" and those who take on the emotional and other burdens of others and do not understand why no one rewards them

Appropriate for:

All ages except the very young who may not understand the baggage handler concept.

Message:

This story shows how an individual can begin to take on the problems of others, how this pattern can develop over time, how individuals can gain a sense of fulfillment in spite of receiving little recognition, and how the only way out of the pattern is to stop doing the work of others.

Symbols and Metaphors:

Baggage: problems/emotions of others

Elements of the Story Which Can be Changed:

Sex of the child; the wise person who explains about baggage handlers

Note:

This story was originally written for a child who had become the main problem solver and "parent" in her home. However, it has broader application to anyone who constantly takes on the burden of other people's problems.

The Baggage Handler

Once upon a time there was a girl who discovered that she was very good at helping other people carry heavy things. Whenever someone in her family or one of her friends found that they were carrying too much stuff, this girl would step in and help them out. Sometimes she would help out a number of different people or she would take on really heavy luggage for someone else. When she took on too much, she would feel weighed down, making it hard for her to do the things that she wanted to do. However, she thought that she was helping other people and she enjoyed helping.

After a while, an odd thing began to happen. Everyone she knew began to feel that helping out was her job. They would get angry with her if she would not take on their heavy bags. This was confusing to the girl because she had always thought that she was doing a person a favor when she helped them out. She thought if she helped other people, they would help her when she needed someone to carry things for her. As time went on she began to feel guilty if she did not offer to help people; her feelings were all mixed up.

One day her brother called her "a baggage handler" because she was always picking up other people's stuff, just like someone in an airport who is paid to carry people's luggage. Part of her really liked being called "a baggage handler" because she did feel that she was "handling" things for other people and she ought to get credit for helping. On the other hand, she didn't like being thought of as somebody whose job it was to carry everybody else's stuff.

After a while she began to stay in her room more and more, because every time she came out she felt that she had to help somebody out. However, even in her room she could feel that people wanted her to come and help them and to carry their stuff for them. Her family began to get angry with her and to treat her a different way since they felt that she had no right to close her door and to stop doing things for people. When they would get mad at her, she would try to do even more carrying for them so that they would like her better.

One day she realized that something that she had started doing to help other people was now becoming a real problem for her. She decided that she needed to talk to somebody. She went to her favorite teacher to talk about being a baggage handler. Her teacher seemed to understand, and she explained how it was very odd that sometimes people who tried to help out other people the most, frequently got the most people angry with them. She said it had nothing to do with lack of gratitude, but it seemed to have something to do with what people expected from each other. She explained to the girl that she needed to change other people's expectations. That meant that she had to carry her own stuff and to leave other people to carry their stuff. The teacher explained to the girl that it was important to trust people, to believe that other people could handle their own things in life. She told the girl never to pick up other people's stuff again. If the girl stopped carrying things for other people then the people around her would stop expecting her to take care of their things for them.

Well, the girl became very concerned about the teacher's advice and at first it didn't seem to make any sense. Surely, everybody around her needed help or they wouldn't always be handing her things to carry. Even at school she was frequently carrying things for other people. One day she became so tired, and it became so much effort to be carrying something that someone had given her, that she decided to take the teacher's advice not to do it any more.

At first this was a very difficult decision. She kept reaching out and trying to take over and take on other people's stuff. As time when on she got better and better at not carrying other people's baggage, until finally she could see somebody carrying heavy things and simply relax. She began to realize more and more how much she was carrying of her own stuff already, and she realized how much effort and how difficult it had been for her to be helping everyone else all the time. She even realized how sometimes she had put down her own things so that she could help someone else carry theirs, and then her own baggage got lost. She found, as time went on, that the teacher was right; that people's expectations could change. They stopped expecting her to be taking on things all the time. Later, when she did sometimes decide to help, it didn't change the way people thought about her. They realized that she was helping that one special time.

She also found that people were much nicer to her, which surprised her the most. Before, everyone seemed to take her for granted and they would get mad if she did not do as they expected her to do, but now they were grateful for her help and noticed how kind and helpful she could be when she chose to be.

As time passed, the girl who used to be all bent over from carrying everyone else's things, and who seemed to be sad most of the time and angry the rest of the time, began to change dramatically. She began to stand up straight and she spent more time taking care of herself and looked better. She was happy and much more relaxed.

She was very grateful to the teacher for helping her figure out what she wanted to do. And even when she saw her teacher carrying a lot of stuff, she did not feel that she had to help her. The teacher knew that her student had learned a very important lesson.

Bobby and the Circus

Problem(s) Addressed:

A child who is a member of an extremely chaotic and dysfunctional family

Appropriate for:

Ages 5 - 10

Message:

You can find a way to clearly see what is going on in your family, remain in the family and be a functional person

Symbols and Metaphors:

Circus: the dysfunctional family

Freaks, trapeze artists, etc.: different members of the family & their roles

Elements of the Story Which Can be Changed:

Sex of the main character; members of the circus

Note:

This story was written for a six year old boy who lived in an extremely dysfunctional family. The goal of the story was to let his unconscious understand that he had choices, and did not have to grow up to be like any member of his family. The beginning of the story mimics his behavior since he acted weird, aggressive or did very strange things.

Bobby and the Circus

Once upon a time there was a boy named Bobby who lived in a circus. The circus traveled from town to town, so Bobby did not know anyone outside of his circus family. Many people make up a circus family—there are clowns, weight lifters, people that ride horses, and people that fly on the trapeze. There is a fat lady and there are side show freaks. (Freaks are the people that look really weird). There are animal trainers who are in charge of the tigers and elephants.

Bobby did not have any choice about being a part of a circus family, but he did have a choice about which type of performer he would be. At first Bobby didn't realize he had a choice, but later he figured this out. After giving it some thought, Bobby decided he would be a clown. Clowns seemed to always be able to get people to laugh. So Bobby tried being the clown. He would act really silly and not pay any attention at all to people who were talking to him. He would play tricks on people and do really crazy things. Sometimes he'd have a flower that squirted water and he would squirt water in people's eyes. Sometimes Bobby would imitate the clowns by messing things up. When the adults would try to get him to quiet down, Bobby would refuse because he thought he was acting just the way a clown should act.

Being a clown was not a happy experience for Bobby because someone was always angry with him. Soon no one in the circus would talk to Bobby. When they saw Bobby coming, they got an angry look on their face. Bobby didn't like having people angry with him all the time so he decided he would be a freak instead of a clown and have everybody look at him with interest.

To be a freak, Bobby would try to look as weird as possible and did really strange things. Everyone looked at him, but they also made fun of him. Bobby didn't like people making fun of him so he decided that he didn't want to be a freak either. "Maybe I can be the person that flies back and forth on the flying trapeze," thought Bobby. "I know they don't use a net, but it looks like fun turning somersaults in the air. That would be much more exciting than being a clown or a freak."

So Bobby watched as the trapeze artists did their flips. He watched as they flew high in the air and let go of the trapeze. Then he watched as they flipped and turned far up toward the top of the circus tent. Although they used a net when practicing, during a performance the net was removed. Bobby started thinking about flipping without a net and decided that hitting the ground would really hurt, so he decided against being a trapeze artist.

Bobby thought about what else he could be. He couldn't be the fat lady because he wasn't a lady and he wasn't fat. He couldn't be a weightlifter either because he wasn't big enough. Although an animal trainer seemed like an exciting job, taking the chance of being eaten by a lion or tiger seemed as scary as turning flips high in the air without a net.

Then Bobby realized there was another member of the circus, the Ring Master. The Ring Master knows what is happening in the circus and helps everyone do what they're supposed to do. Bobby also realized that the Ring Master is the wisest person in the circus family. So Bobby decided that is just what he wanted to be. He spent many hours watching the Ring Master as he ran the circus show.

Bobby learned more and more so that when he grew up, he knew all he needed to know about being a Ring Master. Bobby understood how to run the circus business and how to deal with special people or problems in the circus. He learned how to deal with everybody who was acting like a clown or a freak. He learned how to deal with the people who were doing somersaults without nets. Soon Bobby was the smartest person in the circus family because he knew what was happening in the circus at all times, and because he saw all the crazy things that the people in the circus family were doing and he didn't join in.

©1995
Nancy Davis, Ph.D.

The Boy Who Battled a Giant

Problem(s) Addressed:

Children who must interact with adults who are emotionally abusive or use cruel words that degrade or insult

Appropriate for:

Elementary school children

Message:

You can find a way to disregard and disbelieve the words of those who degrade and insult you without letting them become a part of your self concept

Symbols and Metaphors:

Giant: any adult who is verbally abusive

Battle: the interaction of the abusive adult with the child

Invisible shield: a belief system that protects and disbelieves the abusive words of the adult; a psychological barrier constructed by the unconscious

Elements of the Story Which Can be Changed:

The sex of the child; the words of the abusive adult; the child can practice keeping the words from piercing his heart

Note:

This story was created for a forth-grade boy who had court ordered visitation with an emotionally abusive parent. Repeatedly listening to this story and others allowed the boy to change the way he dealt with his father during the visits, and resulted in a change of behavior by the father.

The Boy Who Battled a Giant

Once upon a time there lived a boy named Roger who was constantly required to battle a giant. As anyone might guess, the battle was not fair because the giant was bigger and older and more educated than Roger. A boy battling a giant is similar to a Little League team playing a baseball game with a professional team like the Mets or the Braves.

The giant didn't battle with weapons, he used words to hurt and injure Roger. The words seemed to go into Roger, hurting his tummy and his heart and his mind. The words wounded in such a way that even when Roger was not battling the giant, his mind was filled with fear of what would happen the next time the giant attacked him.

The feelings that Roger felt about battling the giant were so intense that they spilled over into his whole life. When he was at school, all he could think about was having to go into battle with the giant. When he was sleeping, his fear gave him nightmares. His fear made him sad as he tried to play with his friends.

Because he was a problem solver, Roger tried to forget his fear. He'd daydream and he'd pretend. He'd go someplace else in his mind trying to run from his fear. Nothing worked very well, but he did the best he could.

One day, Roger realized that he needed to find new ways to deal with his fear of the giant. His family and teacher were upset and concerned about him. Of course, he was more upset than anyone. Roger had heard about a magician who lived in his neighborhood so he went to the magician to ask for his help. He told the magician about the battle with the giant. He told him how even thinking about the battle was making him so afraid that he couldn't do his school work.

After listening and thinking, the magician told Roger, "I have a special way for you to deal with this giant. I will put a special shield around you, an invisible shield that will make the words and yelling of the giant bounce off of you. When the words and yelling bounce away instead of going into your heart and mind, you won't feel sad and you won't feel as afraid."

"Will the giant be able to see the shield?" Roger asked.

"No way! No way," said the magician. "He will not see it, but he will figure out that you have found a shield from his hurtful words and yelling. This may make him very angry, but the angry words will bounce off the shield, and away from you."

"This is cool!" Roger exclaimed.

"In order for the shield to work," the magician added, "all the words that pierced your heart in the battles with the giant need to come out of you. Think really hard of each thing that the giant said to hurt you. Then imagine these words moving away from you and back to the giant. When this happens the sadness and the pain and the anger will return to the giant, too."

So Roger thought of all the words that had injured his heart and imagined them returning to the giant. Then he imagined all the pain and anger coming out of him that had been caused by the words. When he closed his eyes, a big red ball with sharp points moved out of his heart and back to the giant.

Then the magician asked Roger to imagine all the nice and kind words that anyone had ever said to him. He told Roger to imagine these words going into his heart to replace what he had returned to the giant. After doing this, Roger noticed how these positive and kind words helped his heart to smile.

The next time Roger had to battle the giant, he made sure his invisible shield was in place. The giant tried screaming and yelling and using words as weapons but they bounced right off the invisible shield surrounding Roger. Roger was delighted that the words of the giant no longer pierced his heart. They didn't bother his ears or his eyes and they didn't bother his mind or his tummy. Just as the magician had predicted, the giant realized that something about Roger was different. The giant yelled louder and said things that were even more cruel. But the shield continued to protect Roger in the battle of words with the giant.

Because the mean words of the giant bounced off the shield, Roger found that he could sleep and do his school work. When he went home, he found that the giant didn't bother his sleep anymore and didn't bother his school work. When he was with his friends, Roger was no longer bothered by fear and sadness.

Each time Roger returned to battle, he made sure that he used his invisible shield to protect him. He realized that refusing to let mean and cruel words pierce his heart was a powerful way to protect himself. And because he learned from his battles with the giant, Roger made sure that no one ever needed a shield to protect themselves from his words.
©1995

The Shadow

Problem(s) Addressed:
Children whose relationship involves one child being in control and demanding obedience of the other in exchange for their continued friendship

Appropriate for:
Ages 5 - 12

Message:
Good friendships involve equal partners and do not equate to submission and control; it is important not to be blackmailed into obedience in exchange for a relationship

Symbols and Metaphors:
A shadow: the obedient child in a friendship with unequal power

Elements of the Story Which Can be Changed:
The interaction between the two friends; the sex of one or both friends

Note:
This story was created for two foster children, ages 9 and 7. Their foster mother complained that the older child controlled the younger one, keeping them both from developing appropriately. The relationship between the two children was loving, but inappropriate. The foster mother indicated that hearing this story several times enabled the younger child to speak up and change their relationship to a more healthy one.

408

The Shadow

Once upon a time there was a boy named Trevor and a girl named Sally. They were like brother and sister and liked each other very much. Because Trevor was older and bigger than Sally, he usually took the lead in everything they did. One day, Trevor said to Sally, "If you want to be like a sister to me, you'll have to be my shadow." Sally was more quiet than Trevor and she liked learning from him, so she said, "Okay."

Being a shadow meant that when Trevor ran really fast, Sally ran really fast. When Trevor went to sleep, Sally went to sleep. When Trevor gave his opinion, Sally had the same opinion. Sally even began to talk like Trevor.

Being a shadow was helpful to Sally in the beginning, because Trevor taught her many things. A problem arose, however, when Sally was invited to a birthday party. Since the party was only for girls, Trevor didn't get an invitation. Trevor told Sally, "You can't go because you're my shadow."

"But I want to go," Sally begged.
"But you can't go because you are my shadow, and if I am not at the party, you can't be my shadow," Trevor responded like he was the boss.

Sally tried to decide what to do, but she felt very confused. When her friend called her to find out if she was coming to her party, Sally said sadly, "I can't come to your party because I'm Trevor's shadow."

"What are you talking about?" demanded her friend.
"I'm Trevor's shadow and I have to do whatever he does," Sally repeated.

"You're not Trevor's shadow. You are your own person. You're not a shadow of anyone," her friend declared.
"But I really like Trevor," Sally replied in confusion.

"You can like Trevor a lot without being his shadow all the time. You can be his friend. And you can come to my birthday party without Trevor," her friend tried to convince her.

"Are you sure? Doesn't that mean I don't like Trevor?" asked Sally.

"You can still like someone, even if they become angry with you for doing something that they didn't want you to do. It's very important that you learn to be a friend both to Trevor and to yourself. That means you may do things that displease him but are right for you," her friend told her. "Trevor may tell you that going to my party without him means that you do not like him, but you can figure out that he doesn't really believe that. He just wants to control you."

Sally thought about this, and it began to make sense to her. She went to the birthday party without Trevor and while she was gone, Trevor found other things to do with some boys from his neighborhood.

Sally had lots of fun at the party. As soon as she returned, Trevor demanded, "You have got to follow me, let's run around the house."

Sally laid down on the couch. "I'm tired, I was running at the party," she said.

"But you're my shadow, you have to do what I do or I won't like you," Trevor told her like he was in charge.

"I'm not your shadow, I'm your friend," Sally said firmly as she sat up to face Trevor. "Being somebody's friend means you can learn from them but it doesn't mean you have to do everything they do, or everything they want you to do. If you don't like me just because I refuse to be your shadow, then you really didn't like me anyway. If you liked me just because I was copying you, you were just liking yourself."

Trevor didn't know what to say, so he sat quietly for a while. "How about being my shadow?" Sally asked him.

"Okay," Trevor replied, jumping up to be Sally's shadow. So Sally sat down and Trevor sat down; then Sally ran and Trevor ran. Trevor wasn't used to being anyone's shadow, so he started telling Sally how to run. "Now listen here, shadows aren't supposed to talk," Sally said frowning.

"I don't like being a shadow either," Trevor muttered, sitting down, "This is no fun at all."

So Sally and Trevor said down and had a talk. They decided that being like a brother and sister meant that they could be good friends and they both wanted to be friends, not shadows. After that, Sally sometimes did what Trevor was doing and Trevor sometimes did what Sally was doing. At other times, they did very different things. Sometimes Trevor would forget and demand that Sally be a shadow. Sally would let Trevor know, very politely, "I am doing what I want to do."

Soon both Trevor and Sally realized that being friends and being close like a sister and brother often means you just be yourself. Being yourself means that there are times that you do what you want to do and there are other times that you can do what other people want you to do. When this happens, you can grow up liking your friends and liking yourself too.

©1995
Nancy Davis, Ph.D.

The Ambulance Story

Problem(s) Addressed:
Children in foster care who go from home to home; lack of assertiveness in expressing needs and feelings; believing that the one is powerless to change the direction of one's life.

Appropriate for:
Children 6-12.

Message:
You may have to be in many homes before you find the home that is right for you; you have some say in your own destiny

Symbols and Metaphors:
The fire truck: the wisdom of the unconscious
Different jobs: the numerous foster homes and placements where the child resides
Reacting to buyers and abusive people: finding ways to take control of one's life

Elements of the Story That Can be Changed:
Sex of ambulance; the behavior of buyers

Note:
Many children go from foster home to foster home with the belief that the world has total control over them. Although many things are not in the control of a child, it is important that they speak up to learn which problems and issues they can influence.

413

414

The Ambulance Story

Once upon a time there was an ambulance that had a hard time finding a permanent place to work. He worked at a fire station with another ambulance for a short time. However, the fire station did not receive enough calls for two ambulances, so he had to leave. Then the ambulance worked at a hospital, but the hospital started using the ambulance from the fire station, so he was out of a job again. Then the ambulance tried working at a nursing home, but the nursing home soon decided that there was not enough work for the ambulance to stay there. So the ambulance had problems finding someplace where he was both useful and needed.

The ambulance was not having problems because there was something wrong with him; he was a very strong ambulance. He had a well-built engine and a siren that was so loud that cars always heard it and stopped when he roared down the street. He had flashing red and blue lights that everyone could see for miles. He had a place in the back to put people who were hurt and he had seats and medicine for the paramedics to use. His tires were in great shape and the body of the ambulance was shiny and perfectly painted. He had just one small problem—sometimes at night, the ambulance forgot to turn on his lights so he had problems seeing where he was driving. However, when someone reminded him, he would turn them on.

The ambulance wanted very much to be useful, so when he couldn't find a place to work and to stay, he became very upset. Because he did not like being upset, the ambulance decided not to think about having no place to go. "I'll just pretend I don't care," said the ambulance. And that's what he did; he pretended he didn't care.

When people asked him, "Where are you going to work?" the ambulance replied, "I don't know and I don't care," or he said, "I don't want to talk about it." Sometimes he changed the subject. But inside, in the very deepest part of his heart, he cared a lot because he was such an excellent ambulance and he really wanted to work.

One day a visitor convinced the ambulance to put a "For Sale" sign on his hood. "Perhaps someone will buy you and give you the job you want," the visitor suggested. So the ambulance decided to give it a try.

The ambulance didn't know what to do when people came to look at him. One time a man stopped by and kicked the ambulance's tires and said really mean words. The ambulance didn't like him at all, but he didn't think he should say anything. He told himself that it would be so much better if he just kept quiet. Another day a woman stopped to look at him. She seemed very nice, but again the ambulance didn't say anything because he thought he should keep quiet. Lots and lots of people who were looking to buy an ambulance came by. Even though the ambulance really wanted to work, he remained silent and tried not to think about the future.

One night snow was predicted, so the ambulance found a garage where he could spend the night. A large fire truck who was also parked there began speaking to him. At first the ambulance remained very quiet until the fire engine called out, "Hey, little ambulance,"..

"Go away," the ambulance responded.

"No, ambulance, I'm not going away," said the fire engine. "Talk to me."
"I don't have anything to talk about," the ambulance said quietly,

Well the fire truck kept coaxing the ambulance to talk until the ambulance was in a conversation with the fire truck before he even realized what was happening. The ambulance began to tell the fire engine how he had no place to work and about the people who came to look at him when the "For Sale" sign sat on his hood. When the fire truck asked what he had said to the potential buyers, the ambulance said, "nothing."

"Why didn't you talk to them?" the fire engine inquired.
"I didn't know what to say," the ambulance responded. "Who cares what I think anyway?"

"You care what you think," the fire truck observed. "If you don't tell those people what you want and how you feel, you may end up somewhere that you do not want to be, with people who push you around and make you miserable."
"Hmm," said the ambulance, thoughtfully. "I thought it would be better to keep quiet."

"Well, you may not always get what you really want, if you speak up," said the fire truck, "but at least you need to tell others what it is you want. When you speak up, those around you will know how you feel so you will have some say in what happens to you."

The ambulance thought about what the fire truck had said. He thought about it and he thought about it. He had been silent for so long he wasn't sure he could change. But the fire truck kept talking to him and challenging him, until the ambulance began to believe that change was possible. In a short time, the ambulance realized that changing was a great idea.

When the snow had melted and the ambulance was once again sitting outside with a "For Sale" sign, people began to come again to look at the ambulance. When someone kicked his tires, the ambulance yelled loudly, "Stop that," and they did. Then as someone seemed interested in buying him, the ambulance began to tell this person about all of his experience. The more he spoke up, the easier it became.

One day some boys started to throw eggs at the ambulance. Instead of being quiet, he put on his siren and lights; this scared them away. Just then, a fire chief walked up to the ambulance. "I have been looking for an ambulance to work in my station," he said. "I need an ambulance that is strong and can let others know what he thinks and feels. After seeing how you handled those boys, I believe you would be perfect for the job."

So the fire chief took the ambulance to his station. Soon the ambulance was feeling very useful. It was exciting to go on runs with his siren blasting and his lights flashing. When the ambulance helped injured people get to the hospital, he was happy and proud. As the ambulance did his job, he also said what he needed to say and he talked when it was important for him to speak up. The firemen and paramedics were good to the ambulance and spent much time polishing and cleaning him. It wasn't long before the ambulance began to feel very happy and content.

One night when it was quiet at the firehouse, the ambulance began to think about his past. He remembered how lonely he had been when he kept his thoughts and feelings locked inside. Then he thought about how discouraged he had been when he couldn't find a place to work and be useful. He smiled when he realized how happy he was now and how much he had changed. "I guess it sometimes happens that one must go to many different places on life's journey," the ambulance said. Just then, the loudspeaker called out that the ambulance was needed for an accident. So the ambulance turned on his lights and siren and happily sped away happy that he had learned that learning and changing is an important part of life..

©1995
Nancy Davis, Ph.D.

417

The Flower That Couldn't Grow

Problem(s) Addressed:
Overprotective parents or caretakers

Appropriate for:
Parents or an adolescent that is overprotected

Message:
Protecting a child from the problems and traumas of growing and living interferes with normal growth and the development of problem solving skills

Symbols and Metaphors:
Flower: a child

Sunlight; wind; cold: life experiences

Covering the plant: overprotection; solving the child's problems

Elements of the Story Which Can be Changed:
For a male child, the symbols might be changed to be more masculine, i.e., an oak tree

Note:
Many parents seem to overprotect their child(ren), because they cannot bear to see their child sad or in pain or because they want to keep their children tied to them in a dependent way. This story might be taped as a collection of stories for a child so that the parents hear the story without conscious knowledge that the message is directed toward them. Alternatively, they may be told the story directly, as part of therapy.

The Flower That Couldn't Grow

Once upon a time in a land not so far away there lived a man and a woman who loved flowers. They admired the flower gardens of their neighbors and the gardens they saw in magazines. Because the man and woman wanted very much to have a beautiful flower garden of their own, they purchased the finest seeds from a nursery. In a gardening magazine, the couple found a picture of a red flower that they very much wanted to have as the centerpiece of their garden. To find the seeds for this rare plant, they searched many stores. The seeds were very expensive, so the couple could only afford to purchase one of them.

"We must be very careful to not let the seed get damaged in any way," they said to each other, "because we cannot afford to buy another." So they planted this seed in a pot, keeping it in the house to protect it from the wind, the rain and the insects that might attack it if they had left it outside.

After the flower began to grow, the pets that were allowed inside the house knocked the plant over on several occasions as they wrestled and played. When this happened, the pot fell to the ground, exposing the roots; the plant seemed to be traumatized from these falls, and the growth of the plant seemed to slow.

Because the seed for this plant had been expensive and the man and woman had given the flower so much attention as it grew, when it was time to plant it outside, they were afraid to put it in their garden with the other flowers. So the flower was planted on the porch, very close to the front door. "We have to protect this plant from intense sunlight and the wind and the cold," they said to each other, so they covered it with a jar in order to protect it. "This flower must stay on the porch so that we can continue to make sure that it gets everything it needs to grow.

When the couple uncovered their plant to see if it had grown or flowered, they were continually surprised that their flower was smaller and had fewer leaves than other flower plants in their garden. "Perhaps we have not protected it enough," they said to each other and built a wall around the flower. But the flower remained small and weak.

"Maybe the flower needs direct sunlight," they said to each other, so they removed the cover. However, the cover had kept the plant from being hardened against the elements and the leaves became white and burned when placed in direct sunlight.

"I guess this plant is very weak and needs to be continually protected," they said to each other and put the bowl over the plant once again. One day the gardeners had a special friend visit, a friend who always had a beautiful garden and they decided to seek her advice. "What is wrong with our plant?" they asked. "The other flowers in our garden are blooming and strong."

The gardener studied the flower for a while, then advised her friends, "You must take off this cover and allow your flower to experience its world."

"But the last time we took off the cover, the flower got sunburned. It started to fall over and it looked like it might die," they replied.

"Because you were so protective of this flower, it has not had time to learn how to grow and develop normally. It must go through an initial period where it looks unhealthy or the leaves become white from the burning rays of the sun. " she told them. "For your flower to reach it's potential, it must learn how to survive in a world that has wind and rain and storms."

The couple was afraid to expose their prize flower to the elements of nature, but the advice of their friend made sense. So the couple placed their flower at the center of their garden. They removed the cover, fertilized it and allowed it to stand on its own.

At first, the plant seemed to be frozen, the leaves turned white and the stem bent with the wind. Soon however, the plant learned to cope with the weather, the sun and the elements. As this happened, the plant began to grow and to flower. The red flowers were brilliant in color and worthy of being the center of the garden.

In time, as the couple viewed their red flower, which was now healthy and strong, they realized that they had learned something very important about growing plants: In order to become strong a plant must be exposed to the elements because overprotecting a plant makes it weak rather than strong.

CHAPTER TEN

Stories for Adolescents and Adults

Although many of the stories in this book may be appropriate for all ages, the stories in this chapter deal specifically with issues more appropriate for adolescents and adults. To determine if stories in other chapters can be used with adults, use the information on each cover sheet or the chart in the back of the book which specifies stories that cover a variety of problem areas.

The Garden

Problem(s) Addressed:
An adult who had a childhood filled with abuse and neglect. When young, she had dreamed of marriage as a way to heal herself; she discovers that relationships are much more difficult to maintain than fairy tales imply. This story also addresses the need to control typical of those in PTSD and lack of problem solving skills.

Appropriate for:
Adults

Message:
A loving and nurturing marriage can heal the lack of love from abuse and neglect, but a relationship requires the constant care of a garden and a great deal of problem solving and determination to keep it growing and healthy.

Symbols and Metaphors:
Slum: The family where a child is abused and/or not loved or nurtured

Hunger: the need for love and recognition

Garden: Marriage, a long-term relationship of love and commitment

Water, fertilizer, weeds: problems that a marriage faces

Storms, hail: a trauma, such as death of a friend or family member, loss of a job, major illness, etc. that all marriages eventually encounter

Elements of the Story That Can be Changed:
Although this story can be changed for males, they tend not to dream of relationships as solutions to their problems (Tannen, 1991).

Note:

      This story was created for a very intelligent and successful woman who, after being married for a short time, was talking about divorce and disappointment. Because abusive parents rarely model appropriate skills at maintaining loving relationships, and because of the lack of problem-solving skills and the need to control that are characteristic of many abused children, continually growing in a good marriage can be very difficult for adults abused as children. This story was an indirect way of helping her unconscious realize that for most couples, a good marriage is very hard work and requires a great deal of commitment.

The Garden

Once upon a time in a place not so far away, a little girl lived in a slum. Now, a slum is a very tough place for a child to grow up because there is much violence and pain. Often there is little to nourish the body or the soul, so hunger can become a constant companion. To cope with growing up in a slum, the girl dreamed that she would someday have a beautiful garden. Nothing but weeds seemed to grow around the slums; almost everything was dead, broken and colorless. So the girl spent much time dreaming of her garden of the future. She dreamed of the beauty of flowers, their colors and fragrances and just how happy she would be when she could someday watch her garden grow and produce flowers.

Although the years of living in the slum seemed to go on forever, at last the little girl grew up and moved to a place where she could plant her own garden. She tilled the soil and purchased packages of seeds and plants from the garden store. After planting them, she waited impatiently for her garden to grow. No rain fell for several days following her planting; many of the seeds did not sprout, and many of the plants began to wither.

"I wonder what's happening to my garden?" she thought. One day as she viewed her garden, she noticed her neighbor watering the flowers that grew beside the house. "Oh," she commented under her breath, "I didn't realize I had to water a garden to make the seeds sprout and the flowers grow."

So the woman began to water her garden. Soon the seeds began to sprout and the plants began to grow. "At last I can sit back and enjoy my beautiful garden," the woman whispered softly to herself. In viewing her garden with expectation, she became aware that her plants were growing slowly. She also noticed that among the flowers, there was a thick crop of weeds. "I wonder what is wrong?" she asked herself. "Why isn't this garden growing the way I envisioned it?"

Because she was a problem solver, the woman returned to the garden store. The manager explained that weeds must be pulled from the garden on a regular basis. The woman also learned that fertilizer would help the plants grow more quickly and be more healthy. "Wow! There are many things about growing a garden that I had not included in my dream," the woman said as she carried the bag of fertilizer out of the store. She fertilized her flowers and pulled the weeds, and soon the plants began to grow tall and produce flowers.

The gardener often sat beside her garden, enjoying the fragrances and admiring all the colors. Once, while picking a bouquet, she noticed with alarm that there were holes in many of the leaves and flowers. "What is this?" she commented to herself. "What else can go wrong with my garden?" As she looked closely at the plants, she realized there were bugs making a meal of her garden. "How did this happen?" she wondered. "These bugs were never a part of my dream. I didn't realize insects would try to destroy my flowers."

A: the garden store, the manager explained to the woman about insects, teaching her about sprays that would rid her garden of these destructive intruders. "Gosh, it takes a lot of work to have a beautiful garden. I never realized this!" she thought as she sprayed the garden with bug spray. The woman continued to fertilize the garden, pull the weeds and water the plants when they were dry. A garden had been her dream for most of her life and she was sure that fulfilling this dream would make her happy.

One day, however, a violent thunder storm accompanied by large hail thrashed her garden. When the storm was over and she viewed the torn and bent plants, she began to cry, "My garden is being attacked by elements that I can't control. When I was a child and dreamed of the future, I always believed that once I grew up and planted a garden, it would grow and produce flowers with ease."

Initially, the woman became sad and depressed and decided a garden wasn't really worth the work required, especially when things she couldn't control could so easily destroy it. Then a power within her, perhaps the child that had always dreamed of a garden, found a voice. This child began to talk to her, encourage her and empower her until the woman realized that a garden was what she wanted more than anything else. Dreaming of the garden had pushed away the dreariness surrounding her childhood. It had motivated her to go on when going on was so difficult. The dream of a garden had brightened her on the inside when the outside was so desolate. Remembering the power of her dream, the woman again surveyed her garden. The storm had not destroyed all of the plants as she had initially believed. Only some of the branches were broken and some of the flowers damaged.

So she went to work, cutting off the broken leaves, branches and damaged flowers. She placed stakes beside the plants that needed support. She spent time tending her garden more and more, discovering that the result was well worth her effort. As summer progressed, her garden was filled with beauty, color and fragrance. The woman discovered that tending to her

428

garden and loving her garden did bring joy to her life and healed the pain of her childhood. The child who had dreamed of a garden to take her out of the slum had been right — a garden was just what she needed. The adult in her had come to realize that a child's dream may be simple, but accomplishing a dream requires work, effort and determination to not give up. As she viewed her garden with pride, the woman was sure that all the hard work required to make her dream come true was worth it.

©1995
Nancy Davis, Ph.D.

The Broken Tree

Problem(s) Addressed:

The techniques or support used to survive trauma can inhibit growth and change if kept in place over time; a parent who is supportive of his/her child during trauma but cannot allow the child to develop independence or emotional health.

Appropriate for:

Adolescents and adults; parents who fuse with traumatized children

Message:

In order to heal from trauma, one must develop a personal source of strength and give up the dependence of childhood.

Symbols and Metaphors:

A great storm: any trauma(s)
Rope: any support or help which is initially appropriate to recover from trauma but becomes growth inhibiting if left in place

Elements of the Story That Can be Changed:

This story can be adapted for parents who cannot let go of a child, but telling it as it is written will probably encounter less resistance from the unconscious. This story can be changed so a male is the main character but would be best if the tree was changed to a male form such as a pecan tree.

Note:

Many things come disguised as help when they are really inhibiting positive growth and self awareness. Dependence or support disguised as love is often the most difficult to perceive and release, especially when the intentions of those involved appear to be positive. It is important to learn to distinguish something that looks like love but is dependence.

The Broken Tree

Once upon a time there lived a woman whose house was surrounded by a well-kept garden. When anyone asked what her favorite plant was, she always named the exquisite, flowering peach tree that grew by the fence. The tree had sprouted from the seed of a peach that had been served at a family picnic. The woman had watched with wonder and great expectation as the tree emerged from the earth, and began to grow, produce leaves and gain strength.

When the tree was still quite young, a great storm, with lightening, thunder and torrential winds moved into the area, attacking the young tree. The branches broke in many places, leaves were torn from their stems and the tree's ability to grow and be strong was challenged.

One encounter with a storm would have been traumatic, but the woman lived in an area where storms were a common part of life. To help the tree survive the storms, the woman used ropes to tie the young tree to a fence for support. The storms had injured the tree in so many ways that many twists and ties of the rope were required to give it stability. The rope was very useful since it gave the little tree a way to hold itself together as a brace against the trauma of the recurring storms.

As time went on, the tree continued to grow, although many scars were hidden deep within its branches. The rope remained as a support, so much so that the tree began to feel that the rope was a part of its functioning.

Because change is a natural part of life, the woman moved to a new place. With her, she brought the peach tree which had grown to be quite tall. The woman also moved the ropes, the fence and all of the structures that bound, supported and made rigid the growth of the tree. The tree was so used to the rope that it didn't even notice or seem to care when the woman once again wound it around the trunk and branches. Although the new home had storms, none were damaging like those that the tree had experienced in the old place.

One day an old friend dropped by to visit the woman. As they talked, the visitor noticed the tree, and asked what kind it was. When the woman told her it was a flowering peach, her friend asked if it had ever bloomed. Her friend's question made the woman realize that the peach tree had never bloomed, although it had been through many springs. The tree, who had been listening, began to realize that it had not experienced the most rewarding part of growing. "Perhaps," the visitor observed, "if you remove all the rope that hampers the growth and allow the tree to be free, it will find a way to bloom and produce flowers."

The woman began to understand that she had not questioned whether the tree continued to need the ropes for support, just as she had not noticed that the tree wasn't blooming. Reaching into her memory, she remembered that the tree had needed the ropes following the storms when it was young and unstable but the storms were now a part of the past. The tree was older, and the woman realized the need for the ropes had passed long ago.

So the woman and her friend removed all ropes from the tree, giving it the freedom to discover its own source of strength against any storms it might encounter. As the woman had hoped, the tree grew stronger and stronger without the ropes to restrict its growth. Soon, flower buds sprouted from each limb, then burst into bloom. Even the tree was not surprised when it was covered with fragrant peach blossoms.

Blooming for the first time gave the tree encouragement to bloom more and more each year. One day some children tied a rope swing to the largest branch of the tree, laughing as they swung back and forth. And for the first time the tree realized that a rope can have many purposes — it can support, it can bind or it can separate.

©1995
Nancy Davis, Ph.D.

The Shelter From the Storm

Problem(s) Addressed:
Becoming a resident of a homeless shelter

Appropriate for:
Any adult who has lived in a shelter

Message:
You can find something positive to take from your journey and use this to improve your life and circumstances. As the 12-step programs often teach, some people must reach a low point before they can begin to change and let go of problem behaviors; let being in a shelter be the beginning of improvement and hope.

Symbols and Metaphors:
The story: any event which results in losing a place to live
The house: any shelter
The old woman: the wisdom of the unconscious to find something positive or to learn from any situation

Elements of the Story That Can be Changed:
The makeup of the family; the events that happen in the shelter

Note:
It is not mistakes that keep people from growing and being successful, as everyone makes mistakes. Successful people use mistakes as a chance to learn and grow. "Optimists tend to believe that defeat is just a temporary setback. Defeat is not their fault: circumstances, bad luck or other people brought it about" (Seligman, 1995). It is useful to teach people to be optimists, as Dr. Seligman has proven is possible.

The Shelter From the Storm

Once upon a time a woman and her children set off on a path in the woods to pick berries. But as fate would have it, this family ran into a lot of problems. First, there were big, mean animals in the woods. Then, when the family tried to pick the berries, they got stuck by thorns. To add to their problems, when they tried to find their way back home, they forgot which path led home. The woman and her children wandered around in the woods, finally realizing that they were lost. Just when it seemed things couldn't get worse, a storm appeared. This storm was very scary, with thunder and lightening that flashed in loud, violent explosions.

The woman and her family were sad and afraid. Whispering to herself, "I've got to find a place to take my kids out of the storm so they can be safe," the woman looked for a place of shelter. Suddenly, she spotted a special house. With her wet and hungry family standing behind her, she knocked at the door of this house. Her knock was answered by a very nice person who asked, "How can I help you?"

The woman replied, "I need to bring my children in from the storm. They're very scared, wet and hungry. Can you help me?"

To the joy of the family, the nice person asked them to come in from the storm and gave them a warm dinner and helped them dry their clothes. It was much better than being outside with those scary animals. The house seemed to offer much to the family, so they decided to stay for a little while.

After being in the house for a short time, however, the children became upset. "We want our cousins and our friends," one child cried.

"Why did we have to get lost?" another asked sadly.

"I don't like the food here," the third child whispered. The more each child cried and talked about what they didn't like about the house, the more they upset each other. Finally, even the mother became upset, and they all felt sad and lost. It was a very strange thing that they could feel lost even when they weren't.

The family became sadder and sadder. They cried and had problems sleeping. The noises in the house bothered them. Other people in the house took their things and bullied them. All in all, things were not going well for the family even though they had a house to shelter them from the storms and from mean animals.

One day the family decided to go for a walk. As they came upon a stream, they all sat on the ground and talked about how sad they felt. As they sat there, an old woman, who was both wise and kind, walked toward the family. After observing them, she asked, "Why are you so sad?"

The family replied, "We have lost our way and everything is hopeless."
The old woman looked at them silently for a while then counseled them quietly, "You are holding onto the past and that is keeping you from seeing what you need to do to be happy."

"But, we have lost everything and we are very sad," said the family.
"Sometimes you have to be lost before you can be found," the old woman said softly.

The family seemed puzzled because the meaning of her words was not yet clear. So the old woman talked to them about homes, about safety, about happiness, about the past and new directions. Then it was time for her to go. As she bid them goodbye, she gave each of the family members a small sparkling diamond. "Remember that coal must go through much pressure to become a diamond. Then a diamond must be cut and polished to bring out its brilliance and sparkle."

When the family returned to the house in the woods, others in the home noticed a change in each member. The family began to sing as they were walking. They began to try new things. Soon they were ready to travel a new path. The family set out in a different direction with new hope, new dreams and new ideas. As they remembered the wisdom of the old woman, they discovered a special strength within. And to make sure that they learned from their experience, each family member kept the diamond they had received from the old woman to remind them that sometimes you have to be lost before you can be found.

©1995
Nancy Davis, Ph.D.

The Evil Eyes

Problem(s) Addressed:

Shame and inability to trust that has been carried from an abusive childhood into adult functioning

Appropriate for:

Adults

Message:

Your abuse did not destroy the part of you that can direct your healing; you can heal, trust and eliminate the shame related to your abuse; you are not responsible for your abuse.

Symbols and Metaphors:

Evil eyes; evil energy: the abusive parents; the acts and words of the abusers
Burned: the symptoms and trauma that are a result of child abuse
Spirit: the essence of emotional health; personal power
Light: healing, truth, wisdom

Elements of the Story That Can be Changed:

The sex of the main character; the behavior of the abusers; the symptoms resulting from the abuse; the different avenues the main character has taken in an attempt to heal

Note:

This story was written for a woman who had been beaten abusively and repeatedly in childhood. She was also given a daily enema by her parents. She carried a great deal of shame from this experience. This story was told to her in trance. In addition, she was asked to visualize her shame. She saw it as a red ball with sharp points. Three sessions were spent as she shrunk this red ball using visual imagery (with her eyes closed). She reports that the shame disappeared and several years later had not reappeared.

439

The Evil Eyes

Once upon a time in a land not so far away, there lived a woman. Life was very difficult for her because she had burns throughout her body. Although she tried to numb herself to the memories of being burned, she often had nightmares in which she relived the far away place and the people with evil in their eyes. The evil energy that came out of their eyes had burned her in many ways. Because she had spent much of her life living with people who had evil in their eyes, their evil energy became very much a part of her existence. As a result, she became more and more burned. It seemed as though the burning extended into her eyes, ears and perhaps even her heart.

As she grew older, she found the power to move to a new place — a land where no one had the power to burn her with their evil eyes. Without wanting to, she brought her fear, sadness and sense of shame and responsibility for having been burned. Relationships were a problem because of her belief that anyone who met her would see that she was severely burned. She was also afraid of meeting people in this new land who would burn her again with their eyes. She had not yet come to understand that the people who burned with their eyes were an ancient power and were now lost in time.

Her pain and sadness motivated her to find ways to heal herself, so she searched in many directions. She tried salves to heal the wounds. She changed her thoughts. She began to act in different ways. All of these solutions were of help, but did not provide her with the healing and relief she sought. But she did not give up; she continued to search for solutions.

A friend came to the woman, understanding there was a way to help her, and directed her to a wise and healing woman.

The wise woman helped her understand that she had protected herself from the burning of the evil eyes by drawing her spirit deep within herself. "Your spirit is not dead or gone. It is within you waiting to unfold. It symbolizes its presence by a light. Search within yourself and locate this light. Then, find the power within yourself to allow the light to expand and grow, becoming brighter and more intense as it fills your body with light. Notice as the light touches your skin, the burns are healed. This light is the true energy of self-love and of healing."

With the healer's coaxing and soothing words, the woman located the light within herself and allowed it to radiate to all parts of her body. As the light touched her skin, her burns were indeed healed. When this happened, the woman experienced a shift, a transformation and a healing. She experienced the people with the evil eyes moving far away from her and disappearing.

"Your burns were from a different time and a different place," the healer gently told her. "The people with the evil eyes have now lost all of their power over you, so you no longer need to retreat to protect yourself."

The woman was astonished that healing was possible, but the healer was not at all surprised. "Within each of us resides a source of power that can heal, direct and empower," she revealed. "In discovering this power, you have used it to heal your burns. It is now available to use in all aspects of your life."

The woman thanked the healer and walked away. As she did so, she understood that a profound change had occurred in her very core. The shame and pain that she had carried for so many years were gone, replaced with a calmness and an inner joy. As she walked, she found herself beside a familiar lake. In the past, as she walked by the lake, she had avoided looking at her image in the water. But she felt very different on this day with no need to avoid or retreat. As she viewed her reflection, she saw someone she had not seen before. This reflection was smiling back at her in recognition of the healing she had accomplished on that day. The burns and scars were gone, replaced by what seemed to be a glow that surrounded her.

As the woman moved through the days and nights of her life, she found herself feeling, thinking and behaving in new ways. She had discovered the ability to see clearly, picking friends who were nurturing and loving, and allowing herself to trust when trust was appropriate. Smiling became a frequent part of her day because the healing had allowed the woman to become friends with herself.

The woman did not completely forget the evil ones from the ancient time. She kept them in a different place within so that her healing would continue. As the final phase of her healing, the woman found a way to make the past a positive experience by helping others who had also been burned by evil eyes.

The Evil Eyes (Second Version)

Problem(s) Addressed:

Shame and inability to trust that has been created because of rape

Appropriate for:

Adults and older adolescents

Message:

The rape did not destroy the part of you that can direct your healing; you can heal, trust and eliminate the shame related to your rape; you are not responsible for your rape

Symbols and Metaphors:

Evil eyes; evil energy: the rapist; the acts and words of the rapist
Burned: the symptoms and trauma that are a result of being raped
Spirit: the essence of emotional health; personal power
Light: healing, truth, wisdom

Elements of the Story That Can be Changed:

The sex of the main character; the behavior of the rapist; the symptoms resulting from the rape; the different avenues the main character has taken in an attempt to heal

Note:

Rape is a crime which is motivated by goals that often have little to do with sex (Groth & Burgess, (1978). Common symptoms in rape victims were first described by Dr. Ann Burgess (1974 & 1983) as rape trauma syndrome. We now recognize that these are symptoms of Post Traumatic Stress Disorder (PTSD) as is seen in rape victims. Many rape victims feel guilty about their own rape because of their relationship with the rapist or their interpretation that they should have behaved in a way that would have allowed them to get away or avoid the rape altogether.

Because guilt appears to increase the symptoms of PTSD in rape victims (McFarlane & Yehuda, 1996), it is important that a therapist deal with the guilt of the rape, through cognitive therapy or by using imagery, hypnosis, therapeutic stories, Multi-Sensory Trauma Process (MTP)or Eyemovement Desensitization and Reprogramming (EMDR).

This story was written for a woman who had been raped by a sadistic rapist. It was combined with "The Necklace" and read to the victim while she was in trance. These stories enabled her to heal to a point that enabled her to talk about her rape and try additional therapy techniques.

The Evil Eye (Second Version)

Once upon a time, in a land not so far away, there lived a woman. Life had been pleasant for this woman until she encountered the evil eyes. These eyes seemed to burn her, leaving scars that moved into the very sense of who she was. The scars from these burns caused the woman to pull away from her friends and to isolate herself. She took many showers and baths because she often felt unclean. Safety became an issue, so the woman was often afraid. But the most destructive symptom that resulted from the burns was her self-hate. On the rare occasions when she allowed herself to look in a mirror, she would tell herself, " I am awful, I am ugly, I am horrible and the burns are my fault. I feel very ashamed and guilty for becoming so burned and dirty."

As a result of her beliefs, the woman became sadder and sadder. Her pain and sadness motivated the woman to find ways to heal herself, so she searched in many directions. She tried salve to heal her wounds. She tried to change her thoughts. She began acting in different ways. All of these solutions were of some help, but did not provide her with the healing and relief she sought. But she was very determined to heal, so she did not give up, and continued to search for solutions.

In her search she found a woman who was known to be a great healer. She told the healer of her burns and her searching. The healer seemed to understand what it was she needed.

"At some time in the past, you met a man with evil eyes. His evil burned your skin, leaving you with pain and sadness. As the spirit or essence within you realized what was happening, it retreated deep within to protect itself from being damaged or hurt. By pulling this essence deep into your heart, your ability to heal, to love yourself and to have personal power has been kept alive within you. This essence has motivated you to continue to search for answers, for you understood that this power was still within you, but you didn't know quite how to reach it or how to heal," stated the healer.

445

"I don't feel this essence within", the woman replied doubting that anything positive or healthy could still remain untouched by the burns.

"Begin by closing your eyes and allowing this tiny light, this essence of who you are within your heart, to be known to you. Can you find this light?" the healer inquired.

The woman sat down and began to focus within. Soon she was able to locate the light that refused to go out. "Yes," she replied to the healer. "I have found it."

"Then allow this light to grow within. Know that your light has the power to heal your burns and dissolve your guilt and shame. This light will cleanse you and chase away the destructive thoughts that have caused you such pain and unhappiness. Allow your light to grow and expand so that it drives out of you all pain and sadness, all self hate and self-blame. As the light touches each part of you and fills you with light, notice that your burns are healing. These burns are from a different time and a different place. Allow the memory of the man with the evil eyes to fade and lose its destructive power. Allow your light, the essence of your personal power, to continue to grow and glow brightly within you until everything that was burned by the man with the evil eye has healed.

The woman experienced a sense of healing as she imagined the light growing within. She felt a shift, a transformation and a sense of freedom. She experienced herself letting go of memories and evil from another time and another place. She sat with her eyes closed until the healing seemed complete.

How can I thank you." she asked the healer.

"Your healing is all the thanks I need." the healer gently replied, "Understand that your healing will continue and you will find yourself very quickly seeing, knowing and understanding in new and different ways".

As the woman left the healer, she understood that something very profound had happened to her. She noticed the shame and the guilt that she had carried with her was gone, replaced with a new calmness and a new inner joy. And as she walked away from the healer, the woman found herself beside a lake. After her experience with the evil eyes, the woman had avoided looking at her reflection in the lake. Now she felt the freedom to look and saw herself smiling from the recognition of the healing that she had accomplished that day. The burns were gone, replaced by what seemed to be a glow that surrounded her.

As the woman went through the days and nights of her life, she began behaving, feeling and thinking in very new ways. She found herself getting close to others again, feeling good about herself and giving up destructive levels of fear and guilt. Most of all she discovered that she had become friends with herself.

The woman didn't completely forget the lesson learned from the evil eyes, because she used what she had learned to continue healing and to help others who had problems related to encounters with those who had evil in their eyes and hearts. And she taught others that although trauma is a part of life; healing and learning from trauma is possible.

The Violet in the Woods

Problem(s) Addressed:

The belief that everyone has the same needs to develop appropriately; believing that a parent or authority figure always knows what is best for a maturing or adult child

Appropriate for:

Adolescents and adults

Message:

That which produces growth in one individual may inhibit or destroy another

Symbols and Metaphors:

Violet: any person or child; a rebel

Gardener: a parent or someone who has control over another

Moving the plant: forcing a person to conform to someone's expectations of what is good or growth-producing

Elements of the Story That Can be Changed:

Sex of the gardener

Note:

A variety of this story was originally created by Karen Custer many years ago. It is also good for therapists and teachers who must learn that people are different from one another and that clients, patients and students are ultimately responsible for their own growth and development.

450

The Violet in the Woods

Once upon a time a plant grew in the shade of a huge and very old oak tree. This plant was a violet that produced bright purple flowers each spring. As the years went by, the plant grew bigger, and each year the blooms increased in number and size. The violet grew in the moist shade of the oak, away from the direct beams of the sun.

One day, an old man was walking on a path by the oak and noticed the bright purple flowers of the plant. "I'm going to dig you up," he told the violet, "and plant you in my garden where your purple flowers will be a welcome addition to my other plants."

The old man walked away and soon returned with a pail and a shovel. He dug up the violet plant, took it home with him and planted it in the bright sunlight of his garden. The violet did not respond by growing bigger and healthier, instead it soon began to shrink and the leaves turned brown. When spring came around again, the plant produced few purple flowers. The old man tried fertilizing the violet and spraying it for insects, but the violet continued to get smaller and more brown.

One day a friend came to visit the old man. In viewing his garden, the old man commented to his visitor, "I don't know what's wrong with this violet. It was so magnificent in the woods. When I dug it up, it was filled with fragrant purple flowers. I brought it from the shade of the old oak tree to my garden, which is so much better. It has sunlight and I can spray for insects and fertilize it. But no matter what I do, the plant seems to be dying. It is drying out and has stopped blooming. What do you think is wrong?"

The visitor understood that there is more to producing healthy plants than fertilizer and bug spray and sunlight. He placed his hand on the old man's shoulder. "When you moved this plant, you believed that what you could offer would improve the way it grew. But this violet doesn't belong here in your garden," the friend explained. "You have taken it out of its element. What is good for one flower is a disaster for another. If you really love this plant, you will return it to the spot beneath the old oak where you found it."

451

"I thought that the sunlight would help the plant grow and it would flourish in my garden," the old man responded.

"Your garden is filled with plants that have flourished under your care," his friend explained, "but this plant is different. Allow it to be free so it can grow to be what it is intended to be."

So the old man and his friend dug the violet up from the garden and replanted it under the old oak tree. "I wanted what was best for you," the old man whispered to the violet. "But you knew what was best for you all along." Then he and his friend walked away leaving the violet to grow and become healthy again in its own way.

The next spring, the old man returned to the oak tree to see how the violet was doing. It was once again filled with purple flowers surrounded by lush green leaves. The old man smiled as he bent to smell the blooms, realizing that even a violet can teach a lesson to an old man.

Nancy Davis, Ph.D.

The Strings (Adult Version)

Problem(s) Addressed:

Families and siblings who are fused inappropriately, too dependant on each other, or sibling relationships in which one older or more intelligent sibling feels inappropriately responsible for the younger or developmentally delayed sibling.

Appropriate for:

Adults and older adolescents

Message:

To become independent and to function as an adult is appropriate and a gift to yourself and your children. Your siblings and your parents must learn to function as an adult. This path often involves pain and struggle. Keeping an adult dependent upon you prevents that person from learning to function in an independent and emotionally healthy way.

Symbols and Metaphors:

Strings: fusion occurring between two people so that they have no sense of where one ends and the other begins

Elements of the Story That Can be Changed:

The name and sex of the main characters; family relationships; the move; what the dependant sister and family say or do when the independent sister breaks free

Note:

Parents may use guilt or emotional blackmail to keep their children from growing into emotionally healthy and independent adults. Often these are the parents who had children in order to fulfill their own needs; their need to keep their children dependent on them comes before the needs of their children to grow up and leave home. Some parents are very appropriate when dealing with young children, but have trouble adapting their behavior to the changing role required as their children grow older. Many of these parents have never grown beyond the emotional functioning of a child themselves. It is important that therapists and counselors help adults to separate appropriately from the dependency of childhood so that they can develop into emotionally healthy adults.

The Strings (Adult Version)

Once upon a time there was a family where everyone was tied together with strings. The mom was tied to the daughter and the daughter was tied to her sister. The sister was tied to her father and the father was tied to everyone. Being tied together was a very big problem because when one member of the family did something, this pulled the strings of the other family members. Because all the family members were tied together, each felt the need to do the same things and be together in order to be happy.

Now, it is unclear where or how this family became tied together. Maybe it happened a little at a time, so no one noticed. Perhaps it occurred because the parents felt that one sister was weaker than the other or because the parents were uncomfortable or unprepared to be adults with their children. After the strings were in place, however, it didn't matter how the family had learned to be connected in that way, because everyone tried to melt together as if they were one.

As nature intends, two of the family members named Molly and Sue moved out of the family home when they became adults. To leave, the two sisters had to untie the strings that connected them to other family members. Because of their belief that all family members needed to remain tied to be happy, there was much crying and moaning by the other members as the two disconnected their strings. Molly and Sue did not disconnect the strings that bound them together.

Even though Molly and Sue started families of their own and moved to different homes, they kept the strings that connected them as they moved. It was as if they were Siamese twins; what one did the other one wanted to do. Eventually, Molly grew tired of being tied to her sister, Sue. "I am untying all these strings," she announced one day.

"No, no, you can't do that," Sue protested loudly. "If you untie the strings, I'll get sick, I'll die, I'll be unhappy. If you untie the strings, something terrible will happen; the earth might open up and swallow me and it will be your fault."

"No, it won't," Molly replied, feeling very determined to disconnect, "when we untie the strings, then we will both be free to be independent and responsible. When we are free of these strings, we can begin to focus on things other than our relationship and how it affects our lives."

Molly, who wanted to untie the strings, and Sue, who wanted to stay all tied up, had many conflicts. But Molly was determined to be free, so she used scissors to cut the strings until the two sisters were completely separated. Sue kept waiting for the earth to open up and swallow her. She kept waiting to get sick or for something terrible to happen because they weren't tied together anymore. She screamed and taunted Molly, demanding that she retie the strings. Family members called Molly advising her to retie herself to Sue or terrible things would happen to Sue, and it would be her fault. Sue and the relatives tried begging, evoking guilt and using threats to Molly, but these techniques no longer controlled her. Molly had experienced the freedom of being untied from her sister and from her family. The heavy burden of being responsible for her sister's behavior and happiness had been lifted.

After they were untied, Sue did have problems in her life. Molly understood, however, that Sue would never learn responsibility or learn to function as an adult if they remained tied together. Whenever family members tried to retie the strings by telling Molly that Sue needed the strings to function, Molly refused to give in. She had her own life to live and her own responsibility to function as an adult, and Molly had acknowledged her own rights by untying the strings.

One day Molly took her children to a field to fly a kite. She helped them let the string out and the kite flew higher and higher. As Molly watched her children fly the kite, she reflected on the string which kept the kite from flying away. She smiled as she understood that disconnecting from Sue was a gift to her own children; they would not have to trip over strings and ties that did not belong in a family. Molly had learned a valuable lesson from her sister; strings help a kite to fly away but they can imprison people who are too tightly connected by them.

©1995
Nancy Davis, Ph.D.

The Necklace

Problem(s) Addressed:
The belief of a victim of rape and/or sexual abuse that the rapist has taken her power

Appropriate for:
Adolescents and adults

Message:
No one can steal your sense of personal power...it is still within you waiting to be discovered and acknowledged; you can heal from the trauma of rape or child abuse

Symbols:
Necklace placed around the neck of babies: a symbol of personal power
Diamond: a symbol of seeing yourself clearly and reflecting light out to the world
Thief: any abuser or rapist
Throwing dirt in eyes: the distortion of perception caused by the belief that the rapist has taken one's personal power; the symptoms resulting from trauma that interfere with recovery
Waterfall: any technique the unconscious can use to clear the distortions and heal

Elements of the Story Which Can be Changed:
Symptoms of the victim; her behavior as she heals; the events that occur before the trauma (the victims life may have been a series of traumas or she might have had a safe and happy childhood prior to the attack(s)). The baby may be eliminated as part of the story; it was added because the victim had stopped having menstrual periods following her attack and wanted to have children. To make this story into a male version, all the feminine symbols should be changed to male symbols.

457

Note:

This story was written for a rape victim who had been brutally attacked. Using EMDR[1] scared her and did not seem to be processing her flashbacks. This story was created because rape is one of the few crimes where the goal of the criminal is to not only totally control the victim (Petrick, Olson & Subotnik, 1994) but to steal the personal power of the victim as well. A victim must believe that it is possible for a rapist to steal their power in order for the rapist to achieve his goal. This story, as well as "The Evil Eye (Second Version)" and the following story were read to the victim as she was in a deep state of relaxation:

I read a book the other day about a woman who had many tragedies. She was very sad, very overwhelmed, very "stuck." This woman was feeling numb and shaky, with her stomach in a knot. She was having problems concentrating, feeling out of control. She was clenching her jaw, she was losing weight, and feeling like she couldn't breathe. I didn't think that she would ever be able to move out of this but, lo and behold, **when I turned to the next chapter of the book, I discovered that the woman had found a way to heal herself**. She found a way to sleep peacefully, she found a way to feel joy and love. She found a way to slow down her thinking to a normal level and to concentrate. She found a way to breathe peacefully, she found a way to relax her stomach, to feel stable, to eat appropriately and to relax her jaw. I was very happy to discover that this woman found power and resources to heal herself that she had never before acknowledged. With this power she solved her problems quickly, she found a way to feel safe. She had taken from the traumatic experience all that was appropriate to learn, all that was positive to learn and left all of the rest of it far, far behind. Know that your heart can listen, your heart can understand, and your heart can heal and is healing very, very quickly. In the coming days you will find that you are sleeping more and more peacefully and are using your dreams to heal yourself.[2]

The victim reported that she listened to the stories (on tape) as well as a tape called, "Letting Go"[3] many hours a day, with improvement in her symptoms. Then she began to have trouble sleeping again. It was discovered that she had told herself that if she had not been sleeping so soundly when the rapist entered her room, then she could have escaped. This belief not only caused her guilt, because she blamed herself for her own rape (according to Crittenden (1996), 80% of women blame themselves for being raped), but also kept her from sleeping since she was afraid she would not wake up if she was in danger. This belief and her guilt were confronted with cognitive therapy. When she intellectually began to see that she could not have

---

[1]Eyemovement Desensitization and Reprogramming. A well researched technique for resolving traumatic memories and flashbacks. For information on training call 408 647-9881.

[2]The idea for the message "reading a book" was suggested ten years ago by my mentor, Karen Custer, LCSW. It can be adapted for any type of problem where someone is stuck.

[3]Available from Dr. Davis; www.therapeutic-stories.com

she was afraid she would not wake up if she was in danger. This belief and her guilt were confronted with cognitive therapy. When she intellectually began to see that she could not have escaped from the rapist, even if she had awakened immediately, EMDR was used to eliminate the message that she was giving herself to prevent a deep sleep.

Since safety is the primary issue of PTSD, it is imperative that any victim of rape or trauma be helped to feel safe. It has been my experience that the symptoms of PTSD (aka rape trauma syndrome) rarely disappear if the victim does not feel safe. Feeling safe is especially important when the victim is at home and sleeping. Recommend a dog, burglar alarms, locks on doors (especially bedroom), curtains on all windows that can be drawn when they are alone, cellular phones and/or someone they can depend on when they are afraid.

The Necklace

Once upon a time in a land not so far away there lived many people. The people had experiences of many kinds, some happy and some sad. They had families and jobs and children of many sizes and shapes. Just as every country has traditions, these people had them too. One of their traditions was to place a gold necklace with a sparkling diamond around the neck of each female child. While the necklace was being placed on the child, someone would whisper, "No one can ever take this necklace from you; it is yours alone."

On one special day in this land a baby girl was born; her proud parents named her Sharon. In following the tradition of the land, a gold and diamond necklace was placed around Sharon's neck. Perhaps because she was a newborn and did not yet understand language, the whispered message was one that Sharon buried deep within her memory as she grew.

Sharon had a very loving family, and she grew up in a home filled with laughter and joy. Her necklace was a permanent part of each outfit that she wore, as it sparkled with brilliant rainbows of light. Because she was protected and loved, Sharon grew to be a woman who felt she could trust everyone. She believed her problems would be small and easily solved. Her life seemed to be almost like a fairy tale, where hard work was rewarded and dreams always came true.

One dark night at a time when Sharon was particularly unprepared, a thief struck without warning. He tore the diamond necklace roughly from her neck, leaving her bleeding and stunned. In order to blind Sharon so that she could not identify or follow him, the thief threw dirt in her face as he ran away.

Once the thief was far away, he reached in his pocket to retrieve the stolen necklace, but it was not there. The thief searched everywhere, but could not find the necklace. The thief was unaware of the power of the whispered message — the necklace was still sparkling around Sharon's neck.

Because of the dirt thrown by the thief, Sharon was unable to understand that she had not lost her diamond necklace. The dirt clouded her eyes, filled her ears and caused a bad taste in her mouth. The dirt bothered her so much she could not sleep or concentrate. It was difficult to read or to talk to her friends. Her laughter disappeared, replaced by a numbing depression and a withdrawal from the world. Sharon continually had flashes of the thief grabbing her necklace and these visions were much more clear than anything else she saw. Sharon no longer felt safe; her trust and joy for living was gone. The dirt changed the way she thought, the way she felt and the way she behaved to such a degree that she did not know if she could continue.

Sharon, however, retained many strengths and she did not give up. She searched for answers and she searched for healing. Many people tried to help. Some did not understand the power of dirt to change her life; others understood but were unable to come up with any techniques to wash the dirt away.

One day as Sharon was walking in a forest, she came upon a waterfall. The waterfall seemed to call to her, whispering for her to stand under the warm, tumbling spray. Sharon listened, for she wanted very much to heal. She moved toward the waterfall until she was standing directly under the warm and comforting spray. This water had special healing powers.... powers to cleanse and to heal. Perhaps the deepest part of Sharon understood this and directed her there.

As Sharon stood under the waterfall, the water began to wash away all of her numbness, all of her shame, all of her sadness and fear. It continued to move through her, washing away all that was destructive or evil that she had taken in from the world and from the thief. As the water moved through her body, down her legs and out of her feet, there seemed to be a drain near her feet. The dirty water traveled into the drain directing it far, far away.

Sharon continued to stand under the water, aware that this was a cleansing waterfall. The cleansing water seemed to move into her mind and her heart and her body, allowing Sharon to let go of the hurt and pain. As the dirt continued to wash away and flow down the drain, Sharon began to realize that she could once again see and hear. Each moment she felt more and more healed, and more and more connected to her own power. After a while, she sensed that she was lighter and the dirt was totally washed away. Sharon remained under the waterfall until she could sense that she was completely free of the dirt the thief had thrown.

As Sharon walked out of the waterfall and moved away she could feel the warmth of the sun as it dried the water from her hair, face and body. She noticed a rainbow in the sky, a rainbow of promise that she had the power to continue healing herself.

Each day Sharon realized that she was thinking and seeing in new ways. She seemed, in many ways, like the person she had been before encountering the thief, yet wiser and stronger. As she returned home, Sharon became aware that she was concentrating; she picked up a book and found herself reading with understanding and memory. Her laughter surfaced again and connected her to a renewed love of life. She re-established connections with friends and had dinner with her family, finding nourishment from the food and the conversation. That night Sharon slept a peaceful and energizing sleep, dreaming about rainbows and babies with diamonds around their necks. Upon awakening, she realized that the memory and vision of the thief had moved far, far away into the past. Upon looking into the mirror as she was dressing the next morning, Sharon noticed her diamond necklace sparkling around her neck, but this did not surprise her. Each day, the necklace shone even more brilliantly than it had when she was a child.

Sometime in the future, Sharon had her own babies. When the necklace with diamonds was placed around each of their necks, she smiled as the message was whispered to them, "No one can ever take this necklace from you; it is yours alone." Sharon was sure that her children would never forget this message because she would repeat it to them again and again as they grew older.

©1995
Nancy Davis, Ph.D.

The Girl Who Never Grew Up

Problem(s) Addressed:

Family relationships in which the parents are self-centered and find a way to inhibit the emotional development of their children. In this situation, even when the children are adults, they function as a child with their parents and have trouble becoming independent and forming emotionally healthy relationships.

Appropriate for:

Adults and older adolescents

Message:

You can see yourself realistically and free yourself of distortions given to you by parents whose needs have inhibited you from development; this will be a gift to them, even if they do not realize the value of the gift

Symbols and Metaphors:

Mirror: self-image
Peeling surface: distortions coming into conscious awareness
Peeling off the cover: understanding and letting go of family distortions that have inhibited healthy development

Elements of the Story Which Can be Changed:

Sex of the main character; family make-up; what the main character does because of the distortions of the mirror

Note:

This story was written for a woman who had searched for years to discover the source of her unhappiness. She had tried 12-step groups, therapy, reading, etc. It became clear that she had been frozen in the role that her parents had chosen for her and that she still related to her parents as a child. To function as an adult, she must talk to her parents as an adult in order to free herself of old ways of acting and feeling. This story was written to help her unconscious understand and chose the correct path for herself. Note that the story does not tell her how to confront her parents, trusting that her unconscious will chose the best way for her. Nor does the story falsely promise that her parents will change or be happy about the new way she relates to them.

The Girl Who Never Grew Up

Once upon a time there lived a couple who delighted in the antics and playfulness of each of their children. One day, as they watched their small children at play, one of them said to the other, "I don't want our children to ever grow up. I like the joyfulness of a three- or four-year-old. Children of this age are very dependent and listen when I tell them what to think and believe. I don't want life to change, because young children never want to be away from me, it scares them."

"I can't imagine a life without children," the other parent agreed. "I want our children to stay this way forever."

The parents understood that they could not stop the bodies of their children from growing, although they really wished that they could. So, they purchased special mirrors which distorted the children's perceptions. As their children looked at themselves in these mirrors, they were unable to recognize that they were growing. Because of these mirrors, as their children grew into teenagers and into adults, they reacted and interacted with their parents as if they were still young children. Even when their children grew up and moved out of the home, the parents insisted they take their mirrors with them.

Most children, as they grow, understand that it is important to separate from their parents, and to grow and become independent adults, just as nature intended them to do. Nature allows a healthy adult to continue to have relationships with their parents, but the relationships change; the parent loses the control and the authority that they had when their child was small and needed the parent for protection. The parents of these children, however, did not understand that the role of the parent is to develop independence and growth in their children, then to set them free. The needs of these parents were so overwhelming that they often disregarded the needs of their children, since their own happiness usually came first.

One of their daughters, named Judy, grew to be a teenager and an adult. She went to college and she learned. Judy had problems relating to and choosing appropriate men because

467

she still used the mirror of her youth, which reflected back the message that her parents wanted her to believe.

An uneasy feeling accompanied Judy as she moved through her life, an awareness that something was wrong and she was "stuck." Judy wanted to change, so she tried many things . . . she read books, she joined groups, she found people to try to help her. Little seemed to change for her, however, because no one understood about her mirror and she didn't understand herself. Therefore, despite her searching, Judy moved in only a limited way.

One day, as she was looking in the mirror, Judy noticed that the corners seemed to be peeling. The corners had been peeling for many years, but this was the first time she allowed herself to notice. As Judy pulled at the peeling edges, she could not recall realizing that mirrors could have covers. More and more curious, Judy pulled and pulled until all of the cover that distorted the mirror had been removed. As she looked at herself in the mirror without the cover, it reflected a true picture of herself. As she did this, Judy saw herself in a new and very clear way. At first, Judy didn't understand what had happened. However, because she was smart and had searched so long for answers, it wasn't long before she understood the message of the peeling mirror.

Freed from the distortion of the mirror, the part of Judy that had been frozen by the reflection of the mirror, began to move rapidly toward her true age. Her dreams helped her to grow, her unconscious and intuitive side helped her to grow, and the part of Judy which was a source of personal power began to flourish.

One day Judy awoke from a particularly empowering dream with the realization that to complete her growth she must talk with her parents. She thought about the best way to do this . . . by letter, by phone, or in person. The adult who had grown to be assertive chose the path that, for her, would be the most healing and empowering. Judy began by formulating, in her mind, what needed to be said. She was sure that she must make it clear to her parents that she now functioned as an adult and she must meet them in a new way. Free of the distortions that had caused her to keep silent and to interact with her parents as if she were still a child, Judy confronted her parents.

Because it is often difficult to shift from one viewpoint to another, her parents were not happy with the grown-up Judy. Trying to shift Judy back into her old role, they tried guilt, threats, and power. Judy, however, had grown and changed and nothing would move her backwards into the role of a dependent child again. Determined to move through the few steps remaining to grow herself up, Judy said all the words that needed to be said to her parents, greeting them in a new way. Although her parents did not realize it at the time, Judy's growth was a gift to them.

After meeting her parents in a new way, Judy found that when she viewed herself in the mirror, the reflected image was a realistic picture of who she was. She was thinking and feeling as an adult, she was relating to men and women as an adult and she was especially functioning as an adult in the relationship with her parents. From that time on, whenever Judy looked into a mirror, she smiled, because she was confident that she was seeing herself through her own eyes and not as a distortion of someone else's needs.

The Woman Who Wasn't Nice to Herself

Problem(s) Addressed:
Self destructive behavior

Appropriate for:
Adolescents and adults

Message:
Loving yourself means treating yourself in ways that reflect that love

Symbols and Metaphors:
This story is straightforward with little symbolism

Elements of the Story That Can be Changed:
Sex of main character; the self destructive behaviors (i.e., drugs); health problems

Note:
This story was created at the request of a seven-year-old patient who was upset that her grandmother was in the hospital having had by-pass surgery as the result of a heart attack. The child was in tears because her grandmother smoked, and did not eat foods that would keep her healthy. She requested a story to help her grandmother try to avoid another heart attack.

The Woman Who Wasn't Nice to Herself

Once upon a time there was a very kind and caring woman who was nice to everyone she met. She was nice to her children, her husband, her friends and her co-workers. Because she was so friendly and agreeable, almost everyone really liked her.

However, this woman who was so nice to everyone else, was not nice to herself. She did many things which were not nice to her body: she smoked a lot of cigarettes, didn't exercise as she should, and ate all the wrong foods. Because neglect can make a heart sad, her heart became sad. "You are nice to everybody but me," her heart cried out. But she ignored her own heart, because she thought everyone else was more important than she was.

So her heart continued to cry and cry. The tears got so hard they stopped up her heart. When this happened, the woman felt sharp pains in her heart. "You haven't listened to me as I cried," her heart said. "So, I'm giving you a pain that's hard to ignore." Her heart was right about that. The pain was so intense, that the woman went to the hospital. The doctors took pictures of her heart and found that the tears had gotten so hard that they had stopped up the arteries leading to her heart.

"We've got to fix your heart," the doctors told her. "We are going to take you to surgery to repair the damage." So, that is what they did.

As she recovered from her surgery, the doctors came to talk to the woman. "We have heard that you are nice to everyone. We have discovered, however, that you are not nice to yourself. From now on, you must be nice to yourself. You must eat foods that are good for your heart, and exercise. You must never smoke again. If you can love yourself and be nice to yourself in these ways, the pain in your heart will go away. Then your heart can be filled with love, not only for others, but for yourself as well."

Because the woman was very smart, and because her heart had taught her a valuable lesson, she found a way to be nice to herself. She stopped smoking, she exercised and ate the right foods. She lost weight and also started to laugh and have fun as a gift to herself. She found a way to be as good to herself as she was to everybody else. And from that time on, her heart began to smile. The woman had discovered that having a heart filled with love means not only loving others, but loving yourself as well.

©1995
Nancy Davis, Ph.D.

Bad Food, Good Food

Problem(s) Addressed:

For disappointed people. People who say "the world always disappoints me" or "the world does not meet my needs" or "I can't depend on anyone". Those who are constantly disappointed in relationships and the world, in general. Those who enter relationships with the belief that people should be always truthful, loyal, and reliable and it is "terrible" when others do not live up to this expectation.

Appropriate for:

Adults and teenagers

Message:

Hopelessness and disappointment often comes from our high expectations and tendency to judge rather than experience the world

Symbols & Metaphors:

Food: relationships or anything that we need to live happily
Bad taste: relationships that go wrong once they are started
The healer: the therapist or the healthier part of the person
Going back to childhood: finding a model for healthier cognitions

Elements of the Story Which Can be Changed:

Sex of the main character; if the client is on medication, have the healer give the woman medicine to help her change; If childhood was an abusive or negative experience, have woman realize that children approach food with trust and joy

Note:

This story was written for a client who was always disappointed and angry. She had been in a very abusive and dependent relationship with her husband until he left her. She was looking for another dependent relationship, but she no longer had the innocence that she had before her marriage. She looked for and found what was wrong with every person in her life as a way of protecting herself from disappointment; her method of protection caused her to be disappointed all the time.

Bad Food, Good Food

Once upon a time there was a young woman with a very serious problem. Everything she ate tasted sour, rotten, spoiled and decayed. This made life very hard for her because she starved for something good and wholesome that she could take in to nurture and sustain her. After living like this for many years, and hoping that things would get better on their own, the woman decided to go to a healer. She went to this healer in spite of her belief that nothing would really help as she no longer thought it was intelligent to hope for improvement in her life.

The healer asked many questions, trying to understand the woman's problem. These questions made the woman wonder if the healer was stupid and slow to understand. She wondered, as well, if her problem was so rare and odd that the healer had just never found anyone else like her before and, therefore, did not know what to do except ask questions. She was irritated by the questions because she wanted someone to fix her problem or leave her alone.

In spite of her reluctance to believe in the healer, as time passed the woman found that together they began to discover many things. The woman explained that when she looked at food, it appeared to be very good. Fruit would seem ripe and ready to be eaten. Meat smelled and looked delicious and perfectly cooked. Milk and bread appeared fresh and wholesome. But, as she began to eat, the food seemed to sour and rot, even as she put it in her mouth.

This experience, the woman had found, was not common among people she had met. Although everyone could tell her of the experience of occasionally eating something that tasted bad or did not agree with them later, most appeared to be able to tell the difference between wholesome, fresh food and bad food. She felt alone, angry, and disappointed by life. However, she was also confused and wanted to change.

The healer found out that the woman had not always been as she was now. She could remember a time in her childhood, when things seemed good and the world seemed much kinder and more supportive. Gradually, as she grew older, the woman had discovered that food could not be trusted. It might appear good, but then would disappoint her. Oddly enough, this discovery seemed to increase her hunger. She searched for the one food that would always taste good and could sustain her completely. Since no food can ever fulfill such a dream, she became even more frustrated.

The healer pointed out that, because food had not always tasted bad to her, it was clear that there was nothing permanently wrong with her. She had not been born this way so it was clear that she could change. It had been a change for her to begin to mistrust food so it was possible for her to change back to the way she had been.

The healer explained that incorrect and useless thoughts and beliefs had somehow grown in the woman. For example, the woman now believed that things, including herself, were either good or bad, black or white. She believed that there were no "in-betweens". She assumed that any food that did not taste good, even one time, could never be trusted again. Because of this assumption, she was very careful to never trust that food again, searching for imperfections and any hint that the food would disappoint her. By doing this, she greatly increased the chances that she would find the food bad in the future. As time had passed she had begun searching for the one perfect food. Whenever she tried a new food, she wanted it to be perfect; to taste good and be all that she needed to live. Thus she expected too much . Her expectations were so high that they could never be met. Finally, and perhaps her biggest error, was her belief that she was so odd and so bad that she did not deserve to find anything to nurture her in the world.

As the healer talked about these beliefs, the woman could see that they were not helpful to her, but she did not understand how she could change the way she was thinking. She had thought differently many years ago. She did not want to return to being a child again, that would be silly, but perhaps she could remember how she thought when she was a child. She remembered herself as very curious and interested in everything, always wanting to learn something new. She felt safe then and failures were temporary things. Perhaps she could be that way again.

The healer gave her some strange advice, telling her to pretend and practice. At first the woman pretended to be curious and interested in how she would experience food. She found, to her surprise, that when she pretended to be a curious person, she actually began to become interested in all kinds of experiences and started to enjoy food more. She no longer looked for the perfect food. She no longer approached food as though it would hurt her. As her feelings of enjoyment increased, she started thinking differently. She became interested in the world, separate from her opinion of it, and learned to approach the world of experience with interest rather than just trying to make judgements about everything. She was no longer eager to decide if things were good or bad, safe or dangerous... she just wanted to learn more about them. As she made fewer judgements, she also found that she was no longer so harsh and unforgiving of herself. Everything, including food and herself, had become much more interesting and exciting.

The change that had begun slowly as she pretended to experience the world differently, eventually became permanent as she practiced her new way of approaching food. She had learned to find joy in new experiences and to take much of life as it comes.

The Princess and The Snake

Problem(s) Addressed:

Women involved in abusive relationships, especially those with sexual sadists

Appropriate for:

Adults

Message:

You can take your experience with an abusive man, learn from it, and find the power to change yourself so that you never again get involved in this type of relationship or attract another man who is abusive or sadistic

Symbols and Metaphors:

Snake: a man who targets a woman to pull into an abusive relationship

Sheltered from the world: a woman who doesn't perceive the signs that a man will be abusive

Energized by fear: sexual sadists are motivated by the fear and suffering of their victims

Chameleon: the manipulation of many abusive men so that many people are fooled into believing they are kind and loving

Revealed his true identity: began to abuse her

Healer: any therapist or healing agent

Coal to diamond: a message to make something positive out of the abusive relationship and finding a sense of personal power

Elements of the Story Which Can be Changed:

This story can be changed to have a female abuser and a male victim since there are many relationships where women are the abusers; this would require major re-writing and changing of symbols from feminine to masculine

Note:

Information about women who get involved with sexual sadists has been taken from the research of Roy Hazelwood and several of my patients. Mr. Hazelwood is a leading authority on criminal sexuality (Dietz, Hazelwood & Warren, 1990; Hazelwood and Burgess; 1987) and has been involved in research of woman who become involved in these types of relationships which he calls "The Compliant Victim" (Hazelwood, Warren & Dietz, 1992 & 1993). Mr. Hazelwood has retired from the Behavioral Science Unit of the FBI and presently works with The Academy Group. [4]

---

[4] The Academy Group, telephone (540) 330-0697, is a private consulting firm in Manassas, Virginia. The firm offers expertise in a number of behavioral science areas, primarily related to law enforcement. They also offer consultation, on a fee basis, to individuals who are being stalked; they assess dangerousness and give recommendations on a course of action to deal with the stalking.

The Princess and the Snake

Once upon a time there lived a princess who had grown up in a castle, sheltered from the world. Now, it's hard to say whether this princess was sheltered because she had never seen much of the world or if her mind created a wall around her because of the scary things that happened during her childhood. Nevertheless, although the body of the princess grew into an adult, she interacted with the world much like she did when she was three or four years old, in an innocent and trusting way.

Now, not far from the castle, although it could have been a million miles away, a large and poisonous snake lived in the marshes. Although most snakes live boring and predictable lives, this snake had big dreams, and often fantasized about how it would be to marry a princess. One day, while slithering close to the edge of the marsh looking for prey, the snake happened upon a royal parade. Riding in a golden carriage, the princess waved happily to the cheering crowd. Immediately interested, the snake watched the parade intently; he was drawn to the beauty of the princess and to her soft air of innocence. This was the princess of his dreams.

The snake's presence was soon noticed by the crowd of people watching the parade. Because most people are afraid of snakes, the crowd began to panic, running in every direction. Seeing the turmoil of the crowd, the golden carriage quickly returned to the safety of the castle walls.

Although he had wanted to spend more time watching the princess, if the snake could smile, the screams of the crowd would have made him smile. The snake enjoyed scaring the crowd. He was energized by fear and the screams were like applause to the snake. But he also understood that the princess would run in terror from a snake, especially because he sensed that she needed, at some deep level, to feel safe and protected by those around her. So, for a time, the snake only fantasized about the princess and what it would be like if she were his.

One day, while warming himself in the sun, the snake reviewed his fantasy about the princess. Suddenly a chameleon darted close to his head to evade a hungry hawk. The snake

483

quickly switched from his day dream to focused attention. He observed the chameleon moving under a leaf, and changing colors so that in blending with the green around him, his presence went unnoticed.

The snake quickly understood how the skills of the chameleon could help him move his fantasy into reality. "Teach me how to change colors so no one will notice who I am," the snake demanded of the chameleon. "I promise I won't hurt you." The chameleon was terrified of the snake, as well he should have been, but realized the snake had watched him and could no longer be fooled by his protective color changes. Hoping to satisfy the snake and get away quickly, the chameleon taught the snake all he knew about the disguises that enabled him to appear to be what he was not. After learning all the chameleon's secrets, rather than thanking him, the snake devoured the lizard, believing that this would give him even greater power. He did not keep promises; he was, after all, a snake.

After learning the ways in which the chameleon deceived the perceptions, the snake began to practice his own. He taught himself to be very skilled at hiding and at blending into the scenery so that the people near to him would miss what they were seeing. He found a way to change himself so that he appeared to be a kind and gentle commoner...the type of person who would live and work in the village outside of the castle walls. He suspected that the princess was intrigued by the world outside the castle and hungered to have a taste of the life that others lived.

One day, as the princess took another ride in her golden carriage, the snake, disguised as a gentle commoner, pretended to be injured as he lay by the side of the road. The princess viewed the scene as the snake had designed it, and telling herself that he was an injured man, stopped the carriage to administer aid to him. As the princess tended to the wounds the snake had created, he used all the charms on the princess that he had learned through a lifetime of practicing deception and deceit.

Because the princess presented herself as naive and innocent, she did not notice the signs that the man whose wounds she tended was really a snake, and invited him to the castle to recover from his injuries. The snake, of course, quickly accepted. He spent his time there quickly making himself a part of the princess' life. He learned just what the princess wanted in a man, so that he could seem to provide it. The snake became especially adept at creating an atmosphere that helped the princess to feel safe and protected with him in her life.

Believing the snake to be a man who was the answer to all her dreams of being accepted and loved, the princess found herself deeply in love. To do this, her heart ignored the danger signals that flashed briefly through her mind during the times when the snake gleefully revealed small glimpses of his real identity.

"I'm really very evil," The snake said firmly one night as he looked directly into the eyes of the princess.
"Don't be silly," she responded. "You're very kind and loving."

The snake whispered to himself that the princess would soon get just what she deserved. After all, he had warned her that he was a snake and she did not believe him. This was, of course, all part of his master plan; deceiving the princess gave the snake as much pleasure as his fantasies about what their future would hold.

And exactly as the snake had planned, the princess and the snake were wed. The snake had fooled even the royal family. The more he pretended to be who he was not, the easier it became to trick those around him.

As husband and wife, the snake and the princess moved into a home of their own. Things went well for a while. But once the snake was sure that the princess was truly his, he began to change back into a snake, a little at a time. When his disguise was not in place, the princess could have seen the snake clearly. But the love she felt for her husband and her need to be taken care of, forced her eyes to deny what they saw. The loyalty and blindness of his wife was just what the snake needed to feel even more powerful, for to be a snake and have someone who loves you deny who you are, is the ultimate in trickery and cunning.

As days passed, the snake revealed his true identity more and more. As this happened, the princess became increasingly depressed and withdrawn. Although she began to recognize some of her husband's evil traits, she believed, as the snake had convinced her, that any evil he exposed was her fault. So the princess tried more and more to please the snake, believing this would bring back the kind and gentle man she believed that she had married. Her efforts to change the snake by pleasing him only led to more pain. As the evil of the snake became a greater and greater part of her life, the princess began to withdraw from the outside world, remaining hidden behind the walls of her home. The snake had engineered this withdrawal by punishing the princess more and more for being with her friends and family. He understood that by isolating his wife, his control over her was complete.

Although the princess had cut herself off from her friends and family, they were still quite concerned about her. Some of them were suspicious of the snake although he usually acted like a kind and gentle man when in their presence. They noticed, on the few occasions when he allowed them to see her, that the princess looked sad and unhappy and begged her to tell them what was wrong. The princess tried to convince everyone that she was fine, and fearing the anger of the snake, isolated herself even more from those who tried to help her. The princess was so afraid that the snake would use his venom to destroy her completely that she told no one about his true identity.

As she became more and more isolated and the snake revealed his true identity to her more and more, the princess protected herself by becoming numb. As this happened, her mind became blank and her face seldom found expression.

Unless one understands the mind of a snake, it would seem that the snake would have been satisfied with making his fantasy a reality. The snake found much glee in moving the princess from a bright and sparkling jewel to a dull and lifeless form that he controlled completely. However, because many snakes do not have long attention spans, this snake grew bored of using his power to control the princess and began to wander more and more back into the marsh.

And after a while, it came to pass that the snake did not want to return from the marsh. The princess quickly moved back into the castle, hoping that the walls would protect her from the venom of the snake. She carried with her the sense of numbness and an overwhelming fear that the poison of the snake might yet completely destroy her. The snake knew of her fear, for he had gleefully created it. He told himself that he was powerful indeed when a princess was afraid of him even when he was far away. Because his sense of power increased in direct proportion to the fear of the princess, if the snake somehow sensed that her fear was diminishing, he would find ways to remind her that he was just outside the castle wall and how easy it would be for him to get inside. For a time, the snake found it took little effort to keep the princess in fear because living with the snake who had chameleon powers had convinced her that no one was strong enough to destroy his power.

Word of the princess' return quickly spread and her friends began to visit her, bringing with them gifts and laughter. They were happy to have her back. It had been a long time since the princess had been around such joy and the sounds of laughter reverberated into her heart, shaking loose a little of her pain. One of her friends, who was a healer, noticed that the princess seemed numb. This healer had learned about snakes and recognized the poisonous effects of venom in her friend.

One day the princess and her friends talked about the times before the princess met the snake. As her friends reminisced about the laughter and sparkle of the princess of the past, the princess saw her younger self in her mind. "I want to return to the way I used to be; I want to be just like that again," she announced. The friend with healing powers understood the danger of snakes. So she put her arm around the princess and counseled her with gentle words, "You can never be like that again, nor do you want to be. The "you" in the past did not understand about snakes and that is why you married one. You can find joy and laughter again by taking wisdom from your experience with the snake and letting that knowledge protect you and guide you and make you stronger."

The princess had kept her mind blank for so long that her friend wondered if she even heard the message about snakes, but apparently the heart of the princess had understood. That night, as she slept, the princess began to dream. In this dream she saw herself as a child, noticing that in the heart of this child was a piece of coal. As pressure and turmoil occurred in the child's life, the coal seemed to decrease in size and power. But she noticed, with new awareness, that the coal had actually grown more solid. She watched as life made further changes in the coal and it became a rough diamond. With cutting and polishing, the princess saw how the rough diamond progressed into a valuable jewel which reflected a single beam of light into a hundred rainbows. Then the focus of the dream changed, as dreams often do.

The princess had concentrated so much on the coal changing into a sparkling diamond that she had not noticed that the girl in her dreams had grown into a woman. The princess saw the woman in her dreams allow the diamond to give her courage, wisdom and a personal power that enabled her to confront the snake. The princess realized, as she continued to watch her dream unfold, that the woman in her dream was more powerful than the snake. She saw that the diamond in this woman's heart enabled her to clearly understand the strengths and weaknesses of the snake. The princess also observed that the woman in her dreams recognized how to get the snake completely out of her life. And with this knowledge, she noticed that this woman developed a special sense that warned her when snakes were near again so that she could move out of the range of danger.

Following that dream, each night when she slept, the princess dreamed again of the woman and the diamond. As she dreamed, there seemed to be a shifting within her heart and soul. All remnants of the poison that the snake had used to control the princess disappeared from her body. Her mind found a way to heal the trauma of living with the snake. The heart of the princess seemed to grow up in a way that allowed her to find new directions in her life and to understand the meaning of personal power. She no longer seemed naive and innocent, nor did she want to function as a child, looking for someone to take care of her. She had come to understand that the innocence of a child is no match for the cunning of a snake. The princess began to search out the wise men and women of the kingdom, listening to their words and learning from their teachings. She endeavored to learn all that was possible to learn about the world, about nature and about people. She began venturing into town realizing that although the walls of the castle had appeared strong, they had not protected her from the snake. The princess had come to understand that protection is not created by walls of a castle, but by the knowledge and vision of your heart.

One day, as she had often done before meeting the snake, the princess took a ride in her golden carriage, joining a royal parade. And, as had happened in the past, another snake was attracted by the noise of the parade. At first, the snake watched the princess from the edge of the marsh. But rather than focusing on the princess and moving toward her, this snake turned away, slithering back into the marsh. He had no interest in this princess since he sensed that she was wise to the ways of snakes and had protection from his poison.

CHAPTER ELEVEN

Stories for School-Related Problems

The stories in chapter eleven, as well as other stories in this book, address a variety of problems that impact on school performance. Many factors influence a student's ability to learn and develop to their potential. In addition to intelligence, family dynamics and belief systems play a major role in the way a student approaches learning, attends school and behaves in an academic setting. Other factors impacting on achievement are: self-esteem, handicapping conditions or illness, optimistic/pessimistic, cognitive beliefs about one's ability to function, poor social skills, personality styles, learning disabilities and brain functioning. Additionally, child abuse has a negative impact on almost every area of a child's development, including his/her ability to perform in school (Briere & Runtz, 1993; Rowan & Foy, 1993).

The issue of Attention Deficient/Hyperactivity Disorder (ADHD) and the spiraling use of medication among students identified as ADHD has received increasing attention from the media (Hancock, 1996). At the same time, research on Post Traumatic Stress Disorder (PTSD) is increasing dramatically with a corresponding increase in the understanding of the impact of trauma on children and adolescents (van der Kolk, 1996; Putnam, 1996). Since children who have acute PTSD may be as active and inattentive as those children who are truly ADHD, it is very important that educators recognize there are important differences in the treatment of these two problems. Since PTSD causes an over-stimulation of the brain, giving a stimulant such as Ritalin to a traumatized child may cause even greater over-stimulation of their brain. In my experience, children who have PTSD may concentrate better when given Ritalin or some other stimulant (as do almost all people who are given this type of medication), but their behavior and emotional functioning does not significantly improve.

One way to differentiate between these two very different problems is to look for trauma in the background of a student. Typical traumas that may cause symptoms of PTSD are abuse, witnessing violence, death of a family member (particularly if the death is sudden and/or violent), surgery, natural disasters, war, or being involved in an accident.

Although the following chart is not supported by research, the differences listed are based on the observations of, Dr. Marcey and myself in our work with numerous children who were PTSD or ADHD:

Hyperactive/ADD	Post Traumatic Stress Disorder
hyperactive behavior	hyperactive behavior
sleeps well	sleep problems-can't get to sleep or wakes up numerous times during night
lack of safety issues no need to control	safety issues, fear of being alone, need to control self or others
problems with boundaries	problems with boundaries
no flashbacks	flashbacks, night terrors
normal range of emotions	problems with rage, temper tantrums, phobias, sadness, depression
problems in paying attention resulting in academic difficulties	problems in paying attention resulting in academic difficulties
future orientation	difficulty planning for the future
impulsive, may grab objects from teacher's hand; getting ahead of instructions	reactive to environment, rather than impulsive
social difficulties resulting from their hyperactive behavior	withdrawal from relationships, as well as social difficulties
may have problems with handwriting and eye-hand coordination that improves when on Ritalin	drawings look more empty or depressed

490

Famularo et. al. (1990) has discovered that children who are in an acute stage of post traumatic stress disorder have a different range of symptoms than those in a chronic state, therefore it is important that educators recognize the differences. These researchers found that children in an acute stage of PTSD have the following symptoms: increase in spontaneously acting as though the trauma were recurring (flashbacks) when re-exposed to the traumatic situation or reminded of the trauma, difficulty falling asleep, hypervigilance, exaggerated startle response, and generalized anxiety/agitation. Children who had a chronic form of PTSD because their trauma was long term and on going or long past displayed the following: detachment from people and withdrawing into themselves, a restricted range of affect (facial expression is absent or looks depressed; little joy or laughter), dissociative episodes (day dreamer or spaced out), sadness and a belief that life is too hard. Children in chronic PTSD may look retarded or "slow" and can be misdiagnosised by the professional unfamiliar with the symptoms of this disorder.

Because therapeutic stories are non-intrusive and indirect, and most students love to hear stories, they provide an excellent tool to help students improve academic functioning. Use the stories in this chapter as an additional tool in helping students to improve school performance.

The Storyteller

Problem(s) Addressed:

Problems in written language, specifically in writing stories and essays

Appropriate for:

Grades 1 - 4

Message:

You have many stories to tell and are finding it is fun to write them down

Symbols and Metaphors:

This story is straightforward with few symbols

Elements of the Story Which Can be Changed:

Sex of the main characters; scene observed

Note:

"The Storyteller" was created for a first grader who had problems writing stories. He was very smart, but convinced himself that he couldn't write. His teacher reported that after hearing this story many times, he wrote more and more and seemed to enjoy written language assignments.

The Storyteller

Once upon a time there was a boy named Luke. Five days a week Luke went to school. He liked school very much, especially P.E. and lunch. Luke also liked to read and do math. However, when a teacher asked Luke to write stories, he would sit and stare blankly at the wall. Luke would search his mind for stories, but he couldn't find any stories there. He convinced himself that he had no stories to tell. The teachers and his parents would sometimes get angry with Luke and demand that he write stories. But the harder Luke tried to write stories, the more difficult it became and his mind remained completely blank. "I can't write or tell stories," Luke told them, "there aren't any stories in me."

One day Luke was walking home from school. His parents had given him money for ice cream, and Luke loved ice cream more than almost anything in the world. As he was approaching the ice cream store, Luke saw a robber run out the door and get into his car. Luke realized that the robber was stealing all the ice cream from the store! This made Luke very angry and he watched the robber carefully. He noticed his appearance, his car, and the numbers on the car license plate. Luke also paid attention to the direction the robber took when he raced off in his car.

Soon the police came. They questioned the store manager and the adults in the store. One policeman said to the others, "I'm going to ask that kid over there if he saw anything." "Don't bother," another policeman told him. "He's only a kid and kids don't pay attention, even to a crime." But this policeman was very thorough, so he asked Luke if he had noticed the robbery.

"I saw everything," Luke told him. Luke related to the policeman all the details he remembered about how the robber looked, the description of the car, the license plate number and the direction the car went when the robber drove away. He even remembered all the flavors of ice cream he had watched the robber put in his trunk. "You saw more than any adults we've interviewed," the policeman said patting Luke on the back, "Thanks."

The police soon found and arrested the robber because of all the detailed information Luke had provided in his story about the robbery. Luke was interviewed by reporters from newspapers and TV news programs; again and again he told his story. What a hero he was! The news people asked him to talk about himself, and Luke was soon telling stories about all parts of his life.

When Luke returned to school, his teachers and the other students also wanted to hear him tell how he had helped the police catch the robber. Luke enjoyed telling the story over again, and the teacher asked him to write it down so that it could be published in the school newspaper. Luke found writing the story very easy. When the story was printed in the school newspaper, Luke became the hero of the entire school. Soon Luke was writing stories about all kinds of things in his life; in fact, story writing became his favorite part of school. Luke had discovered that all life is a story, just waiting to be written.

The Red Tow Truck

Problem(s) Addressed:

Inability to stay focused or follow directions because of a learning disability, attention deficient disorder or post traumatic stress disorder; lack of problem-solving skills; lack of insight

Appropriate for:

Ages 6 - 10

Symbols and Metaphors:

Red Tow Truck: the forgetful person or child

Elements of the story which can be changed:

Sex of the child; the type of things that are forgotten; specific suggestions to match a child which will help him/her to remember

Message: There are techniques to compensate for forgetfulness and you can discover the techniques that help you; you can change and succeed

Note:

Regardless of the reason for a learning disability, becoming aware of this problem and using problem-solving techniques increase the chances that these learning disabilities will have minimal impact on functioning.

The Red Tow Truck

Once upon a time there was a Red Tow Truck with "Mike's Service Station" painted brightly on each door. The Red Tow Truck was responsible for many jobs that helped the service station run smoothly. He would drive to cars that were wrecked or stalled, and bring them back to the station for repair. When a car ran out of gas, The Red Tow Truck carried gasoline to the owner so they could get on their way.

Working at a service station required that The Red Tow Truck remember many different instructions. This was a big problem because he would often start a job and forget what he was doing. The Red Tow Truck would get a call on his radio from Mike, the owner of the service station, to pick up a wrecked car. He would start in the right direction, but after driving by a park or a new car lot, The Red Tow Truck would forget what he was supposed to do as he stopped to admire the new cars or watch the kids playing in the park. The wrecked car and its owner would wait and wait for The Red Tow Truck who never arrived. Then Mike would yell through the radio of The Red Tow Truck, "Where are you, Red Tow Truck? Why haven't you done what you were told to do?"

When this happened The Red Tow Truck would feel sad and embarrassed. He didn't like the boss yelling at him. So he would start off again to get the wrecked car, but soon he was distracted by other things and would again forget what he was doing. Sometimes The Red Tow Truck would get angry at other cars and run into them on purpose, causing wrecks and confusion. When this happened, traffic backed up causing even more problems. Then Mike, the boss, would yell at The Red Tow Truck again through the radio and The Red Tow Truck would concentrate very hard and find the wrecked car. Sometimes when The Red Tow Truck went on a run that should have taken ten minutes, he would be gone five hours. When he finally returned to Mike's Service Station, everyone would be very angry with him.

At night, when Mike's Service Station was closed, The Red Tow Truck would ask himself, "Why is everybody so mad at me?" He did not understand what he was doing to cause all the yelling. Mike tried to tell The Red Tow Truck what he needed to do, and so did the mechanics who worked there. Customers talked to him too. Even though The Red Tow Truck listened, he really didn't hear.

Although Mike was a patient man, after many weeks of yelling at The Red Tow Truck with little change in his behavior, Mike said, "I'm going to get another tow truck if you won't do your job. We are losing business because you take so long to bring back the wrecked and stalled cars and to take gasoline to customers who run out. The customers are always yelling at me and they are starting to use another service station with a more reliable tow truck."

The Red Tow Truck was very sad when Mike said he would replace him. "Please give me another chance," he pleaded, "I'll try really, really hard."
Mike liked The Red Tow Truck and he was a nice man, so he said, "I'll give you one more chance."

So that night, when the tow truck was in the garage, he began to think about his problem. He knew that he had promised to try harder, but he didn't understand what he had done to make everyone so unhappy. Then one of the mechanics who had worked on The Red Tow Truck when it needed repaired, entered the garage. "I'm going to show you why you are always in trouble," the mechanic told him, "It's important to see yourself as others see you so that you can change if you want to."

There was a TV and video player in the garage that the mechanics watched when there was no work. "I followed you today," the mechanic told him, "I took a videotape of everything you did and I'm going to show you why people are always angry with you." At that, the mechanic put on the videotape and a picture appeared on the TV. As The Red Tow Truck watched the videotape, he noticed how he had forgotten what he was supposed to do. He saw that he was doing many things that he wasn't supposed to do. Then he noticed how he was sent to get a wrecked car and did everything but that. The Red Tow Truck was amazed. "I never knew I acted like that," he mumbled.

"I knew that," the mechanic commented, "That's why I decided to show it to you. I hope seeing yourself in this way helps you." Then the mechanic went home for the night leaving The Red Tow Truck to think about what he had learned. He decided that if he had trouble remembering what he was supposed to do, that he would find ways to remind himself.

The next day, The Red Tow Truck asked Mike to write down what he was supposed to do each time he went on a run to get wrecked or stalled cars. Then he also asked Mike to repeat the instructions on a tape recorder so that he could play it again and again to remind himself what he was supposed to do. The Red Tow Truck talked to himself as he was out on a run, reminding himself again and again what he was sent to do. He also asked the mechanics and Mike if they could recommend other things that would help him to remember, and he tried each new idea until The Red Tow Truck found the combination that worked for him.

It wasn't long before The Red Tow Truck would go directly to a wrecked car and quickly return to Mike's Service Station. Then he would take gas to drivers who had forgotten to fill up and they would quickly be on their way. The Red Tow Truck soon was driving to cars who had dead batteries and recharging them in what seemed like no time at all. Not only was Mike very happy with The Red Tow Truck, but customers called with compliments and the service station got more and more business.

Every day The Red Tow Truck found more and more ways to remember where he was going and what he had been sent to do. He liked the compliments and he liked doing his job well. When problems arose, The Red Tow Truck figured out what he had done to cause the problem. ...then he worked on how to solve the problem. One day The Red Tow Truck heard Mike tell a customer that he was the best and most reliable tow truck in town. If tow trucks could smile, The Red Tow Truck would have smiled at hearing this, because he loved being responsible and getting his job done right.

®1991
Nancy Davis, Ph.D.

Andy and the Golden Path

Problem(s) Addressed:

School phobia or refusal to attend school in kindergarten and first grade

Appropriate for:

Ages 5 and 6. (This story should not be told to children whose mothers constantly desert the family)

Message:

You can find a way to ignore your fear and go to school; your mommy will be fine without you and will be there when you return

Symbols and Metaphors:

The golden path: school learning
The pot of gold: a degree

Elements of the Story That Can be Changed:

Name and sex of the child; family member child is afraid to leave

Note:

This story was written for a five year old who was afraid to go to kindergarten. He had a baby sister with an extremely serious heart condition; his mother also had a heart condition and had been hospitalized in critical condition shortly after the birth of his sister. When this story was written, his mother and sister were doing well. "Andy and the Golden Path" and other stories enabled the boy to go to school and significantly reduce his level of fear.

Andy and the Golden Path

Once upon a time there was a boy named Andy who lived in a country where all children were required to walk along a golden path. Each child who walked to the end of the golden path was rewarded with a pot of gold. When it became Andy's turn to walk along the golden path, he wasn't sure he knew how to do it. He wasn't even sure he wanted that pot of gold at the end. When Andy's mother told him it was time for him to walk along the path, Andy replied, "No, I'd rather just stay home and never walk along the path at all."

To encourage Andy, his friends in the neighborhood knocked on his door, calling "Andy, come on. Let's go." But Andy was afraid. "Maybe I'll just stay here in my house and never leave," he told himself. "Who cares about gold anyway? I don't need any gold."

Then more children Andy's age came to the door calling to him, "Andy, come out and walk the golden path with us and we'll be your friends. We can learn a lot and have fun, too." Part of Andy wanted to go with the other kids but part of him was afraid.

"What if Mommy gets lonely without me?" Andy asked himself. "Maybe Mommy needs me here to help take care of her."

The other children kept calling to Andy, "Come on. Let's go and walk the golden path."

"No, I think I'll just stay here with Mommy," Andy told them. So the children went away.

One afternoon, Andy saw a television program with children laughing as they walked along the golden path. Then Andy watched a video that had children learning many things as they walked the path. "Walking the golden path looks like it might be fun," Andy told himself. "But I'm scared that Mommy won't be here when I get back."

Then Andy decided to play with his dog and her puppies. He loved to watch the puppies play and he noticed that the mother dog left them for a while, but she always came back. Andy paid attention as the puppies wandered far away from their mother. He saw that they played and had fun when their mother was in another place. Andy continued watching the puppies and their mother and thought about what he was learning.

When the next morning came and the kids called to him again, "Andy, come and walk the golden path," Andy replied, "I'm ready." He had breakfast and kissed his mom goodbye. "I'll be back this afternoon," he promised. Then Andy went with the other children and walked the golden path. Sometimes he was scared and sometimes he was happy. Sometimes he didn't want to go but that changed as soon as he got to the golden path. Each day when Andy arrived home, he noticed that his mother had done fine without him, but she was always glad to see him again and gave him a big hug and kiss.

The day came when Andy wasn't afraid to go to the golden path at all. Andy had gotten rid of his own fear by doing what he was afraid of until his fear disappeared. He had learned that fear can keep you from growing and Andy wasn't going to let fear be smarter than he was.

©1995
Nancy Davis, Ph.D.

Problem Child

Problem(s) Addressed:
Problem behavior in school and at home when a child is smart and has the skills to achieve and be appropriate

Appropriate for:
Ages 12 and under

Message:
The problem behavior is under your control and you have the ability to change your behavior; you can heal the tears in your heart and be successful

Symbols and Metaphors:
Tears in your heart: any sadness or pain from rejection or trauma

Elements of the Story Which Can be Changed:
Sex of the main character; characteristics of the main character to more closely reflect the behavior of the child for whom the story is being told

Note:
Andrew was a child with many losses. His mother did not know the identity of the father. She then deserted Andrew, leaving him with a boyfriend and the boyfriend's mother, who took on the role of a grandmother. The boyfriend was later sent to jail and the grandmother became very sick. Although he became a problem child, Andrew was a survivor. He was able to reverse his behavior. He was adopted by a wonderful family and is hopefully continuing to use his skills to be successful rather than a problem child.

Problem Child

Once upon a time there was a boy whose name was Andrew. Andrew was very handsome and very smart. He had good skills when dealing with people. But Andrew didn't believe there was anything good about him at all. When Andrew looked in the mirror, all he saw were problems. The mirror told him that he was ugly and stupid and he would be a failure in life.

But Andrew didn't want to be a failure at everything, so he decided he was going to be a problem child. "I can succeed at being the best problem child that anybody around here has ever encountered. I can be successful and really good at that. I wouldn't have to be smart to be a problem child and I wouldn't have to be handsome and I wouldn't have to be nice and friendly. I can succeed at being a problem child!" Andrew told himself.

So Andrew immediately began to work toward his goal and he succeeded very well at being a problem child. When he arrived at school, he hit his classmates. While sitting at his desk, Andrew kicked and tripped students unlucky enough to be anywhere near him. During recess, he muttered curse words. Andrew also refused to do his school work. The principal came to Andrew's classroom to talk to his teacher. He heard her say, "Andrew is a problem child." Then Andrew smiled because a problem child was exactly what he wanted to be.

When Andrew walked around his neighborhood after school, he got in fights with the kids on the playground and punched them in the nose. The kids would get very angry and they would say to each other, "Andrew is really a problem child." Then Andrew would smile and say to himself, "I'm doing exactly what I want to do."

When Andrew was at home, he refused to clean up his room. He wouldn't pick up his clothes or the things he played with from the floor, so the place was a mess. Andrew refused to eat dinner and he screamed when someone in the house was watching television because he wanted to watch another channel. Then the people in his house would say, "Andrew is a problem child." And Andrew would smile because he had made the decision to be a problem child.

One day, after everyone had yelled at him, Andrew looked in the mirror and talked to himself. "I have succeeded, I am the worst problem child that anybody has ever experienced. So, why am I so sad? I thought being a problem child would make me happy, but it hasn't. I don't understand what's wrong."

That night, Andrew went to sleep and began to dream. In his dream, Andrew saw himself as older. This older self had come from the future to talk to him. The older Andrew came with a message: "Andrew, you have decided to be a problem child because you have so many tears in your heart. You thought those tears in your heart would go away if you could be the worst problem child anybody had ever encountered. But they didn't go away, they just got worse."

Andrew had to agree, "You're right, the tears in my heart are worse." "Well it's time to do something about it," said the Andrew from the future. "You are a different person than you think you are. You're very smart. You know how to make friends when you want to and you know how to do your schoolwork. It is time to heal the tears in your heart. Why not make a decision to give up being a problem child? Then you can succeed at things that will make you happy and other people will be happier with you."

Andrew was sure he needed help in changing what he wanted. So the Andrew from the future and the Andrew from the present talked and talked in the dream. They spoke about trouble and love, about school work and goals, about being the best you can be and being the worst you can be. When Andrew woke up the next morning, he was very still for a moment as he lay on his pillow; he felt that his heart was somehow changing. The tears in his heart seemed to have gotten smaller and his body didn't feel like such a problem.

On the day after the dream, Andrew went through his day without being a problem to everyone. Each day he seemed to be less and less of a problem until the day came when Andrew even got a hug from his teacher. As the days went on, the tears in Andrew's heart disappeared and his heart found a way to heal. Andrew changed the way he acted with friends, the way he acted at school, the way he acted at home and especially the way he talked to himself.

In no time at all, Andrew was treating kids his own age in a way that allowed him to have lots of friends. People were happy when Andrew walked down their street. Andrew's teacher was happy to see him in the morning because she realized that he was smart and was going to be successful in whatever he tried. At home, Andrew cleaned up his clothes, he brushed his teeth, took showers and became a different person.

One day, after all these changes had occurred, Andrew was looking in the mirror and he realized something new about himself. As he looked in the mirror, Andrew saw himself in a very different way. "I don't want to be a problem child anymore. I want to be someone special." And Andrew smiled to himself, because he realized he already was someone special.

©1995
Nancy Davis, Ph.D.

The Boy Who Couldn't Put Things Together

Problem(s) Addressed:
The effect of the symptoms of abuse and/or trauma on a child's ability to read

Appropriate for:
Grades 1 - 4; any child who has been traumatized or abused and is having difficulty learning to read

Message:
Talking about your trauma, feeling safe, and finding ways to protect yourself in the future can help you to learn to put things together; the technique which protected you from being overwhelmed by trauma or abuse is hurting you now and keeping you from learning

Symbols and Metaphors:
Inability to put things together: a metaphor for fragmented thought processes and fragmented memory

Elements of the Story That Can be Changed:
Sex of the child; the subject that the child finds difficult; the details of what happened to the child and the solutions that help the child to feel safe and to talk about their trauma. The person to whom the child can talk about his/her trauma can be changed, e.g., school counselor, principal, therapist.

Note:
Daniel was a second grader who had a very traumatic life. His father went to jail for abuse, the mother's boyfriend was never charged with abusing him, although the abuse was severe. Daniel's mother had been an exotic dancer. Daniel learned to read as his self image improved, his mother's functioning improved and he began to feel safe.

514

The Boy Who Couldn't Put Things Together

Once upon a time there was a boy named Daniel. From the time he was a very little baby, many things happened in Daniel's life that were very scary and very difficult. People moved in and out of his life a lot. People hurt him. Sometimes he didn't have enough to eat and sometimes he was very cold. Children need love and security and a feeling of safety, but Daniel had few of these.

Because Daniel was a child, he had few skills to change his life. Knowing and remembering what was happening to him was so painful, that Daniel just stopped putting things together in his mind. He didn't plan to do this, it was caused by his pain and his fear. He stopped remembering what would happen when adults got angry with him and had belts. He didn't think about what might happen if he didn't have enough food. When it was afternoon, Daniel did not remember the morning. And Daniel's memory often went blank when he thought about the abuse in his past, although his body never forgot.

As Daniel grew a little older, things in his life improved very little. So Daniel still didn't put things together and he still didn't remember. By doing this, he was able to help himself feel a little better. When Daniel did not put things together, he wasn't as afraid all the time. He didn't have to think about what was going to happen because he didn't have to know.

When Daniel grew bigger and older his life improved, but he continued to have difficulty in putting things together. He had taught himself to disconnect everything so well, it became automatic . . . Daniel wasn't even aware he was doing it.

When Daniel was old enough to attend school and learn to read, his teacher, Mrs. Cook, showed him a page with words, saying, "Daniel, it's time for you to learn how to read." But Daniel's mind couldn't read because he couldn't put things together. When Daniel looked at the words on the page, they didn't make any sense to him because that's the way he had learned to deal with his life . . . if things didn't make sense and he didn't put them together, he wouldn't have to be scared and sad.

Daniel did not realize why he was having problems reading and neither did his teacher. Mrs. Cook tried everything she could think of to teach Daniel to read. She tried different books and she tried different reading groups. She tried praising Daniel and she tried punishing him. She used tapes or colored beads or videos. But Daniel still couldn't read because he couldn't put things together.

After the teacher tried every technique she knew and Daniel still couldn't read, Daniel accepted the fact that he couldn't read. When a new student entered his class, Daniel would introduce himself by saying, "My name is Daniel and I can't read." Perhaps Daniel was comfortable with his inability to read, believing if he learned how to read, that all the feelings he had tried not to feel would return and he would feel very sad and very scared.

As the days went by, Mrs. Cook continued to be confused about Daniel's inability to read; Daniel just tried not to think about it. One day Mrs. Cook asked all the students to put a puzzle together but Daniel couldn't put the puzzle together. Then, Daniel tried to put together a toy he bought and he couldn't put that together either. His teacher noticed this and decided to challenge him. "Daniel," she said, "I know you're very smart and I know you can put things together. Somehow you have just tricked yourself into believing you can't."

After thinking about all the things he couldn't put together, Daniel began to talk about what happened when he was a baby, and what happened when he was a little boy, and what happened when he was a bigger boy. The teacher was a special person who helped Daniel to feel safe as he put together all the things that had happened to him. She helped Daniel to think of what he could do if these things ever happened again, so he would not feel so helpless. And she gave Daniel a phone number to call that was especially for children who needed help when there was nothing to eat, or they were being hurt.

As Daniel talked to his teacher day after day about all the things that had happened to him, something changed inside of him. He began to be able to put things together. First Daniel was able to put together puzzles, then he was able to put his toy together. After that, Daniel understood that he had tricked himself into thinking that he couldn't put things together. The more Daniel talked about what was inside of him and what he had been through, the more Daniel improved in putting things together. Soon he was putting together words. Then he put together sentences. After that, Daniel learned to read so quickly, that he even surprised himself. By the end of the school year, Daniel no longer said, "I can't read." He told anyone who would listen, "I'm the best reader in the class because I learned how to put things together."

When Daniel grew up, he became a builder because, after all, putting things together is what builders do.

©1995, Nancy Davis, Ph.D.

The Confused Car

Problem(s) Addressed:

The problems of others interfering with the functioning of a child; holding onto past events that need to be "let go"; pessimism; prior trauma interfering with functioning, i.e., flashbacks.

Appropriate for:

Ages 6 and up

Message:

You can find a way to "let go" of everything that you are carrying with you that is interfering with your ability to function properly; you can be repaired

Symbols and Metaphors:

Hitchhikers: any problem or trauma that hangs on, becoming a focus of thoughts

Teenager: the wisdom of the unconscious to fix the problem

Elements of the Story That Can be Changed:

Sex of the car; color of the car; sex of the teenager; type of problems that the car has because of the hitchhikers

Note:

This story was designed for a child whose mother had multiple problems and used him as her therapist. It is an appropriate story for any child who holds on to things or who is given problems that are not his or hers to solve.

The Confused Car

Once upon a time there was a green car who seemed very confused. When this car tried to stay on the road so it could go where it was supposed to go, the engine would stop running. When it tried to keep the engine running, it couldn't stay on the road. Now this was a very difficult problem, indeed, because the green car rarely got where it wanted to go.

Because of his confusion, the green car was always in trouble with somebody. When it ran off the road and crashed into things, he was in trouble with himself. When he stopped running, he was in trouble with the driver for getting stuck in traffic. People were constantly yelling at the green car, "Why can't you watch where you're going? Why do you keep stopping?"

Being yelled at only made the green car more confused. It was as if the green car couldn't do two things at once. He couldn't watch where he was going and keep running because something had happened to him and he really didn't know what had happened.

Because the green car was always hitting something, and because his drivers were always getting stuck, it wasn't long before the green car was abandoned along the road. As the green car sat and sat alone, his paint began to peel and fall off. Teenagers stole his hubcaps and he became covered with mud.

One day a teenage boy who had little money, but needed a car, noticed the green car. He found the owner and asked if he could buy him. "I can't charge you very much," the owner told him. "The green car has an unusual problem and it can't be fixed." Then the owner told the teenager how the green car seemed unable to stay on the road and keep the engine running at the same time.

The teenage boy was not discouraged; he believed he had the ability to fix the problem. So they agreed on a fair price and the owner handed the teenager the keys. However, when the teenager tried to drive the green car home, they crashed into a telephone pole.

"The old owner is right," the teenager commented to himself. "This green car does have problems." So the teenager had the green car towed to a garage where he worked part time. He put the green car on a lift and raised it above his head so he could look under the bottom. He was very surprised at what he found; the green car had hitchhikers all over its engine.

Hitchhikers are seeds from plants that attach and stick to whatever comes close. They hold on and "hitchhike" to a new place, usually on the fur of an animal or the pant legs of a person. The teenager had never seen hitchhikers attached to a car. But, as he looked more closely, he saw that the green car had hitchhikers in his air cleaner. He had hitchhikers in his exhaust pipe. He had hitchhikers in the carburetor and the power steering fluid. He had hitchhikers everywhere the teenager looked. The teenager understood that hitchhikers do not belong in a car where they can interfere with the engine and the steering.

"Ah ha," smiled the teenager, "Green Car, I have found the source of your problem." Quickly the teenager began to clean the hitchhikers out of every part of the green car where they had attached themselves. He threw the hitchhikers in a field so that they could grow into plants as they were supposed to. He removed all of the hitchhikers from the green car where they did not belong.

When all the hitchhikers had been removed from the green car, the teenager took the car for a test drive. To the amazement of the green car, he could both watch where he was going and run at the same time. "How interesting," the green car thought to himself, "that those hitchhikers interfered with my ability to do what a car is supposed to do."

After that, the teenager drove the green car everywhere he wanted to go. He fixed the peeling paint and worked on the engine until it purred. When his friends commented that he was lucky to have gotten such a bargain, the teenager knew that having the green car had nothing to do with luck. He had gotten the green car because he believed in his ability to fix it, and he had not given up when other people told him that the car could not be fixed.

©1995
Nancy Davis, Ph.D.

The Puppet

Problem(s) Addressed:
Children who allow others to manipulate them into angry outbursts or inappropriate behavior

Appropriate for:
Ages 6 - 13

Message:
When you react to the taunts or dares of others, you are allowing them to control you

Symbols and Metaphors:
Pulling the strings: knowing what to say to someone to get them to act inappropriately or to get them to react in such a way that gets them in trouble
Puppet: anyone who is reactive to others in a self-destructive way

Elements of the Story That Can be Changed:
Sex of the main character; the kinds of behavior that gets the main character in trouble

Note:
Some children have explosive anger because of PTSD. Others learn it. Still others are rebels that do not want anyone telling them what to do. Most believe that they are in control of their anger. This story helps them to see how they are being manipulated, and how to deal with it.

The Puppet

Once upon a time there was a boy named LeRoy. LeRoy was smart and could have done very well in school, but LeRoy had an anger problem. Day after day, LeRoy would go from being calm to being enraged in the blink of an eye. When this happened, LeRoy would hit, curse and call other students names.

LeRoy would be in trouble with the teacher, but he would smile as he was being punished. He believed he was in control of his anger. "I'm acting just the way I want to act!" LeRoy muttered to himself as he was being sent to the principal's office again. "No one tells me what to do." LeRoy smiled as he waited for the principal to call him into his office. He had convinced himself that he wanted to be angry; he thought everyone saw him as powerful and independent.

As he sat outside the principal's office, LeRoy began to listen to the voices coming through the door as he heard someone mention his name.

"LeRoy is a puppet," someone said to the principal. LeRoy recognized the voice as belonging to his PE teacher.

"You're right," the principal replied, "any student in his class can pull LeRoy's strings at any time. Then LeRoy acts just the way they want him to. If they call LeRoy — the puppet — a name, he always hits them. They know exactly what to say to LeRoy to make him angry. Then LeRoy gets in trouble and gets sent to my office. When this happens, all the students laugh at LeRoy behind his back because they've been controlling his puppet strings. LeRoy thinks he is independent, but LeRoy is really a puppet."

LeRoy did not like hearing this at all, because he had thought he was tough and thought all the students admired him. Knowing that the students were laughing at him because they thought he was a puppet, really made him angry. LeRoy remembered the story of Pinocchio and he could picture someone pulling Pinocchio's strings. He also had been in the audience when puppet shows were given in the school auditorium. These puppets had strings attached to their arms, hands, feet and head. The person who pulled the strings of the puppets had total control over the movement of the puppet.

"I am not a puppet!" LeRoy said to himself, but the tears in his eyes meant that he wasn't sure.

The principal had LeRoy wait for so long in the office that he fell asleep. As he slept, LeRoy dreamed that he was indeed a puppet and the other students were pulling his strings. Waking up suddenly, LeRoy didn't feel so tough anymore. "This is really scary," he said. "I don't want to be a puppet."

After talking to the principal, LeRoy returned to class. He thought and thought about what he needed to do to stop being a puppet. "I have to change so no one can pull my strings," LeRoy told himself. "I can figure out what I need to do."

The next day, some of the students called LeRoy a name. The old LeRoy would have punched them, but LeRoy was changing. "I'm not a puppet," LeRoy said firmly and walked away without hitting anyone. "What is he talking about?" the students asked themselves. So they tried calling LeRoy even nastier names than usual, attempting to get LeRoy upset. When LeRoy did not react as he used to, the students were the ones who got angry.

"Now that I am not a puppet, they are the ones getting mad and I'm winning. Maybe those students will become my puppets," LeRoy said to himself.

For days after that, the students tried all kinds of techniques to get LeRoy to lose control. They wanted to get him in trouble and sent to the principal's office, but nothing they tried was successful. LeRoy had cut the strings between himself and those students. They weren't able to pull his strings anymore; LeRoy had given up his strings. He had wised up when he realized that the students were controlling his behavior to constantly keep him in trouble.

After a few days, the students stopped trying to pull LeRoy's strings because they realized that LeRoy had changed — he was no longer anyone's puppet. When LeRoy changed the way he was acting, he began to make friends. He liked going to school and was doing well.

One day LeRoy's teacher announced that the class project was to give a puppet show for the school. LeRoy volunteered to pull the strings of one of puppets in the show. This helped to reinforce LeRoy's understanding that only real puppets should have strings and to make him certain that he would never again become someone else's puppet.

The Boy and the Bullies

Problem(s) Addressed:

Children who are taunted by bullies; lack of problem-solving skills

Appropriate for:

Children under 13 years of age or children who are developmentally delayed

Message:

Bullies will leave you alone when you discover the techniques for handling them; there are many ways to solve problems; if the solutions you try do not work, there are always many other solutions to try

Symbols and Metaphors:

Old woman: the wisdom of the unconscious to find solutions to problems
Invisible shield: not being bothered by the words of bullies
Apple trees: metaphor for problem solving
Bull: bullies

Elements of the Story Which Can be Changed:

Sex of the child; what the bullies say; family make up; the person who talks to the child; additional ideas for handling bullies

Note:

This story was written for a boy who had been sexually abused by a babysitter and developed Post Traumatic Stress Disorder. His behavior at school was so out of control that the other kids began to taunt him. As his PTSD symptoms diminished, he had to find a way to handle the bullies. This story and others allowed him to find solutions to this age-old childhood problem.

The Boy and the Bullies

Once upon a time in a land not so far away there lived a boy named Tyrone. He was a typical boy. He loved to play basketball and baseball. Tyrone was a success in school and he had many friends. Tyrone, however, had a big problem in his life because he was bothered by bullies.

Many children are bothered by bullies. Bullies are people who try to make themselves feel good by making others feel bad. They say mean things to many people until they find someone who is bothered by their mean words. The bullies in Tyrone's school had said mean things to many students but these students just ignored the bullies. When they began to taunt Tyrone, however, he became really upset. This was exactly what the bullies wanted. When Tyrone became distressed by the insults of the bullies, they picked on him more. The more the bullies picked on Tyrone, the more upset he became. The more upset he became, the more the bullies picked on him. Tyrone soon found that he did not want to get out of bed on school mornings; his stomach was always upset and his grades fell.

Tyrone knew he had a problem with bullies but he didn't know how to solve it. He asked his family for suggestions, but they just told him to ignore the bullies. Tyrone told himself that he couldn't ignore them. Tyrone told his teacher about the bullies, but that did not solve his problem either. His teacher spoke to the bullies and told them not to pick on Tyrone; after that the bullies would wait until the teacher wasn't around and be even meaner to Tyrone.

"I've asked two people how to stop the bullies and they haven't been much help," Tyrone said sadly to himself. "I guess I'll just give up. I'm going to be miserable forever." Then Tyrone got even more sad.

One day Tyrone was playing near his home when some bullies spotted him and began to taunt him. It just so happened that there was a very old woman who lived near Tyrone who saw what was happening. Now this old woman was very smart; she was a retired teacher and had learned much about life. She had a special understanding about bullies and the pain they cause. So she called to Tyrone to come and sit with her.

"I see that those bullies are saying very mean and cruel things to you and you're getting really upset," the old woman remarked to Tyrone.

"There's nothing anybody can do," Tyrone said, hanging his head. "I've asked my teacher and I've asked my family what I can do to solve this problem; their solutions did not work. I guess I'm going to have to learn to live with it." The old woman was not discouraged by Tyrone's belief that there was no solution; she understood what it was Tyrone needed to learn about bullies and about problem solving.

"I can help you with those bullies," she remarked. She explained to Tyrone that he could find many different ways to respond to bullies so that they would leave him alone. "There are many ways to solve problems," she said. "Just because you pick the first two apples off the tree and they have bugs in them, it doesn't mean that all the apples have bugs. There are always many more apples on a tree and many more trees with apples."

The old woman and Tyrone sat and talked for a long time about all the different ways he could respond to bullies. As Tyrone returned home, he thought about some of her suggestions. She told him to make jokes about what the bullies said. "When they see that you are laughing at their behavior rather than letting it upset you, they will leave you alone." She also told him that he could think of ways to talk to the bullies so that they realized he was not bothered by their taunts.

"Tonight when you are sleeping and every night after this, your dreams will help you deal with bullies," the old woman said. "You'll find that in your dreams, you are able to put up a big, invisible wall around yourself that shields you from the taunts of bullies. Whenever the bullies say mean things to you, their words will bounce off this wall. The shield will keep the words of the bullies from entering your heart and making you sad like they used to. This shield will only keep out mean and cruel words, because it's important to let in the positive words and love from those around you."

Tyrone was not sure he believed that his mind could create an invisible shield to bounce off the words of bullies, but he knew it was worth a try. The old woman had helped him think of many other things that he could do to handle the bullies. That night during dinner, Tyrone told his family about the old woman. His family thought that the old woman had many good ideas. When Tyrone slept that night, his dreams did help him. He found himself building an invisible wall around himself to keep the words of bullies from injuring his heart. In his dream, Tyrone practiced what he could say to bullies and he practiced making jokes of what they had said. Tyrone found that he was thinking of many new ideas to help him handle bullies.

The next morning, Tyrone felt good about going to school. When the bullies said mean things to him, their words didn't bother Tyrone . . . they just seemed to bounce off of him. Tyrone also watched other students who handled bullies well and learned from them. He became more sure of himself because he realized there were ways to solve his problem. Other students had figured out ways to handle bullies and Tyrone was sure that he could too.

As Tyrone tried new ways to handle the bullies, they bothered him less and less. Each night as he slept, Tyrone came up with more ways to deal with bullies so that they would leave him alone. Mean words continued to bounce off his invisible shield. Soon, Tyrone was confident that he could handle the meanest bullies in his school.

As word got around, other students who were having trouble with bullies began to ask Tyrone to help them. When Tyrone realized how much he was helping the other students with their problems, he began to smile. He had a hard time remembering the old Tyrone that had not been able to handle bullies. The new Tyrone knew what to say and how to act to keep bullies away from him.

To remind himself that there are many ways to solve problems, Tyrone kept a picture above his bed of a bull sitting in the middle of an apple orchard. And to thank the old woman for her help, Tyrone gave her a cookbook containing recipes of hundreds of ways to serve apples and he even baked her an apple pie all by himself.

The Wish That Came True

Problem(s) Addressed:

Low self-esteem, social difficulties, poor problem-solving skills

Appropriate for:

Elementary school children

Message:

You can learn how to have friends, just as you learn math and reading

Symbols and Metaphors:

Being invisible: the desire to run away from problems rather than to find ways to change them

Elements of the Story That Can be Changed:

The name and sex of the child; the types of difficulties encountered with peers at school; the academic success of the student; family members that the child talks to; what he/she decides to do with his life as a consequence of learning how to have friends; e.g., may have many parties at home, may teach his/her own children how to have friends, or may grow up to be a school counselor and help other students

Note:

This story was written for an eight-year-old boy who was depressed and having great difficulty in peer relationships at school. Rather than try to change himself, the child decided to run away. The story helped motivate him to behave in new ways and take responsibility for dealing with his problems, instead of trying to hide from them.

The Wish That Came True

Once upon a time there was a boy named Matt who hated going to school. Schoolwork was not the reason Matt hated school; he was really smart. He hated school because the other students were mean to him. They called him names, called his mother names and made fun of him. When this happened, Matt didn't know what to do or say. Sometimes he punched the bullies in the mouth, but that didn't help because fighting somehow encouraged them to say even meaner things. In addition, fighting resulted in being sent to the principal's office. When mean things were said to him, he said mean things back. Then the bullies would say even more cruel things to Matt. On the playground, Matt was ignored or tormented. At lunch, no one wanted to sit by him. Consequently, Matt did not want to go to school because no one likes to be bullied and hurt.

To feel better, Matt often daydreamed, especially of being invisible. "If I were invisible," he thought to himself, "I could come to school and learn everything I needed to learn, but no one could give me a hard time." This seemed like a silly dream because Matt had never known anyone who was invisible, but it helped him get through the day.

One day, as Matt walked home from school, he found what looked like a magic lamp. Matt rubbed the bottom of the lamp just as he'd seen on cartoons. To his surprise, out popped a genie. As genies usually do, this one announced, "You have three wishes. What do you wish for?"

Matt asked "Can I have one wish and then come back and ask for the other two?"

The genie thought this was an unusual request because most people can't wait to get their wishes right away. But he said, "Okay, what would you like for your first wish?"

Matt told the genie that he wanted to be invisible. So, with a wave of his hand, the genie made Matt invisible.

At first, Matt thought being invisible was great. He walked by all the bullies in his neighborhood without being taunted by cruel words. When he got home, Matt heard his mom

533

saying, "Matt, take out the trash and do the dishes." But Matt didn't have to do his chores, since his mom couldn't see him.

After a while, Matt's mom realized that she had not seen him come home from school and she called the police. When the police were unable to find Matt, his mom got very upset and began to cry. Matt tried to let his mother know that he was in the house, but Matt was invisible so his mom could not see him. That night, Matt went to bed just like he usually did, but his mom was too upset to notice that the covers were turned down and that he'd slept in his bed.

Matt got up the next morning and went to school. At first, being invisible in school was a lot of fun. He arrived late for class and he didn't get in trouble because no one could see him. After a while, however, being invisible started causing him problems. First, the teacher asked for volunteers to help with the Ice Cream Social. Matt loved ice cream and he knew that if he worked at the Ice Cream Social, he would get lots of free ice cream. Matt raised his hand to volunteer but did not get chosen because the teacher couldn't see him. Then, a girl in his class, who he really liked, gave out invitations to her birthday party. Matt noticed, to his surprise, that he was invited. Since the girl could not see him, however, she threw the invitation in the trash. When Matt went to the cafeteria for lunch, he got in the line but no one would give him any food because he was invisible.

As the day wore on, Matt began to believe that being invisible might not be such a great wish after all. He realized that he would rather have people notice him and give him a hard time than not notice him at all.

So, on the way home from school, Matt retrieved the magic lamp from its hiding place. He rubbed the lamp and the genie reappeared. The genie had special powers to see Matt even though he was invisible. "What do you want now? How do you like being invisible?" the genie asked.
"It is terrible being invisible," Matt replied, "I hate it."
"What are you going to do it about it?" asked the genie.

"I want my second wish," said Matt. "I want to be visible again."
The genie raised his eyebrows. "That's interesting. You wish one thing and then you unwish it with the next wish. You've used two wishes. What do you want with the third wish?" the genie asked as Matt again became visible.

Matt considered asking for all the video games in the world, but he realized that wouldn't make him happy. Although video games were fun to play, they never made Matt happy in the deepest part of his heart. Then Matt considered wishing for lots of money for his mom. Perhaps, Matt thought, if he lived in a really nice house he would be happy. After talking to the genie, however, Matt realized that money wouldn't make him happy either. He'd still be lonely and the students in his class would still make fun of him.

After thinking a little more, Matt told the genie, "What I really want is friends. I want to know how to have a friend and how to be a friend. I want to learn how to get people to like me. I want to be invited to parties and have students in the hall smile and say 'hello' when I am at school. I also want to know what to say if bullies say something mean to me."

The genie looked at Matt with new respect, "That's one of the wisest wishes anyone has ever asked for. Knowing how to have a friend and be a friend is an important part of happiness. I will find a way to help you with that. I grant that your wish will come true. Every night, while you sleep, I will send a special counselor to talk to you in your dreams. This counselor will tell you about friends — how to make friends, how to be a friend and how to be really happy with yourself."

So Matt returned home. At first his mother was so relieved that he was okay, she was overjoyed to see him. After a while, however, she asked Matt where he had been. When he told her that he had been invisible, she didn't believe his story. In fact, Matt's mother got very angry and punished him for being gone for a whole day and scaring her to death. Matt spent so much time talking to his mother, that when he went to bed that night, he forgot all about the assurance of the genie.

Just as the genie had promised, when Matt began to dream, a counselor appeared. The counselor talked to Matt about friends. Each night the counselor talked to Matt more and more. Soon, Matt noticed that he was acting in different ways. He found more ways to be friendly, listen to other people, handle bullies, and do all the things he needed to do to have friends.

He carefully watched TV to see what people did when they had friends. He watched the other kids in the classroom who were popular to learn what they did. Matt paid special attention to any student who handled bullies well. He also watched carefully to see what the students who didn't have friends were doing to cause other students to reject them. He talked to his relatives and teachers to find out what makes them like or dislike someone. He checked out books from the library on how to handle bullies, and he asked students who were not bullies what they had done to keep the bullies away. Matt took all this information and tried out one technique and then another. He kept trying new things. If one idea didn't work, he had many more to try.

It wasn't long before Matt had friends. He looked forward to going to school and learning and seeing the other students. He looked forward to lunch and recess.

The day came when the counselor said to Matt, "I don't need to come back in your dreams anymore. You have learned much that you need to know about how to have a friend and how to be a friend. I also know that if you have difficulties with your friends, you have learned many techniques to help you solve your problems."

Matt was very satisfied with himself after that. He learned that having friends takes a lot of work and time, but they are worth it. He read and listened and learned more about being a friend.

One day the principal called Matt into her office to tell him his school was starting a peer counseling program. She explained this program used students to help other students with their problems. She asked Matt if he would like to be a peer counselor. Matt, of course, said, "yes." When the principal asked Matt what kinds of problems he would like to talk to the students about, Matt smiled as he replied, "The wish to be invisible" — then he explained.

©1995
Nancy Davis, Ph.D.

The Boy Who Won the Gold

Problem(s) Addressed:

Inability to trust; problems in asking for help from authority figures or teachers

Appropriate for:

Grades 1 - 9

Message:

Winners understand that learning from those around you is important to success

Symbols and Metaphors:

Hurdles: any problem encountered in life; skills that must be learned

Flower: a metaphor for a child and what is needed to grow

Gardener: a teacher, counselor, parent or anyone that can teach and assist

The gold: a goal achieved

Elements of the Story Which Can be Changed:

Sex of the main characters; characteristics of the main character

Note:

This story was created for a seventh grader who refused to ask for help from anyone. He would not ask his teachers or his coaches for assistance when he did not understand something, nor would he ask his parents for help. Consequently, his grades were very poor. This story allowed him to ask for help in therapy and to express his feelings for the first time, an added bonus.

538

The Boy Who Won the Gold

Once upon a time there lived a boy named Sean who could run like the wind. Sean ran every place he needed to go because he lived in the country where people and places were far away. Sean loved to run and rather than riding in a car, he would run up mountains and jump over logs. He would run down roads and over bridges. Sean would even run down streams. Everyone who watched Sean as he ran commented, "Sean could win the Olympic gold someday. He is the best runner I have ever seen."

As Sean got older, his parents realized that he needed special training to help him improve his running. So they sent him to a private school that specialized in training Olympic champions.

On the first day of school, the running coach watched with excitement as Sean ran, jumping over anything in his path. "You can be an Olympic hurdler because of your speed and the ease with which you jump," the coach said to Sean. So Sean became a hurdle jumper. Sean wasn't convinced that jumping hurdles was what he wanted to do, but the coach continued to tell Sean that he could be a great star.

Sean silently began to train for the hurdles. Each morning before academic classes began, Sean would run the track and try to jump the hurdles set up in each lane. The hurdles were new to Sean and he had trouble clearing them with his legs. Often he knocked the hurdles over, hitting and bruising his legs. Even though his legs hurt each day, Sean continued to try jumping over the hurdles without telling anyone how much trouble he was having.

When the coach asked Sean if he would like his help, Sean would either answer "No" or he would just remain silent and jog away. Sean had made the decision that he could become the best hurdle jumper in the world all by himself.

One day Sean's school was competing against another school. When Sean ran the hurdles in the first race, he didn't do very well. Sean — the runner who had amazed everyone who had seen him run — had problems getting his legs over the hurdles. He kept knocking them down. He came in a disappointing last in his first race and began to get discouraged. "I guess I'm not the champion everyone thought I was," he said to himself. Although no one else seemed to notice, Sean began to get sad and withdrawn.

At practice, Sean asked his teammates what he was doing wrong. Each of them had a different opinion of what he should do. One told Sean to hold his legs straighter. Another thought he should jump higher. A third thought he should think of running in the mountains instead of running on the track. He listened to all of their conflicting advice . . . ran some more, jumped some hurdles, but continued to knock them down. Sean improved a little, but he still came in near the end of the pack.

The coach noticed that Sean was beginning to get sad and disappointed at his performance. He asked Sean if he would like individual coaching sessions in hurdle jumping. "I have watched you run, Sean, and I believe that you can be the best huddle jumper I have ever coached," he announced to Sean. "How about meeting me on the track tomorrow an hour before class and I'll work very hard to help you."

"I need my sleep," Sean responded while turning away to study a textbook. "Thank you anyway."

That night Sean's parents called to see how he was doing. Sean told them he was doing fine. He didn't want to tell them about the sadness in his heart because he had come to believe that all the predictions about his future greatness were proving to be wrong.

Sean ran two more races and continued to come in near the end of the pack. Sean was very disappointed with himself. "Maybe I'll just quit track and go back home. I guess I was never destined to be a track star anyway."

That night, Sean had a dream about a plant that was grown to be a prize-winning flower. When the seed sprouted and the plant began to grow, it grew more slowly than the other plants. When the gardener came along, the plant refused to take in the fertilizer she put around him. Then it refused to let the bug spray help it; it even kept the rain and the sunshine away. Soon the plant that was supposed to be prize winning, grew smaller and more withered. As the dream progressed, Sean watched as the gardener talked to the plant about fertilizer, about bug spray, about sunshine and rain, about opening yourself up to all that you need to be the best that you can be.

When Sean woke up, he lay very still letting the message of the plant and the gardener be clear to his heart. Then Sean got out of bed and got dressed. He found his coach and asked him for some special help. The coach was, of course, happy to work with Sean individually.

Each day Sean and the coach spent an hour or more training and videotaping Sean's performance. The coach then used the tapes to show Sean how to improve his running and hurdle jumping. With each race, Sean improved his performance. Soon he began to come in first.

When the Olympic trials were scheduled, Sean qualified to run with the United States team in the hurdle races. No one who had predicted Sean's greatness was surprised when he won the gold medal at the Olympics. As the gold medal was placed around Sean's neck, a little girl handed him an armful of flowers. As Sean looked at the flowers, something in his heart smiled as it understood the connection.

©1995
Nancy Davis, Ph.D.

The Car That Couldn't Stay on the Road

Problem(s) Addressed:

Hyperactivity caused by Attention Deficient Syndrome or Post Traumatic Stress Disorder; poor problem-solving skills; pessimism

Appropriate for:

Ages 5 - 9

Message:

You can learn techniques to help you pay attention and to slow down

Symbols and Metaphors:

Running off the road and bumping into things: hyperactive behavior
Slowing down the carburetor: slowing down the accelerated electrical activity of the brain common in PTSD
Changing the fuel mixture: allowing the brain to use glucose from the blood

Elements of the Story Which Can be Changed:

Sex of car; type of person who buys the car; the way in which the engine is changed, based on the child's problem

Note:

Research from the National Institute of Mental Health (Zametkin, Nordahl, Gross & King, 1990) suggests that hyperactivity and attention deficient disorders are caused by the inability of the brain to use glucose from the blood. (10% of the most extreme activity is thought to be caused by excess thyroid.) PTSD has been shown to accelerate the electrical activity in the brain, particularly the hippocampus, causing behavior similar to that of hyperactivity (van der Kolk, 1996). Even though there are physical causes of both types of hyperactive behavior, the unconscious can sometimes figure out how to normalize its own functioning (Haley, 1973; Siegel, 1986).

The Car That Couldn't Stay on the Road

Once upon a time there was a car whose dream was to be a police cruiser. He wanted to have flashy lights and a loud siren. He wanted to be painted in blue and white and race by cars that had pulled over to let him pass.

The family that owned the car had no idea that he wanted to be a police car. They just wanted a car that drove them safely to work, to school and shopping. But this car was a big problem. When the family drove the car, he often went so fast that he ran off the road. The car didn't seem to pay attention to where he was going and always seemed to be bumping into things. The more he ran off the road and ran into things, the more dented and rusty his body became. He seemed to always be in trouble because he did not seem able to pay attention to where he was going and what he was doing.

After the car had scared the owners one too many times, they decided to buy another car. "You're not good for anything," they told the car. So they covered him with a big piece of canvas and parked him in a field.

As he sat alone in the field, the dream of being a police car seemed to fade further and further into the distance. He was lonely and couldn't see what was happening because the canvas covered his body from back to front.

One day a thief was running from a policeman and spotted the car. Thinking the car would be a great hiding place, the thief pulled up the canvas and jumped inside. The policeman soon followed with his dog who smelled the trail of the thief even though he was hidden from view. When the dog began to bark at the car, the police officer threw the canvas off and quickly arrested the thief. After putting the thief in his cruiser, the police officer began admiring the car that he had uncovered and wondered why such a nice car was not being used. Just then the owners of the car ran over to determine why the police were running through their field. After telling the owners about the thief, the police officer asked them about the car.

"Oh, that old thing," they said with disgust. "He won't stay on the road, he only has one speed—fast—and he doesn't pay attention."

"Well, the car sure looks good to me," the policeman responded.

"You can have that car if you want it, it's just taking up space in our yard," they told the policeman. The policeman asked his partner to drive the police car with the thief back to the station so he could drive the car home.

Sitting quietly had not taught the car a thing. In fact, being still had pushed the car to be more out of control. Even with the expert driving of the policeman, the car went on and off the road, and ran into a parked car, denting the bumper.

Because the policeman also was a car mechanic, he looked at the car in a far different way than the previous owners had. When they had looked at the car, they saw it in terms of problems. When the policeman looked at the car, he saw it in terms of solutions. "I can fix you so you pay attention," he told the car, "And I can repair you so you stay on the road."

He put the car in his garage and found his tool kit. First he opened the hood and slowed down the carburetor. Then he changed the fuel mixture. He tightened the steering and fixed the accelerator pedal so the driver controlled the speed of the car. After that, he washed the car, and polished it until it shined.

When he drove it again, the car stayed on the road. It seemed to pay attention to what was happening around it and to slow down. Each time the policeman drove the car, it seemed to gain more and more control. Soon it was acting like every other car on the road. When the policeman was sure that the car was safe, he began taking his family for outings in the car. The car loved being a family car and realized that being a police car might have advantages, but so did having a family who cares about you.

As the car sat in the driveway in front of the police officer's home, he realized how lucky he was to be owned by a man who looked for solutions as a way to deal with problems.

©1995
Nancy Davis, Ph.D.

The Turtle and the Mouse

Problem(s) Addressed:

Withdrawal from learning; poor problem-solving skills; poor social skills

Appropriate for:

Elementary school students

Message:

Knowledge is power and protection; withdrawal from learning and people is risky

Symbols and Metaphors:

Pulling into shell: withdrawal, depression, turning-off

Falling down the hill: any difficult problem

Turned upside down: any problem which throws life off balance

Elements of the Story Which Can be Changed:

The sex of the main characters; the way the turtle withdraws; the message from the mouse

Note:

Students withdraw from learning for a variety of reasons...modeling of parent behavior; Depression, Post Traumatic Stress Disorder, low self esteem, personality style, social difficulties, or poor problem-solving skills. School can be the place where many of these problems are reversed.

The Turtle and the Mouse

Once upon a time there lived a turtle and a mouse who were the very best of friends. Although the mouse and the turtle were very different animals, sometimes differences can be helpful, especially when one friend has problems.

The mouse was a very curious and friendly creature who loved new experiences and unfamiliar situations. He constantly explored his environment, and as he did this, the mouse learned much about the world. The furry rodent met many animals and made lots of friends, finding each day to be a new adventure.

The turtle, on the other hand, was quiet and fearful. Whenever a problem arose, rather than face it, the turtle withdrew into his shell and waited for the problem to go away. The turtle didn't learn much by doing this, but having a shell that was attached to his back made his style of problem solving very difficult to change.

The mouse constantly challenged the turtle to stay out of his shell and find a way to solve the problems that he faced. However, whenever the mouse tried to convince the turtle of the harm of running away from problems, the turtle pulled into his shell and ignored the mouse.

Despite the problems the mouse had in convincing the turtle to stay out of his shell, he refused to give up on his friend. He constantly knocked on the shell of the turtle, reminding him that there was a world outside of his shell and it was time for the turtle to come out and face it.

The mouse talked to the turtle, brought food to the turtle, and tried to teach him much of what he had learned about the world first hand. He told the turtle about animals that hunt mice and how a mouse had to be smarter than these animals in order to survive.

"If you had a shell," the turtle said to the mouse one day, "you wouldn't have to be afraid of all those mean animals. You could just pull inside to be safe. I have my own natural hiding place."

"Hiding is not safety," the mouse replied. "Knowledge is the best protection that I have, because I can figure out the best way to get out of danger; you stay hidden so much you don't know how to do anything else but hide!"

The turtle, however, was not convinced. He continued to hide in his shell even when the mouse tried to talk him into exploring the forest and meeting new friends. "I don't need to learn anything," the turtle told himself. "The safety of my shell is the only thing I need to know."

One day, the turtle was walking along on a hill where he walked every morning to drink from the creek. Because he didn't pay attention to his world, the turtle was unaware that a storm had loosened the dirt near the edge of the hill. Without noticing the danger ahead, the turtle walked into the loose dirt, tumbled down the hill, and landed upside down.

An upside down turtle is a turtle in big trouble. His legs were too short to flip himself over, and without help, a turtle can quickly die of thirst or hunger. No one had seen the turtle fall, and he had so few friends that the turtle realized that he probably wouldn't be missed. To make the problem even worse, the turtle was covered by tall grass, hidden from view of any animal that might happen to walk by on the hill and look down.

The turtle tried pulling into his shell to forget his problem, since withdrawal was the only technique the turtle had learned to solve problems, withdraw is just what he did. "I just won't think about this problem," he told himself. So the turtle went to sleep.

After several hours, the turtle woke up hungry and thirsty. He was still upside down and alone. He tried going back to sleep and withdrawing into his shell, but this didn't seem to help when his stomach began to growl. Then the turtle began to get scared. He realized that he was trapped and he had no way to help himself. However, he couldn't think of anything to do but pull back into his shell and try not to think about his problem.

Night came and went, and the turtle remained upside down. He tried to think of some way to help himself, but his mind was blank. He remembered how his friend, the mouse, had told him that learning was important and how he had ignored the mouse, time and time again.

Without water, the turtle's mouth became dry; all the turtle could think about was getting a drink of water from the creek. He moved in and out of his shell trying to take his mind off of his thirst, but the technique that had worked in the past to help him avoid problems, didn't help at all this time.

All at once, the turtle felt a nudge on his shell. To the surprise of the turtle, his friend the mouse, had appeared and was trying to turn him over. "How long have you been here?" the mouse asked, "I've been looking everywhere for you."

"I don't know," the turtle replied weakly, "I never learned to tell time or how to count."

The mouse was not strong enough to turn the turtle, but he studied the upside down turtle for a while, thinking of solutions to this problem. All at once, the mouse grabbed a long and thick stick. Putting the end of the stick under the turtle and over a rock, the mouse jumped on the other end. The turtle rocked and then flipped over; he was on his feet again. The mouse helped his friend walk to the creek for a much needed drink.

"How did you find me?" the turtle asked his friend.

"When I discovered that you had disappeared, I walked the paths that you always travel," the mouse told his friend. "I looked and looked for you. When I couldn't see you from the paths, I moved away from the trail and walked in and out of the trees and grass, searching until I found you."

The turtle was so grateful, that he couldn't thank the mouse enough. "Thank me by staying out of your shell and learning about the world," the mouse told him. "If I had been lost, you would have withdrawn into your shell and never found me. I need a friend that can help me to feel safe too, so it's time for you to quit hiding!"

So the turtle learned from being upside down and lost. He followed the mouse as he explored his world and learned many new things. The turtle learned how to solve problems and how to make friends. He learned how to look forward to adventure and to think rather than keep his mind blank. He learned how to enjoy life rather than to withdraw from it.

One day the turtle became lost in some tall grass as he tried to find his friend, the mouse. In the past he would have pulled into his shell and tried to forget that he was lost. But because he had learned so much from the mouse, the turtle did not withdraw...he used the new techniques he had learned to find his way out of the tall grass, and was soon proudly telling the mouse how he had learned to solve his own problem. The turtle had discovered that hiding from problems never helps you find solutions.

® 1996
Nancy Davis Ph.D.

CHAPTER 12

Modern Fairy Tales

Most fairy tales were created when woman were considered property and had no rights. The most popular fairy tales have women as both the villains (witches, step-mothers) and victims, often because of their own lack of awareness of the world. Men are considered powerful rescuers that can carry off a woman to live "happily ever after." Just as listening to therapeutic stories again and again can give powerful messages to the unconscious, so can watching the modern video taped versions of fairy tales with outdated messages of a woman's role in society. What is happening to the values of little girls in our society who repeatedly listen to messages in these fairy tales of the passive and powerless role of women? The fairy tales in this chapter have been re-written to help the modern woman move out of the role of victim and find equal status in their own values and in the world.

Little Green Riding Hood

Problem(s) Addressed:
Distorted perceptions; problems in seeing evil in others

Appropriate for:
Any age

Message:
It is easy to tell the difference between a wolf and a person if you have eyes that see clearly

Symbols and Metaphors:
Wolf: abusive male

Elements of the Story Which Can be Changed:
Sex of the main character; sex of grandparent

Note:
If a woman (or man) can learn to tell the difference between someone who is nurturing as compared to abusive, she/he will not need to be rescued.

Little Green Riding Hood

Once upon a time there was a little girl named Crystal who wore a hood just like Little Red Riding Hood, except Crystal's hood was green. One summer day, Crystal decided to go to her Grandma's house to bring her cookies she had baked.

Grandma lived alone in a house with big windows. Because Crystal had not called to let her know she was coming to visit, Grandma had left to go to the grocery store. While Grandma was out of her house, a wolf broke in. He was going to steal everything in sight, but when he heard Crystal at the door, the wolf got other ideas. He decided to pretend he was Grandma. He put on Grandma's nightgown and got under the covers of her bed. The wolf had heard the story of Little Red Riding Hood. Having noticed that Crystal was wearing a green hood, he believed that she would say, "Oh, what big ears you have, Grandma," when she walked in the bedroom and saw him.

However, Crystal was not Little Red Riding Hood. She entered the bedroom, took one look at the figure in the bed, and demanded, "Where's Grandma?"
"I'm Grandma," whispered the Wolf trying to disguise his voice. "I've been feeling sick this morning, so I stayed in bed."

"Nooooo, you're not Grandma," Crystal said firmly. "You're a wolf!"
"How did you know I wasn't Grandma?" the Wolf asked. "This disguise fooled a girl your age who was dressed in red."

"You must think I'm stupid; I can certainly tell the difference between my grandmother and a wolf," Crystal yelled, turning around and running as fast as she could to get away from the wolf before he could hurt her.

Little Green Riding Hood soon found Grandma at the grocery store. "Did you know that there is a wolf in your house?" Crystal asked her grandmother, grabbing her hand to get her attention. "He was in your bed, with your nightgown on and he tried to get me to believe he was you," she added.

"You're kidding me?" Grandma said with a frown, "Let's get the police."

So Grandma and Crystal called 911 and soon were riding in a police car to Grandma's house. The wolf was still inside, packing the things he wanted to steal into a pillowcase. The police arrested the wolf, charging him with trespassing, breaking and entering, robbery and impersonating a grandmother.

Crystal received an award from the police for helping capture the wolf, and the police hired her to teach classes to women who can't tell the difference between a wolf and a person who loves you.

©1995
Nancy Davis, Ph.D.

Cynderella

Problem(s) Addressed:

The empowerment of women

Appropriate for:

Females of any age

Message:

Education, mentors, motivation and self esteem are the keys to getting away from abusive relationships and being successful

Symbols and Metaphors:

Wicked stepmother and stepsisters: any abusive family

Elements of the Story Which Can be Changed:

The details of Cynderella's life can be individualized.

Note:

This modernizes the old story of Cinderella in which a woman needed a fairy godmother and a prince to rescue her from an abusive family.

Cynderella

Once upon a time, not very long ago, there lived a girl named Cynderella. When Cynderella was quite young, her mother deserted her father and ran off with another man. That left Cynderella and her father trying to fend for themselves. Because her father thought that Cynderella really needed a mother, he searched far and wide for a woman who was suitable. Learning little from his experience with Cynderella's mother, the woman he chose for a second wife was even more heartless than the first.

Although initially appearing quite kind and caring during the courtship period with Cynderella's father, after they were married, this new wife revealed a side of herself that she had been hiding. Cynderella and her father soon learned that Cynderella's stepmother was very mean and cruel. In addition, she brought with her to the marriage two mean and self-centered daughters, slightly older than Cynderella.

Cynderella's father was not much of a problem solver. Rather than try to deal with this new wife, he began to stay away from the family more and more, closing the local bars in town each night. When he finally came home, Cynderella's father was often so drunk that it really didn't matter to him how the new wife acted — he was numb.

With Cynderella's father out of the way, the stepmother proceeded to turn Cynderella into her slave. She degraded her and humiliated her. She demanded that Cynderella do all the cleaning, cooking and washing around the house. She refused to let Cynderella talk to her friends or go out on dates. The stepmother and her cruel daughters spent many hours at the mall buying new clothes; Cynderella got whatever clothes they discarded after they were tired of wearing them.

Cynderella appealed to her father for help, but being a man who ran away from problems, she might as well have kept silent.

When the stepmother first came into her life, Cynderella was already depressed and withdrawn due to her mother's desertion. So it was easy for Cynderella to believe the cruel words of the new members of her family and follow their orders to clean, to cook and to stay put. The

When the stepmother first came into her life, Cynderella was already depressed and withdrawn due to her mother's desertion. So it was easy for Cynderella to believe the cruel words of the new members of her family and follow their orders to clean, to cook and to stay put. The stepmother, however, could not keep Cynderella from school. It was in the classroom that Cynderella first began to feel safe and competent. In one of her classes she met a teacher with exceptional understanding and the ability to motivate even the most troubled students. This teacher recognized Cynderella's potential and began to counsel her, eventually making Cynderella her teaching assistant.

With this teacher's encouragement, Cynderella began to secretly spend many of the hours that she was supposed to be cleaning the house studying her books instead. She hid her library books under her bed. She watched videotapes supplied by the teacher that gave her extra knowledge, and she learned to repeat the words of encouragement to herself that the teacher said to her at school. Soon, Cynderella's grades were at the top of her class. She hid her report card from her stepmother, who really wasn't interested enough in Cynderella to notice that she never saw her grades. The stepmother assumed that Cynderella was doing so poorly in school that she was hiding her grades for fear of punishment.

As Cynderella studied, she decided that she was going to be a doctor. The inspiring teacher remained her counselor, her encourager, and her friend, as she passed from grade to grade. Cynderella began to check out medical books and books on being successful in college and medical school. When the fire department offered CPR classes and training in the Heimlich Maneuver, Cynderella was the first to sign up.

One weekend day, Cynderella's wicked stepmother sent her to the mall to buy more cleaning supplies and new curtains. Unbeknownst to Cynderella, an important prince was also paying a visit to the same mall. As Cynderella walked past the stores, admiring the many things which she had no money to buy, she stopped outside a restaurant where the prince was enjoying a fine steak dinner. At just that moment, the prince swallowed a very large piece of steak which became lodged in his throat. He began to choke, turn blue and panic, pointing to his mouth. The people with him began to panic as well. Not knowing what was wrong with the prince, they screamed to the waiter to call 911. Cynderella recognized from her class exactly what was happening and, although she was much smaller than the prince, she ran into the restaurant, put her arms securely around his stomach and pulled very hard. At the second squeeze, a piece of steak projected across the room from the prince's mouth. The prince was so happy to be saved that he forgot to ask Cynderella her name as she walked quickly away.

In the hours and days that followed, the prince had flashbacks of his experience and saw the face of the exceptional Cynderella, who knew exactly what to do to save him. He decided that he had to find her and marry her. The prince sent the people who worked for him to hire a detective agency. It wasn't long before a clerk in one of the stores where Cynderella bought cleaning supplies was able to tell them who Cynderella was by pulling out a charge card slip and looking at her address.

The prince put on his finest suit, purchased a huge diamond engagement ring, and took a limousine to Cynderella's house. As the prince emerged from his limousine, the cruel and self-centered stepsisters and their mother recognized immediately who he was; they had read about him and seen his picture in the society section of the local newspaper. Cynderella was in the back room cleaning the floors, but heard the commotion. She moved quietly to a window and peeked out, seeing the prince that she had helped coming up to the door.

When the prince knocked on the door and asked for the woman who had saved him, the stepsisters tried to pretend that it was one of them. It wasn't difficult for the prince to figure out they were not who he was looking for. For one thing, he wasn't blind and these women didn't look like Cynderella at all. He also asked them about the Heimlich Maneuver and they had no idea what he was talking about. He demanded to see Cynderella; her wicked stepmother declared that no one by that name lived in her house.

Cynderella, however, had begun to get assertive while attending school and walked boldly into the room, letting the prince know that she was the woman for whom he searched. The prince fell to his knees, offering the diamond to Cynderella and asking for her hand in marriage. The stepsisters almost turned blue as they choked on their tongues, wondering how Cynderella could charm this rich prince when they had tried to keep her a slave, dressed in hand-me-downs. Cynderella asked the prince if they could go to dinner and talk about his request. He agreed, asking if she would allow him to buy her a dress befitting her radiance.

Cynderella could not remember ever having a new dress. She agreed. The prince accompanied her to a store and bought her the dress of her choice. This purchase was followed with an expensive dinner at the best restaurant in town. The prince and Cynderella talked and talked through dinner. At the end of the evening, the prince asked again for her hand in marriage, stating that she had saved his life and by doing this she had become the woman of his dreams.

Cynderella thanked the prince for his offer. But she told him that if he really wanted to repay her for saving his life, he could loan her the money for college and medical school. Cynderella may have been a slave in her own home, but she had learned something from her father's two mistakes in picking wives. She explained to the prince that she didn't even know him and that her saving his life was no basis to start a marriage. If the prince would help finance her education, Cynderella told him, they could date during the years she was in college.

The prince was again astounded by the ways and wisdom of this American girl. He called his lawyer and had a contract drawn up stating that he would pay for the schools of Cynderella's choice. The prince made sure that this contract also guaranteed money to live on campus, far away from her wicked stepmother and selfish stepsisters, as Cynderella had requested.

Because her grades were very high and she was very smart, Cynderella was quickly accepted into college. She studied hard and did well; she was determined to be different from her mother, her father and her stepmother. She dated the prince, at times, during the years she attended college, but they found that they had very little in common.

Her stepmother and stepsisters wanted to attend Cynderella's graduation, so they could gain status by claiming they were related to a doctor. Cynderella did not invite them, and was happy the tickets to attend the graduation ceremony were limited. After giving one ticket to the teacher who had inspired her and another to her father, she gave the third to the prince. The prince brought five-dozen roses, which he handed to Cynderella as she received her diploma. Inside the box with the roses were the torn up pieces of the loan contract. The teacher was very happy for her, and her father gave her a hug. He had sobered up, learning to take care of himself by following his daughter's example. Cynderella and the prince parted friends.

That night as Cynderella looked at her medical degree, she was proud of herself for understanding that she didn't need to marry a rich prince to take her away from a wicked stepmother and a bad situation. With a little determination, a lot of work and the support of someone who could inspire her, Cynderella had figured out how to rescue herself.

©1995
Nancy Davis, Ph.D.

Beauty and the Prince

Problem(s) Addressed:

Women with distorted perceptions who ignore signs that a man is evil or abusive; women who "look but don't see."

Appropriate for:

Females all ages

Message:

You can give up the distorts in your perceptions and learn to see people as they really are; it is necessary to see clearly in order to protect yourself from abusive relationships

Symbols and Metaphors:

Costume: the tricks that abusive men use to distort the perceptions of the women that they victimize

Elements of the story that can be changed:

This story can be changed to a male form since many men are victims of abusive women.

Note:

Victims of childhood abuse often have distorted perceptions that are the result of the abuse and help to continue the cycle of abuse, as well (Putnam, 1996). Therapists and teachers must help children learn to have perceptual processes clear of distortions in order to build self esteem and the ability to protect oneself from abusive relationships.

566

Beauty and the Prince

Once upon a time there lived a princess named Beauty. She was a cute child, and as she grew, she changed into a gorgeous young woman. Word of the stunning princess spread far and near, to many kingdoms. As she grew old enough for suitors, many men visited the castle, hoping to claim her hand in marriage. If one succeeded in marrying the princess, not only would he share her riches, but would also gain power since the princess would one day inherit the throne.

When Beauty grew of age, the king and queen gave a dance to introduce their daughter to the world. They invited suitors to present themselves to Beauty, so all would have an equal chance. The princess sat on a throne as each man introduced himself. If the princess was interested, she would ask the man to dance.

The princess was more than ravishing that night. Many men lined up to greet her. But among these men was a monster disguised to look like a handsome man. His costume was well done, but anyone who looked closely would notice that he wore a costume.

Beauty chose to dance with many men that night, among them the monster in disguise. Because he was a monster, he had developed more skills than the average handsome man to charm a princess. The monster impressed her more than the other suitors, and was asked back for dinner the next night. The princess had not noticed the zipper in the back of his costume, nor the fur that peeked out from the seams. Beauty believed that all men were good, and made sure that her eyes saw only what she believed. This, of course, made the monster quite happy. He loved to find a woman who looked but did not see.

The monster brought flowers and gifts to Beauty, wooing her with words of love and praise. He complimented her on traits that she viewed as flaws, making her feel even more special than a princess usually does. Soon Beauty began to see the monster exclusively, and seeing him occupied most of her time.

One night, after drinking wine, the monster flew into a rage at Beauty, slapping her across the face. The monster immediately apologized, telling her that the wine had hit her, not him. The princess told herself that the man who hit her was not the man she was beginning to love and believed his lie.

The costume of the monster became more and more shabby as he wore it, but the princess did not seem to notice. She ignored the claws when they protruded from his hands. She paid no attention to the monster smells that penetrated his costume. She did not listen to the growls that the monster sometimes made when he was upset.

One night, the monster held Beauty in an embrace. As their lips touched, the monster's costume fell to the ground. Instead of the beast becoming a kind and handsome prince, the man who had seemed to be a kind and handsome prince now clearly was a monster.

The monster thought that he and Beauty were alone, but the princess's brother was close by, and happened to see the monster emerge. The prince had eyes that saw very well and quickly summoned the guards. Over the protests of the princess, the prince and the guards soon had the monster in the dungeon where no one could mistake him for a kind and loving man.

When her brother returned, the princess was crying and kept insisting that the monster was really a nice man. Her brother knew better. He took his sister to an eye doctor so she would be sure that when she looked, she saw without distortion. Then her brother had wise teachers work with the princess day after day until she understood about monsters and costumes. To complete her education, the prince threw away the princess's book titled, "Beauty and the Beast." When the princess protested, her brother told her that it was time for her to stop believing in fairy tales. "Love cannot make a prince out of a monster," her brother informed her. "Have you ever seen a man change a wicked witch into a beautiful princess by kissing her? Men know better than to believe in that kind of fairy tale."

It wasn't long before the princess was seeing in a very different way. She decided that she didn't need to be put on display at a dance so that men could beg to dance with her because of her beauty. She now understood that seeing a man at his best behavior at a dance was no way to pick a partner.

So the princess became a writer and wrote stories based on reality, rather than fairy tales. And she made sure that she was smart enough to never again kiss a handsome prince who turned into a monster.

The Beauty Who Slept a Long Time

Problem(s) Addressed:

A victim's inability to place responsibility for abuse on the abuser instead of themself; a victim who has difficulty in getting angry at the behavior of an abuser

Appropriate for:

Ages 13 to adult

Message:

See abuse for what it is and hold abusers responsible for their behavior

Symbols and Metaphors:

Sleeping: the distortion of responsibility for abuse held by many victims of child abuse, rape and battering

Elements of the Story Which Can be Changed:

This story can also be changed into a male version, since men often fail to report abuse or to acknowledge the abuser as responsible for his/her acts (Putnam, 1996).

Note:

Victims often remain in denial, sadness, shame and guilt because they blame themselves for their own abuse. Anger is a progressive step in healing, since it is an emotion which acknowledges that someone other than the victim is responsible for their abuse. Anger can be healthy and motivating and the beginning of healing.

The Beauty Who Slept a Long Time

Once upon a time there lived a king and a queen who had a very large, but empty castle because they were unable to have children. The queen and the king wanted children very much, but after years of trying, they were still childless. Hoping to get some advice, they got an appointment with the most famous fertility doctor in the kingdom. The royal couple asked that the doctor keep their visits confidential while providing the most up-to-date treatment available.

This doctor was very self-centered and loved money far more than he loved people or babies. He let the king and the queen know that there was only about a 40% chance that the treatment would be successful and that it would require a lot of their money to insure that they produced a child. The doctor was crafty and thinking about his retirement. He told the royal couple that they would only have to pay if he were successful in providing them with a baby. Even after the birth of their child, the doctor informed the royal couple, they could wait sixteen years before paying his fees. This sounded like a great deal to the king and queen until they heard the doctor say that his fee for successful treatment was five million dollars.

"No!" the king responded and stood up to leave the clinic. The queen began to cry and the king could not stand to see his wife cry. So, with a great deal of trepidation, the king and queen signed a contract guaranteeing payment of five million dollars on the 16th birthday of their first child.

Because they wanted a child very much, the king and queen followed the treatment the doctor prescribed day after day. With the thought of five million dollars constantly on his mind, the doctor did much research and used every current medical procedure available to insure that the royal couple were successful in producing a child. On a beautiful spring day, the doctor announced that the queen was pregnant. Nine months later, a baby girl was born as church bells rang throughout the kingdom. The king and queen named their daughter Joy, because of the happiness she had brought to their lives. The royal couple became so absorbed in raising their daughter that they soon forgot their contract with the clinic doctor.

571

Princess Joy grew taller, wiser and more lovely with each passing year. The king and queen had several other children after the princess was born, and were so busy raising their family that Princess Joy's sixteenth birthday approached almost before the royal couple realized the significance of that date. On the morning of the princess' birthday, the clinic doctor knocked at the castle door demanding his money. Unfortunately, hard times had fallen on the kingdom during the sixteen years. Although the king and queen were happy, they were not rich. The king reluctantly informed the doctor that they did not have five million dollars and offered to pay him in installments.

The doctor had planned on receiving payment in full and had already spent three million dollars even before he had received the money. He had planned to pay off his creditors as soon as he got the check from the royal couple for five million. When the doctor learned that he would not be paid in full, he became enraged. He tried many techniques to get his money, to no avail. After exhausting all of his own ideas, the doctor hired a credit collection agency. The agency also tried every technique that had been successful in other cases. But the king and queen just did not have the money to pay them, no matter what techniques were used.

The doctor's creditors began to hound him, wanting their money, too. In desperation, the doctor hired a shady character that used less than legal methods to collect accounts. Harassing a royal couple was a risky business, so the doctor promised him $500,000 when he received the payment. This collector also tried every dirty trick in his book. He viciously threatened to break the king's legs. Although this had worked with other people, the king had guards, so he was not intimidated. Although the shady character used every other technique he had learned in a lifetime of intimidation, the king and queen had no money so they could not pay their debt.

When the collector realized that his normal techniques were not going to succeed, he became enraged. He talked to the doctor, who was also angry and desperate. They concocted a scheme. They decided to give Princess Joy a drug which would put her into a deep coma. The doctor would tell the king and queen that only he had the antidote for the drug. They were sure that once the princess was in a coma, the royal couple would pay five million dollars in return for the antidote to awaken her.

The doctor provided the collector with a potent drug and it was quickly placed into the breakfast of the princess by the sneaky collector. When Princess Joy ate her cereal, she instantly fell into a deep coma. Soon, a letter arrived for the king and queen promising to provide the antidote to wake up the princess in exchange for the money they owed. As much as the king and queen wanted to pay, they could not. They still had no money and little hope of getting that much at any time in the future.

The court doctor was unable to wake the princess, neither could all the other doctors that offered their help. The king and queen were broken-hearted and watched day after day as their daughter lay in the grip of a deep sleep. The drug was amazing, because the princess looked exactly the same as she had when she first fell into a coma. Because the king and queen wanted Princess Joy near to them, she was placed under glass in the lobby of the castle. People often came to visit when they heard the story of the sleeping princess.

Months went by and the doctor gave up trying to collect his money. He moved out of the kingdom to escape the collectors who hounded him, taking the antidote with him. All hope of reviving Princess Joy seemed lost.

One day a handsome prince from another kingdom heard about Princess Joy and arrived to see her for himself. He entered the lobby of the castle, standing beside the princess in admiration for some time. Then, looking around to make sure no one was watching, the prince lifted the glass cover and began to kiss the princess again and again. Then the prince began to rub his hands all over her body.

For a reason understood by many women, even though she was in a coma, Princess Joy began to get angry. The more the prince touched her and the more he kissed her without her permission, the more angry she became. Because anger has a special power to wake up even those in the deepest coma, the eyes of the princess popped open. As the prince leaned to kiss her again, the princess hit him in the jaw as hard as she could.

"You pervert," yelled the princess, "What kind of man kisses and touches a woman who looks like she is dead?" Princess Joy became more and more angry and she screamed so loud that the guards arrived. They were amazed to see that she was awake.

The king and queen were elated to discover their daughter was back. They told her about the doctor and the drug and Princess Joy told them about the prince. Soon the prince was arrested and there was a trial. The princess' anger allowed her to be a vocal and convincing witness.

In the time that followed, the princess decided to become an attorney and teach a class in contracts. She spoke to others about making promises that can't be kept. She began by teaching her mother and father. Life was very good for her and, more or less, she lived happily ever after.

The prince, on the other hand, did not live so happily, as he was found guilty of assault in his trial. He was sent to prison where his status as a prince became a source of scorn. While serving his sentence, the prince had many days to think about his judgment and why he had kissed a princess who looked like she was dead.

Bibliography

American Psychiatric Association, (1995). *Diagnostic and Statistical Manual of Mental Disorders-Revised.* (4th ed.). Washington, D.C.: Author.

Briere, J. (1992). Studying delayed memories of childhood abuse. *The APSAC Advisor:* Summer.

Briere, J., & Runtz, M. (1993). Childhood sexual abuse: Long-term sequelae and implications for psychological assessment. *Journal of Interpersonal Violence.* 8 (3) 312-330.

Brett, E. A., and Ostroff, R. (1985). Imagery and post-traumatic stress disorder: An overview. *American Journal of Psychiatry.* 142, 417-424.

Browne, A., & Finkelhor, D. (1986). Initial and long-term effects: A review of the research. In D. Finkelhor (Ed.), *A sourcebook on childhood sexual abuse.* (pp. 143-179), Beverly Hills, CA: Sage.

Burgess, A. W. (1983). Rape trauma syndrome. *Behavioral Sciences & the Law.* 1(3), 97-113.

Burgess, A. W. & Holmstrom, L. L. (1974). The rape trauma syndrome. *American Journal of Psychiatry,* 131, 981- 986.

Ceci, Stephen J. & Bruck, Maggie. (1996). *Jeopardy in the Courtroom.* American Psychological Association: Washington, D.C.

Cole, P. & Putnam, F. W. (1992). Effects of incest on self and social functioning: A developmental psychopathology perspective. *Journal of Consulting & Clinical Psychology.* 60, 174-184.

Conte, J. R. & Schuerman, J. R. (1987). Factors associated with an increased impact of child sexual abuse. *Child Abuse & Neglect.* 11, 201 - 211.

Creamer, Mark. (1993). Recent developments in post traumatic stress disorder. *Behavior-Change.* 10(4), 219-227.

Crittenden, Patricia M. (1996). Attachment and memory systems in maltreated children. *Psychological Trauma.* 133-134.

Davis, Nancy. (1985). *Therapeutic Stories to Heal Abused Children.* Psychological Associates. Oxon Hill, MD: Author.

Demi, A. S. & Miles, M. S. (1987). Parameters of normal grief: A Delphi study. *Death Studies.* 11, 398- 412.

Dietz, P. E., Hazelwood, R. R. & Warren, J. (1990). The sexually sadistic criminal and his offenses. *Bulletin American Academy of Psychiatry and the Law.* 18(2), 163 -178.

Doris, John. (Ed). *(1991). The Suggestibility of Children's Recollections.* American Psychological Association. Washington, D.C.

Downs, W. R. (1993). Developmental considerations for the effects of childhood sexual abuse. *Journal of Interpersonal Violence.* 8 (3), 331-345.

Ellen, P. & Van-Kammen, D. P. (December 1990). The biological findings in post-traumatic stress disorder: A Review. *Journal of Applied Social Psychology.* 20, 1789-1821.

Elliott, D. (1994). Trauma and disassociated memory: Prevalence across events. Paper presented at the meeting of the International Society for Traumatic Stress Studies: Chicago, IL.

Ellis, A. & Harper, R. (1974). *A Guide to Rational Living.* North Hollywood, CA: Wilshire Book Company.

Epstein, Richard. S. (1993). Avoidant symptoms cloaking the diagnosis of PTSD in patients with severe accidental injury. *Journal of Traumatic Stress.* 6(4), 451-458.

Erickson, M., Rossi, E. and Rossi, S. (1976). *Hypnotic realities: the induction of clinical hypnosis and forms of indirect suggestion.* New York: Irvington Publishers, Inc.

Everly, George S. Jr. (1993). Psychotraumatology: A two-factor formulation of post traumatic stress. *Integrative Physiological and Behavioral Science.* 28(3), 270-278.

Everly, George S. Jr. (1994). *A Clinical Guide to the Treatment of the Human Stress Response.* New York: Plenum Press.

Everly, George S. Jr. (1994). *Post Traumatic Stress Disorder.* Educational Associates: New Jersey.

Famularo, Richard; Kinscherff, Robert and Fenton, Terence. (1990). Symptom differences in acute and chronic presentation of post traumatic stress disorder. *Child Abuse and Neglect.* 14(3), 439-444.

Finkelhor, D. (1984). *Child Sexual Abuse: New Theory and Research.* New York: The Free Press.

Foa, E. B.; Riggs, D. S. & Gershuny, B. S. (1995). Arousal, numbing & intrusion: Symptom structure of PTSD following assault. *American Journal of Psychiatry.* 152 (1), 116-120.

Friedrich, W. N. & Reams, R. A. (1987). The course of psychological symptoms in sexually abused young children. *Psychotherapy: Theory, Research and Practice.* 24, 160 -170.

Goldfield, A. E.; Mollica, R. F.; Pesavento, B. H. & Faraone, S. V. (1988). The physical and psychological sequelae of torture: Symptomology and diagnosis. *Journal of the American Medical Association.* 259, 2725-2729.

Goodman, G. S.; Taub, E. P.; Jones, D. P. H.; England, T.; Port, L. K.; Ruby, L. & Prado, L. (1992). Testifying in criminal court. *Monograph of the Society for Research in Child Development.* 57 (5).

Groth, A. N. & Burgess, A. W. (1978). Rape: a pseudosexual act. *International Journal of Women's Studies.* 1(2), 207- 210.

Haley, J. (1973). *Uncommon Therapy: The Psychiatric Techniques of Milton H. Erickson, M.D.* New York: Norton.

Hammond, D. Corydon. (1990). *Handbook of Hypnotic Suggestions and Metaphors.* New York: Norton

Hancock, LynNell. (1996) Mother's litle helper. *Newsweek.* March 18, 51- 56.

Hazelwood, Robert R., & Burgess, Ann Wolbert. (1987). *Practical aspects of rape investigation: a multidisciplinary approach.* Elsevier: New York.

Hazelwood, Robert R., Warren, Janet & Dietz, Park. (1993). Compliant victims of the sexual sadist. *Australian Family Physician. 22(4), 474-479.*

Holaday, M. & Whittenberg, T. (1994). Rorschach responding in children and adolescents who have been severely burned. *Journal of Personality Assessment.* 62(2), 269-279.

Holmstrom, L.L., & Burgess, A.W. (1975). Assessing trauma in the rape victim. *American Journal of Nursing.* 75 (8) 1288 - 1291.

Janet, P. (1909). *Les nervoses.* Paris: Flammarion.

Kinzie, J.D. (1993). Posttraumatic effects and their treatment among Southeast Asian refugees. In J.P. Wilson & B. Raphael (eds.), *International Handbook of Traumatic Stress Syndromes (pp.311-319).* New York: Plenum Press.

Lanning, Kenneth.V. (1991). Personal communication.

Lanning, Kenneth V. (1986). *Child Molesters: A Behavioral Analysis for Law Enforcement.* U.S. Department of Justice.

Lindemann, E. (1979). *Beyond Grief: Studies in Crisis Intervention.* New York: Aronson.

Loftus, E.F.; Polensky, S., & Fullilove, M.T. (1994). Memories of childhood sexual abuse: remembering and repressing. *Psychology of Woman Quarterly.* 18, 67-84.

577

Madakasira, S., & O'Brian, K. (1987). Acute posttraumatic stress disorder in victims of a natural disaster. *Journal of Nervous and Mental Disease,* 175, 286-290.

Marcey, Marcella M. (1995). *A Comparison of the Long-Term Effects of Bereavement After Four Types of Death: Anticipated Death, Sudden Death, Drunk Driver Crash and Homicide.* Unpublished doctoral dissertation: George Mason University.

McFall, Murburg, Michele; Roszell, Douglas & Veith, Richard. (1989). Psychophysiological and neuroendocrine findings in post traumatic stress disorder: A review of theory and research. *Journal of Anxiety Disorders,* 3, 243-257.

McFarlane, Alexander. C. (1993). Abnormal stimulus processing in post traumatic stress disorder, *Biological-Psychiatry,* 34 (5) 311-320.

McFarlane, Alexander C. & Yehuda, Rachel. (1996). Resilience, vulnerability, and the course of posttraumatic reactions. *Traumatic Stress.* Guilford Press: New York.

Mills, J.C. & Crowley, R.J. (1986). *Therapeutic Metaphors for Children and the Child Within.* New York. Brunner/Mazel.

Nemiah, J.C. (1995). Early concepts of trauma, dissociation and the unconscious: Their history and current medications. In D. Bremner & C., Marmar (Eds.), *Trauma, Memory, and Dissociation.* Washington, D.C: American Psychiatric Press.

Parkes, C.M. (1975). *Bereavement: Studies of Grief in Adult Life.* New York: International Universities Press.

Perry, B.D. (1993). Medicine and psychotherapy: Neurological development and the neurophysiology of trauma: Conceptual considerations for clinical work. *APSAC Advisor.* 6 (1).

Petrick, N. D., Olson, R. E., & Subotnik, L. S. (1994). Powerlessness and the need to control. *Journal of Interpersonal Violence.* 9(2), 278-285.

Putnam, F. (1996). Developmental pathways in sexually abused girls: psychological and biological data from the longitudinal study. Research presented at conference: Psychological trauma: Maturational processes and therapeutic interventions. Boston, MA.

Rauch, S.; van der Kolk, B.A.; Fisler, R.; Orr, S.P.; Albert, N.M.; Savage, C.R.; Fischman, A.J.; Jenike, M.A. & Pitman, R. K. (1994). *Pet imagery: Positron emission scans of traumatic imagery in PTSD patients.* Paper presented at the annual meeting of the International Society for Traumatic Stress Studies. Chicago, IL.

Riggs, D.S., Rothbaum, B.O., & Roa, E.B. (1995). A prospective examination of symptoms of post-traumatic stress disorder in victims of nonsexual assault. *Journal of Interpersonal Violence.* 10(2), 201-214.

Rosen, E. (Ed.) (1982). *My Voice Will Go With You: The Teaching Tales of Milton H. Erickson, M.D.* New York: W.W. Norton & Company.

Rosen, Jules, & Fields, Robert. (1988). The long-term effects of extraordinary trauma: A look beyond PTSD. *Journal of Anxiety Disorders,* 2(2), 179-191.

Rossi, E. & Ryan, M. (Eds.) (1985). *Life Reframing in Hypnosis. Vol. II. The Seminars, Workshops and Lectures of Milton H. Erickson.* New York: Irvington.

Rowan, Anderson B. & Foy, David W. (1992). Post traumatic stress disorder in child sexual abuse survivors: A literature review. *Journal of Traumatic Stress.* 6(1), 3-20 .

Sample, William E.; Goyer, Peter; McCormick, Richard, & Morris, Evan. (July 1993). Preliminary report: Brain blood flow using PET in patients with post traumatic stress disorder and substance-abuse histories. *Biological-Psychiatry.* 34 (1-2), 115-118.

Saunders, B.E.; Kilpatrick, D.G.; Resnick, H.S.; Hanson, R. A. & Lipovsky, J.A. (1992). *Epidemiological characteristics of child sexual abuse: Results from Wave II of the National Women's Study.* Paper presented at the San Diego Conference on Responding to Child Maltreatment, San Diego, CA.

Saywitz, Karen J.; Geiselman, R. Edward & Bornstein, Gail K. (1992). Effects of cognitive interviewing and practice on children's recall performance. *Journal of Applied Psychology. 77(5). 744-756.*

Saxe, G.N.; Chinman, G.; Berkowitz, R.; Hall, K.; Lieberg, G.; Schwartz, J. & van der Kolk, B.A. (1994). Somatization in patients with dissociative disorders. *American Journal of Psychiatry.* 151, 1329-1335.

Schreiber, S. & Galai-Gat, T. (1993). Uncontrolled pain following physical injury as the core-trauma in the post-traumatic stress disorder, *Pain,* 54(1), 107-110.

Seligman, Martin E.P. (1995). *The Optimistic Child.* New York; Houghton/Mufflin Company.

Shapiro, Francine. (1995). *Eyemovement Desensitization and Reprogramming: Basic Principles, Protocols and Procedures.* New York: Gilford Press.

Siegel, B. (1986). *Love, Medicine & Miracles.* New York: W.W. Norton & Company.

Swedo, Susan; Leonard, Henrietta; Mittleman, Barbara; Allen, Albert; Rapoport, Judith; Dow, Sara; Kanter, Melissa; Chapman, Floresta and Zabriskie, John. (1997). Identification of children with pediatric autoimmune neuropsychiatric disorders associated with streptococcal infections by a marker associated with rheumatic fever. *American Journal of Psychiatry.* 154:1, 110 - 114.

Tannen, Deborah. (1991). *You Just Don't Understand.* New York: Ballantine Books.

Trickett, P.K., & Putnam, F.W. (1993). Impact of child sexual abuse on females: Toward a developmental, psychobiological integration. *Psychological Science*. 4(2), 81-87.

van der Kolk. (1996). The role of memory and attention in the integration of experience. Workshop presented at conference: Understanding Trauma and Memory in Clinical and Forensic Settings. Boston, MA.

van der Kolk. (1995). Post traumatic stress disorder. Workshop presented at conference: Third World Congress on Stress, Trauma & Coping. Baltimore, MD.

van der Kolk, B.A., & Ducey, C.P. (1989). The psychological processing of traumatic experience: Rorschach patterns in PTSD. *Journal of Traumatic Stress*. 2(3), 259-74.

van der Kolk, B.A. & Fisler, R.E. (1994). Childhood abuse and neglect and loss of self-regulation. *Childhood Abuse and Neglect* 58 (2), 145 - 168.

van der Kolk, B.A., & Kadish, W. (1987). Amnesia, dissociation, and the return of the repressed. In B.A. van der Kolk (Ed.) *Psychological Trauma* (pp. 173-190). Washington, D.C: American Psychiatric Press.

van der Kolk, B.A., & van der Hart, O. (1991). The intrusive past: The flexibility of memory and the engraving of trauma. *American Imago*, 48(4), 425-454.

Vargas, Adriana M, & Davidson, Jonathan R. (December 1993). Post-traumatic stress disorder, *Psychiatric Clinics of North America*. 16 (4), 737-748.

Williams, L.M. (1992). Adult memories of childhood abuse: Preliminary findings from a longitudinal study. *The APSAC Advisor*. Summer.

Williams, L.M.(1994). Recall of childhood trauma: A prospective study of women's memories of child sexual abuse. *Journal of Consulting & Clinical Psychology*. 62 (6), 1167-1176.

Zametkin, Alan J.; Nordahl, Thomas E.; Gross, Michael & King, A. Catherine. (1990). Cerebral glucose metabolism in adults with hyperactivity of childhood onset. *New England Journal of Medicine*. 323(20), 1361-1366.

SUBJECT INDEX

Although each Chapter contains stories grouped broadly by the primary problems they address, many stories are useful for dealing with a number of different issues. Listed below are many of the issues covered, followed by the beginning page numbers of the stories which address each problem.

Post Traumatic Stress Disorder/Problems sleeping: 17, 23, 301, 307

Post Traumatic Stress Disorder/Pulling away from people: 17, 23, 31, 37, 43, 57, 79, 83, 75, 85, 117, 133, 145, 155, 191, 481, 503, 507, 517, 531, 547

Prejudice: 173, 201

Problem Solving Ability/Resources: 69, 91, 105, 149, 159, 187, 197, 207, 211, 215, 221, 225, 237, 297, 301, 307, 343, 393, 425, 497, 507, 531, 543, 547, 559

Reality contacts/Poor: 231, 317, 321, 475

Removing destructive anchors/Triggers: 117, 127, 255, 457, 517

Satisfied/Never: 475

School/Daydreamer, spaces out, problems focusing: 23, 37, 43, 275, 317, 493, 497, 513, 517, 543, 547

School/Fear of making mistakes: 197

School/Inability to access information: 43, 53, 47, 97, 275, 317, 493, 497, 513, 517

School/Making friends: 75, 159, 165, 203, 507, 535, 531

School/Problems learning: 37, 47, 97, 493, 497, 507, 513, 517, 537, 543, 547

School phobia/School refusal: 503

School/Reading: 47, 97, 513

School/Refusal to accept help: 177, 193, 537, 547

School/Written language: 47, 493

Self understanding: 123, 145, 149, 159, 165, 191, 199, 221, 237, 313, 431, 465, 481, 497, 507, 517, 521, 525, 547

Self-abuse: 91, 111, 145, 165, 191, 197, 221, 247, 313, 343, 349, 471, 385, 393, 507, 521

Thinking/Rigid: 155, 159, 169, 201, 211, 221, 225, 231, 237, 371, 381, 385, 425, 449, 453, 475, 521, 547

Thinking/Thought disturbances: 53, 101, 139, 247, 317, 321

Trauma/Symptoms of: 17, 23, 31, 37, 43, 47, 53, 57, 61, 65, 69, 75, 79, 83, 91, 97, 101, 105, 111, 117, 123, 127, 133, 139, 145, 169, 191, 207, 247, 255, 259, 265, 271, 275, 291, 297, 301, 307, 321, 343, 349, 357, 361, 365, 371, 399, 403, 419, 425, 431, 435, 439, 453, 457, 465, 481, 507, 513, 559, 565, 569

Trying new things: 91, 105, 111, 133, 149, 155, 159, 165, 169, 173, 177, 187, 197, 207, 211, 215, 221, 225, 237, 297, 301, 307, 313, 343, 375, 371, 399, 425, 493, 497, 503, 507, 521, 525, 537, 543, 547, 559

Withdrawn/Depressed/Shy/Building walls around self: 17, 23, 31, 37, 43, 47, 57, 79, 85, 97, 127, 133, 145, 155, 191, 203, 339, 357, 361, 419, 431, 457, 481, 507, 547

About the Author

Nancy Davis, Ph.D., is a licensed clinical psychologist who has specialized in treating children, adolescents and adults traumatized from experiencing child abuse, rape, domestic violence and job-related trauma related to serving in combat, as a law enforcement officer and emergency services. Dr. Davis uses an eclectic type of therapy including techniques with an Ericksonian emphasis, therapeutic stories, hypnosis, visual imagery, NLP, EMDR and cognitive-behavioral therapy. She is completing a book describing **Multi-Sensory Trauma Processing (MTP**), a brief treatment technique she created for treating job-related trauma and complicated PTSD. Dr. Davis has administered over 3000 psychological evaluations, the majority of which have been of children. Dr. Davis is a recognized expert witness in the areas of child abuse and post traumatic stress disorder. She has testified in more than 130 criminal proceedings, trials and juvenile court proceedings. She taught graduate school at Towson University for two years, worked as a school psychologist for Fairfax County, Virginia schools for 10 years and in private practice for over 20 years. Dr. Davis served as Chief of Counseling Services for the Employee Assistance Unit of the Federal Bureau of Investigation (FBI) from April 1998 to December, 2000.

Dr. Davis provided treatment to rescue workers and their families following the Oklahoma Bombing in 1995 and the World Trade Center Bombing on 9-11. She is also the author of **Therapeutic Stories to Heal Abused Children** (also translated into Norwegian, Dutch, Romanian and Hungarian).

Dr. Davis presently lives in Florida with her husband of 47 years, who retired from the FBI after 26 years of service as an agent and Chief Counsel (Assistant Director). They have three sons: Eric and Luke, both FBI agents and Cliff, a medical doctor specializing in Interventional Radiology.

Dr. Davis has presented workshops and training to a wide variety of professional groups including: state associations for play therapy; centers for treatment of victims, sexual abuse and/or child abuse; psychological associations; conferences on family violence, law enforcement agencies and conferences; the Defense Department, as well as therapists and counselors in Norway, Great Britain and Ireland. Workshop topics have included:

- "Therapeutic Techniques that Teach & Heal; An Introduction to Multi-Sensory Trauma Processing (MTP) & Therapeutic Stories"
- "Healing the Traumatized Child"
- "Understanding the Impact of Trauma and Grief on Children"
- "The Use of Therapeutic Storytelling in Play Therapy to Treat Traumatized Children"
- "Identifying and Treating the Student with Post Traumatic Stress Disorder"
- "Post Traumatic Stress Disorder"
- "Understanding and Treating the Trauma of Sexual Abuse"
- "Why Don't They Just Leave? Understanding Victims of Domestic Violence"
- "Moving Past Trauma; Education Event for Crisis & Emergency Workers"
- "Recognizing & Treating Post Traumatic Stress in Law Enforcement Officers"
- "The Abusive Woman"
- "Sexual Sadists"

Dr. Davis has created a variety of materials for use by therapists and others seeking to understand and heal problem behaviors and functioning available on her website: www.therapeutic-stories.com or www.drnancydavis.com. These include articles on PTSD, job-related trauma, child abuse and other subjects related to trauma. She has also created a variety of CD's/DVD's to promote healing in a variety of areas, such as job-related burn-out, self-confidence, breast and prostate cancer, and becoming pregnant. To schedule workshops, contact her at: www.nancydavisphd@yahoo.com

3/18/2012